Year of the Smuggler

Year of the Smuggler

A Memoir of 1984

By Jim Finucan

Lighthouse Point Press

Pittsburgh, Pennsylvania

Year of the Smuggler
A Memoir of 1984
Jim Finucan

Published by Lighthouse Point Press
Pittsburgh, Pennsylvania

www.lighthousepointpress.com

ISBN: 978-0-9792998-7-2

Printed in the United States of America

In loving memory of Shawn Patrick Finucan

3/19/60—1/31/85

CHAPTER 1

God is strong.
God is with me.
Therefore, I am strong.

August, 2019 Merrill, Wisconsin

"The rumor in our house was that your brother, Shawn, was murdered," my cousin, Mike Talbot, said to me. He had been a dear friend to Shawn when growing up. I listened, knowing that his mother, my dad's sister, would have been the source of that line of thought. "The people that your dad was involved with killed him because your dad wanted out of the criminal drug ring. This was the price he had to pay. Mentally and emotionally, he was collapsing, and so they were trying to gain a hold on him. They were trying to persuade him to stay in. It was a threat they made good on."

"Collapsing?" I asked, but I knew well what he meant. He was collapsing. I knew because I was there to witness it.

"Yes, well, you know, you wrote the book on it in fact." He was referring to Wild Counselor; 1977—The Summer of the Hunt, the book I wrote about hanging out with Dad when he was homeless, and I was eleven. Someone tried to kill him that summer by shooting ten rounds at him through a window. No charges were ever filed.

"Yeah, he was…collapsing," I said tenderly. I was remembering Dad, what we were doing, our international criminal venture, the madness of it all, and then Shawn's death, which turned life into horror and unrelenting sorrow for us all.

My brother, Tim, Dad and I had suspected foul play in Shawn's death. It all never added up.

What I felt, as I heard Mike's words, was shame. Not shame that my Dad had gotten into criminal enterprise and I had gone with him. I was feeling shame for what I hadn't done.

My brother, Shawn Patrick, was the oldest of us four kids. He had always looked out for me. When I was about nine, he protected me from an assault from an older kid, gave me good advice, and was always gentle and kind to me.

He had died at the age of twenty-four when I was eighteen. He had become a born-again Christian five years prior to his death. Shawn had completed his four years in the United States Marine Corps with an honorable discharge and the rank of Lance Corporal. He had returned home to Wisconsin and began study at a Christian college in Pembine, Wisconsin, to become a missionary. He died in the woods while target shooting at five a.m. on a cold January morning when the temperature was close to twenty-four degrees below zero.

That was thirty-seven years ago, I realized as Mike went on talking, being pleasantly funny and wonderful like he always was, but the comment about Shawn and Dad had sent my mind down a dusty hallway of memory and feelings that were sensitive again. Being sober now, I cannot tell what will trigger unfinished business. I smiled and joked with Mike but the inner tumblers were moving.

I had never had the guts to probe into the matter. I had been a private investigator and a cop, at one point in my life. It wasn't like I didn't know how to ask questions and investigate. I didn't do it because it had been a painful topic and I had lacked the courage and fortitude to face it.

If it is true, let it be said.

I thought of the many times I had been asked "What happened to Shawn?" by people who didn't have the tact not to ask such a question. I often replayed a stammering sentence like: "We think he leaned a rifle against a tree, walked down range to check the target, and the rifle fell down as he walked.

The bullet entered his back and exited the pectoral muscle." The faces stared at me waiting for more information to make sense. "It…the bullet had exited out his chest," I said in my own befuddlement, and I would look away hoping for an interruption.

"What?" a man had asked me at a social gathering. "Give me that again," he said, like I owed him an explanation. I thought of the long barrel on a 30.06 rifle and couldn't imagine it playing out myself. "I have been around firearms all my life, how is that even possible?" he asked. The urge to twist on the balls of my feet and deliver a solid right cross to his jaw flashed across my mind.

"He was out in the woods at five-thirty a.m. target shooting," I said with nothing else to offer and the bile rising up in my throat.

"In January? It's dark outside at that time, and cold as Hell," Mr. Obnoxious said. The temperature that winter was twenty-seven degrees below zero. "The sun isn't even up yet," the faceless figure from my memory would say. I had never liked this conversation and resented myself for answering questions to strangers who wanted to satisfy their own morbid curiosity and who had a lack of social grace.

Dad's friend, Tom Samboni, had attended Shawn's funeral dressed in an expensive pinstriped suit. He was tall, lean and looked like a young Steven Segal with his hair slicked back. Dad and I had been to his house in Madison and his apartment in Los Angeles. Tom was many things, notably a record producer promoting a band he was trying to make famous called The Cause. I suspected him as being part of "the team", the international drug group that Dad worked with to hide their money in tax shelters and smuggle cocaine out of Columbia, though I didn't know this to be true. When riding in his car, and when he and Dad wanted to talk about something sub rosa, he handed me a Sony Walkman with his band's music on it and asked me to listen to it. I remember hearing four songs, one called "Dear Love" that he thought would be a big hit. The rest of the tape was another guy he was promoting who played a guitar and sounded like Pat Metheny.

Tom was Italian to his core and was one slick dude. When I had stepped away from the reception line he pulled me aside. "Listen to me, Jamie. I heard the details of Shawn's death—what they're saying, okay? I want to tell you this: its bullshit, something is up." His eyes locked on mine. "You get me?"

"Yeah."

"I'm sorry about the loss of your brother."

"Thanks, Tom." He slapped me on the shoulder and handed me three, crisp, tri-folded hundred-dollar bills and stepped out of the funeral parlor into the sub-zero winter wind. He got into a Mercedes Benz and drove away in the perpetual gray sunlight of winter. I stuffed the bills in my suit coat pocket next to a prayer card for Shawn and would find the items there two years later when I attended another funeral.

My cousin Mike went on, being funny and sharp with the Irish wit he had inherited from my Aunt Mary as my mind flashed around, recalling imagery of the funeral, and stirring up the sense of loss that would haunt me throughout my life.

After the funeral, life marched on with or without us. Routines would start again; the conveyor belt didn't hesitate. "Clear the moving walkway," an automated voice might say. Teeth needed brushing again, showers taken, chores done. We moved around or stepped over the hole of the loss in our lives. We were forced to press on like all death marches.

Time was like an impatient cab driver. We all had things to get back to. I had to finish High School, my brother Tim had to go back to college at Eau Claire, and my sister Deirdre had to go back to Hutchinson, Minnesota, to raise kids. "Hey, buddy, you getting in or what?" the impatient cab driver said. I got in the vinyl-covered back seat that smelled of leather and cigarette smoke and shut the door. The cabbie would look back over his shoulder at me.

"I guess he's not coming," I would have to say, looking at some door on the street that Shawn was behind, that door would never open again. The driver flipped the lever on the meter, checked for oncoming traffic over his left shoulder and we pulled away from the curb of life.

And I never had the guts to even look back out the fucking rear window.

I never had a chance to say goodbye to my brother.

The memory was interrupted by my cousin Mike looking at me across the conference room table in my office. He had asked me a question. "I said I'm going to Rome, I want to take a copy of your book *The Spear*, and I'll leave one in the Vatican. Someone will find it, maybe get a kick out of it." He gracefully lifted me out of the memory alley with humor and we chuckled about an old family story.

Mike was fixing to retire soon. I tried to imagine what Shawn would have looked like if he had aged to sixty years old. I drew air into my lungs and expelled sorrow and regret. It was time to be present.

As we sat in my office in Merrill talking, I had formed a resolve. I was going to look into my brother's death. With my newfound sobriety and the power I had from God, I would find out what happened to Shawn.

I owed him that.

I would need to look at the events leading up to the incident. Since Shawn died in January of 1985. I would examine the year 1984. The notebooks and journals I keep in boxes would need to be gone through. Painful and sometimes joyous memories would need to be touched. Photos pulled out and interviews conducted with family members and friends.

I would need to experience tears and pain, laughter, discomfort, and awkward silence. There would be anguish and regret, broken-hearted longing and tender memories cradled; this was growth.

I would need to reflect and remember…

January, 1984 Merrill, Wisconsin

"I got a report that you have been drinking during the school day, Mr. Finucan," Strand Wedul said to me. He was the Vice Principal of the Merrill High School. He and the Principal, Lanny Tibaldo, ran the school and if I was having a conversation with either of them, it was most likely for unflattering reasons. The legal drinking age was eighteen at that time, and being seventeen, it wasn't that hard to look eighteen, especially with me sporting a big "Cookie Duster" mustache.

In fact, the thick mustache was the reason why I was the official booze buyer for my buddies, frequenting Mr. Goldie's liquor store on Third Street just a few blocks from the High School.

"Who would tell you I was drinking during the school day?" I asked Mr. Wedul with an expression of surprise.

"Who told it to me doesn't matter as much as whether the report is accurate."

I had been drinking and isolating from childhood friends and taking up with people who shared my compulsion to consume alcohol. I had been cutting sixth-hour study hall and going to Harold and Marge's Bar, where I enjoyed a Bloody Mary or two, then going back with a renewed sense of vigor about my education.

Mr. Wedul sat in his suit, behind his desk, waiting for my reply. Even then, before it became a principle in my sobriety, I hated lying.

"Yes, I had a drink or two. I came back to Political Science class in time." He looked at me stunned.

"Where did you do that?"

"I prefer not to say." I didn't want Harold or Marge getting any heat. They had served me and my friends alcohol without asking for I.D. I didn't want to slap a gift horse in the mouth.

"You're on the swim team, aren't you?"

I felt my casual demeanor become quite formal.

"Yeah…."

"Well, Mr. Finucan, not anymore. This infraction is a violation of our code of ethics in our athletic curriculum. I'm afraid you are officially kicked off the swim team and will serve three afternoons in detention."

The swimming team and the Olympic-size pool were brand new to Merrill High that year. I liked sports and kept in the school's programs of cross country, wrestling, track and now swimming.

The workouts in the pool after school were important. I was fighting a growing hysteria of some kind that was developing in my mind. As I swam the mile, lap after lap, flipping off the wall at each turn, a claustrophobic fear had infected my crawl stroke giving me a suffocating sensation with each stroke.

Each practice and every meet, as I rolled to grab a breath between strokes, I was experiencing the feeling that there was not enough air. With my face in the water, then out of it for just a second to grab a breath, I was trying to keep calm and not go bug shit. Each stroke was becoming a challenge to keep my sanity. But I was dealing with it, and it was important that I kept working on it. A critical battle of self-control was going on in those swimming workouts against a form of anxiety and I felt I needed to continue to engage in the sport.

It would take me years of addiction to figure out that this type of terror was a result of drinking. The challenge of the swim team was one of the last things keeping me rooted to the world.

"I'm the only one who swims the mile, Mr. Wedul. You don't want to do that."

"I'm certain that I don't need you to identify my wants, Mr. Finucan. That's the policy in our school. You just confessed to the infringement."

"So that's what I get for my honesty? I get kicked off the swim team?"

"Yes. You are a senior here in this school and set the example for the underclassmen. And don't forget the three night's detention." He scribbled out a note of detention like he was a parking attendant writing me a ticket on a curbside yellow line. He stood up in his three-piece suit and handed me the paper, looking handsome and poised, like an out-of-work actor.

I stood up, took the paper, and walked out of his office deflated like I always did after I had a kick in the ass for something I did.

The next day I turned over my Speedos, rubber headcover and eye goggles to Coach Hatfield. He was managing a practice of the girls' swim team. He didn't say much as I handed it to him. His expression might have been shame or indifference, I couldn't tell. I walked away with a "that's that" feeling. In order to show my contempt for the whole establishment, when I got out into the hallway and as I moved past the big floor-to-ceiling window of the pool, I yanked my pants down and mooned the entire girls' swim squad.

Mr. Hatfield reported my behavior to Stand Wedul and I was called into the office of the vice-principal the next day—the second time in forty-eight hours. Mr. Wedul let me know that after consulting with Mr. Tibaldo, the Principal, the two of them had decided to suspend me from school for three days for "Mooning." He shook his head as he wrote the word on the disciplinary slip.

"Well, this is a first," he muttered under his breath. I looked around his office at the knick-knacks: a golf trophy, a picture of someone who looked like Woody Allen on the wall, and scales of justice made of wax. I felt a burning resentment. I thought of my senior year here in this establishment of formal education as wading through knee-deep manure. Growing within me each day that year was the feeling that I didn't fit in here.

I went home feeling betrayed by Mr. Hatfeld, who I thought liked me, and by the entire educational establishment. The response from the Administration for a few minor infractions was heavy-handed. I took their harsh treatment of me as a rejection, so I rejected them.

I had spent some time with Shawn when he was home for the Christmas of 1984.

Shawn had gone through a major transformation as he completed his tour in the US Marines. He had become a born-again Christian. All of us kids were raised Catholic and attended Catholic school but Shawn had plunged into something more fundamental and had no problem telling the rest of us that we needed to get "saved."

We were going to hell and that was that in his opinion.

Shawn no longer went to movies or used foul language. He woke up early in the morning to read his Bible and pray. He already was a kind, gentle guy who never spoke a harsh word about anybody, but now he became even more considerate in his speech to all. He looked for an opportunity to share what he had found with others. As he began his transformation, he confused us all by reaching out to "any and all" whom he felt he may have wronged in some way and apologized. I would recognize this as standard procedure in a spiritual program of twelve steps when I got older, often called "making amends."

Christmas in northern Wisconsin is a season of lights, snow and cold. In our house, we feasted on a turkey dinner.

"I have a peace now that I have never known in my life," he said at Christmas dinner. It was clear that he had found something that had transformed him with happiness. "I have purpose now, because I have given my life to Christ."

"That's good," I said to this new man who was still in the form of my brother. I shook my head and speared another piece of the juicy dark meat of the dead, cooked bird. He noticed my reaction and started laughing.

"You must think I'm crazy. All of you, you must think I've lost my mind."

"Well then, in this family, you should feel right at home," I responded. His eyes became reflective and he thought before he spoke to me.

"Listen, if Dad ever wants you to go with him, to live with him, don't do it. Don't go. He doesn't like to be alone and I know you love him, but you've got a life mission of your own."

Shawn had lived with Dad through some of his high school years. He had transferred and lived in Minocqua, Hazelhurst and Eagle River.

"When I moved around with him, I was the new kid in school frequently. I ate all my meals alone in numerous cafeterias. I didn't have any friends and wasn't around anyplace long enough to get to know anyone. I tell you this to spare you heartache. Dad doesn't always use the best judgment in the decisions in his life. So stay in school, don't be drinking or using drugs, and study. You're a smart guy."

He gave me a gentle smile.

As I touch that memory, I recall in my research that I had found an essay Shawn had written in high school dated 4/17/78. The teacher had given it an A-plus and an admonishment to use paragraphs.

My First Party by Shawn Finucan

A few years ago, I lived up in the backwoods of Hazlehurst and went to school at Lakeland in Minocqua. Entertainment in the Northwood's of Wisconsin consisted of drinking, hunting and fishing, in that order. There were lots of parties. One night in April of my sophomore year, a friend of mine decided to take me to one.

Darrel is a red-haired guy with a fast temper nobody liked to mess with. He told me he just got his license last week and we climbed into his car. We sped off down the narrow, curvy road that went six miles to Highway 51 which would take us into the town of Minocqua. He drove with one hand, the radio blaring, talking directly at you, giving little attention to the road ahead of him.

Arriving in Minocqua, we stopped to pick up his friends. They were all shady looking characters. They were ruffians and natural clowns. There were five of them: an Indian, Bob, Jeff, Joe and Darrel. All of them had reputations of being sadistic and practical jokesters. One guy, Bob, exposed himself to our female vice principal. The Indian was charged a month ago with assault and battery. Darrel had to go to court next week to pay 200 dollars for shooting a deer out of season. Jeff burned down the Lakeland School sign. The other guy I didn't know about.

We left to go for the party but stopped at a supermarket to get beer. Two of them went in a side door and a few minutes later they came running out skipping because of the enormous amount of beer they had just stole, $25.00 worth under their arms. After our quick getaway and showing up at the party, I just sat around playing pool, talked to a few people, just drinking a Coke.

After a while, I had a beer. I didn't want to lose too many points with the boys. The fifteen or twenty people that were there were getting very intoxicated and conducting themselves with extreme anti-social behavior. Somebody threw up on the carpet. Two people stepped outside to fight. An attractive girl who was a freshman came inside the house crying. I found out she was just raped. The place was really a mess. I wanted to get out of there.

The police came to break up the party so everybody made a hasty exit. As we headed home on this dark night, I wondered why I even went to that party. I was riding with some drunken moron driving 80 miles an hour down that dark curvy road with his thumb and forefinger on the wheel while at the same time looking nonchalantly out his left window. Somehow I made it home but he totaled his car on the way to his house. Since then I haven't gone to many parties.

The teacher commented on the bottom, "This has so much power it rivets you to the page."

Shawn was into health food when no one else was, like the way my brother Tim was into bow hunting at age twelve.

Shawn would drink goats' milk, make his own whole-wheat bread and eat yogurt from his yogurt maker. He had a sensitive stomach and was careful about all things.

"And one more thing…you need to accept Jesus Christ as your personal Lord and Savior."

"What are you talking about? I go to church every Sunday, don't I?"

"Yeah, that's not the same thing."

"Ok, this is where you start to lose me," I said. He shook his head and smiled.

"I'm not worried, know why? Because I'm praying for you."

At dinner, Shawn talked about a trip he was taking. "I'm going on a mission trip to Greece, Yugoslavia and Romania."

"Romania? Like Transylvania, Romania?" I asked. I had just read *Dracula* by Bram Stoker on a night with a thunderstorm pounding outside like cannon fire and rain splashing against the windows. I was enthralled by the creepy story and unable to put the old book down.

"Yes."

"What are you doing there?" Tim asked, dishing up more cranberries.

"I'm smuggling Bibles behind the Iron Curtain. Those people need to hear the word of God as much as anyone else."

"Smuggling Bibles?"

"I've been studying in Northland College in Pembine on how to be a missionary. This will be my first mission. Pray for me."

I looked at him with deep admiration; out of the Marines now, he was going back into action.

"Well, it can't be like smuggling drugs. Is it a big deal if you get caught?" I asked.

"It could be a death penalty, certainly prison. They take it seriously, like you are undermining the authority of the government of the country, so they look at it like spying."

The turkey was moist, Mom's homemade cranberries were tart and the biscuits were still warm. Her fresh tapioca pudding, made from scratch, was still steaming with the sugary sweet aroma rolling out of the big glass bowl. I tried to keep away from it until the end of the meal because once I started on it, I would fill up on the rich, sweet warm pudding.

"Spying?" The thought was audacious to me. "Is there any profit in it?" I asked more as a joke.

"All of heaven rejoices at one saved soul," Shawn opined. He looked at me with a smile that drifted off his face. "Listen, if Dad wants you to go with him, to live with him, don't do it. I did it and it's very lonely. Dad is not…well. Do you understand me?"

"Sure," I said, not really understanding him. I would remember that warning later in detail, many times throughout the next year.

What I didn't know was that as we were having that conversation, Dad was smuggling kilos of cocaine from Bogotá, Columbia through customs at LAX International Airport in a hollowed-out golf bag. He walked it through customs and out to a car that was waiting for him. He threw the bag in the trunk, got in, and rolled out onto Sepulveda Boulevard, then into the traffic of the 405 freeway in the bright sunshine.

CHAPTER 2

"And that which fell among thorns are they, which, when they have heard, go forth, and are choked with cares and riches and pleasures of this life, and bring no fruit to perfection."

Luke 8:14

"There is no greater agony than bearing an untold story inside you."

Maya Angelou

13th of July—29th of August, 1984
Ministry in Europe
A Sojourn for Christ
Shawn Finucan

After arriving in Europe Pastor, Rodenhorst picked us up from a missionary's home in Mainz, West Germany, and took us to his residence in Tannusstein, West Germany. We also stayed with Billy Sutton, a missionary in Austria. He resides in a home not far from Salzburg, Austria.

From Shawn's mission notes

October, 2019 Merrill, Wisconsin

I took a deep breath and dialed the phone number of Florence County Wisconsin Sheriff's office. A deputy answered. His tone was low, official—even his voice was wearing a uniform.

"This is Jim Finucan. I'm looking into an incident and I wonder if you might have records on the death of Shawn Patrick Finucan. I am hoping you have a file I could see."

"What was the date of the incident?"

"January 31st of 1985."

"No, we don't keep records longer than ten years. We expunge them and throw them away."

"You...what?"

"Yeah. Where did the death occur?"

"In Dunbar near Pembine, Wisconsin."

"Oh, that's Marinette County. You'll have to call them."

"Do you think they have records?"

"I have no idea. Each county has its own way of handling record keeping. You'll have to ask them."

I took a deep breath and called the Marinette County Sheriff's office. The lady who answered the phone was kind and helpful. I explained, "My brother died in Dunbar at a Christian college and I am wondering if there is a file I could take a look at." I told her the date and spelled out the last name. She put the phone down and returned a few minutes later.

"Yes, there is." She said sweetly. I sat down in my chair.

"Fantastic, could I come and get that?"

"Sure, would you rather have me mail it to you?"

"Certainly. Can you tell me...are there pictures with the file?" The phone fumbled and then went quiet.

"I don't see any here."

I asked her to mail me the file and thanked her. My wife was babysitting our one-year-old grandson, so I stayed and had breakfast with them, reveling in family time. Work beckoned to me as it had so often, tearing me from the four kids I had raised to get done what must be done, and so I left the safe fortress to face the challenges of the day.

I had begun the process of finding out what happened to Shawn, finally.

January, 1984 Merrill, Wisconsin

At 4:10 PM in the winter of northern Wisconsin, the soft light dims to opaque sunsets of hollow light smeared across the west for twelve minutes, and then the winter night descends like a bird of prey.

Darkness falls like a big collapsing circus tent. I ventured out for a walk and looked at wondrous starlight holes punched through the black northern sky in dazzling winter constellations.

I then walked to the coziness of home enhanced by the subzero temperatures surrounding the walls. I found myself behind the walls of a heated fortress under siege by the season itself. The winter was maddening in its isolation. Restless agitation smothered me in a chilly black vapor of night. It would be a long time and much self-medication before I figured out a name for it *–anxiety*. I paced the floor, then picked up a novel I was working my way through, *Look Homeward Angel,* by Thomas Wolfe, and identified with Eugene Gant. Certain books were finding me in that lost stage in my life, connecting to me like a kite string.

When my bedroom got too small, I sat at the Royal typewriter with the ink ribbon and cranked out a few pages on a story I was writing. It was about a kid who was bow hunting the Hodag. The Hodag is a giant mythological lizard-like creature that is the mascot of the city of Rhinelander, about thirty miles north of my hometown. I was scraping my mind for words, rather than letting them flow. I could find no solace in this activity and went downstairs for a glass of milk.

The lights of a vehicle pulled into the driveway of Judy and Bob's house, my mom and stepfather. It was a Jeep, CJ5 ragtop. I flipped on the backlight and noticed a distinctive powder-blue color to it. No rust. It seemed to shine in the light that cut the night.

My Dad got out of the Jeep wearing an Irish tweed cap and a down vest over a nylon jacket. He was lean and in shape, living a hard life. He got to the door as I open it and smiled. His eyes were tired, his face haggard and frayed from fatigue.

I was delighted and surprised to see my best friend here in the winter. Usually, Dad slept in the parks in Merrill during the summer and went to California for the winter where the parks were warmer.

With a warm smile, he sat down while I made coffee. He ran to the bathroom on several occasions after clutching his stomach. "I picked up some dysentery in Columbia," he reported.

"Columbia? Like the country in South America?"

"Yes," he confirmed. I waited for an explanation but nothing came just yet.

"Whose Jeep?" I asked, looking out the window.

"It's mine. Payment for some work I've been doing." I sat down—astounded. At one time, he had been a prominent attorney, but after his emotional breakdown, he had been unable to work, other than physical labor. The family had watched him struggle for years, dreaming that one day he would pull it all together. Could it be that he had? He reached into his pocket and pulled out a half-eaten Toblerone white chocolate bar and pushed it across the kitchen table toward me.

He was a gift-giver, endlessly. I could never tell if it was his language of love or if it was to alleviate some guilt.

Dad leaned to the side, digging into his vest pockets, then pulled out an envelope that had my name written on it in his distinctive block-letter handwriting. He handed it to me, flapping it out like a badge, as though he had practiced this presentation and had been waiting to do this for a long time.

It was thick, heavy, and had Grosvenor House, London, on it along with a coffee stain. "What's this?"

"It's two grand, in cash. That's for you and I have more for all the other kids, and some for your mother. I guess we can call it late child support." I flipped through the crisp one-hundred-dollar bills. I couldn't remember ever having seen so much money.

"Whaaat?" I heard myself say. Dad smiled at me.

Last winter was a low point for Dad. He had been financially broken for a long time but that winter he had left too late and got stuck here in Wisconsin with no money. He had nowhere to go and was hit with a severe attack of depression that left him hardly able to sit upright. With nowhere to sleep, he stayed in our basement on a couch next to the washer and dryer. "I'm sleeping in my ex-wife's basement," he had said to me, evaluating the new low in his life, looking up at a pipe in the ceiling structure. Some people at school found out about that, forcing me to field questions in front of people like, "Is your Dad living in his ex-wife's basement?"

Now Dad showed up in the dead of winter with a new Jeep and a wad of cash. An uneasy feeling was coming over me and clashing with my gladness to see him.

He had envelopes for all four of us kids. He seemed to be set on getting rid of his resources as fast as he had made them. Through his fatigue, he had about him a self-satisfaction that I had not seen in a long time. But it tarnished as a thought crossed his mind. "I stopped and saw Shawn at that Christian college up in Dunbar. He wouldn't take the money. Can you imagine that?"

"Why not?"

"He said it was blood money. He wouldn't touch it because he said it was ill-gotten gain. I told him, 'Listen, Kid, money doesn't have any memory,' but he wouldn't even touch it. Can you imagine treating your father that way?"

I had been around Shawn since his transformation and I could imagine it. Right after he had gotten out of the Marine Corps, he and I decided to go camping. Shawn said he found a great spot with a trout stream running near a great spot to pitch a tent. So we packed up sleeping bags, some food, and a few fishing rods with some fat Canadian nightcrawlers and set out.

But as we drove into the property, there was a sign that read "No overnight camping." We were way out in the woods where no one was around; I told him not to worry about it. We would eat and fish through the evening, head out in the morning and no one would even know we were here.

As we settled in by the bank, I started baiting a hook but he was quiet and I could tell something was bothering him.

"This isn't right," he lectured. "We have to go. Come on." Upon his insistence, we packed our stuff back up, got into the car, and headed home.

"All because of some stupid sign?" I asked Shawn on the drive back home.

"It's not right. Overnight camping is prohibited. We have to respect those who God placed in authority over us. God wants us to do that."

"Man, I'm not so sure. We rose to take this country from the British in 1776. I'm pretty sure God was behind us in doing that."

"The British were abusing their authority. We didn't own that property. We should respect the wishes of those who do," Shawn said in a calm voice.

I could see him not accepting money from Dad if he knew something about its origin that he didn't like.

Dad jumped up to go to the bathroom again, holding his stomach as he hurried down the hallway.

We went for a ride in the Jeep, as Dad had to find a place to stay. The interior of the Jeep was built for rugged handling. There was even an "Oh, shit!" handle mounted on the straight-up dashboard. Chinese music wafted over the sound system from a cassette tape. As I listened to the flute and twanging guitar play, I glanced over at him.

"This music helps me relax," Dad confided. While driving around town in the dark winter night, he asked me questions about how everybody was doing, then stopped at a bar that had rooms to rent upstairs. He paid and got a key for one.

"How long are you in town for?" I asked, both hoping that he was staying and fearing that he would. Thinking of him being around, I began to feel a burden and then felt guilty for feeling it. Yet it was good to be around my Dad—my old friend. I still looked up to him like a little kid would.

"I'm not sure. Right now, I just need to rest and lay low. I'll drop you off. Come over and see me tomorrow for coffee," he said.

The next day was one of my suspension days from school, so I went to see Dad in the morning for a delightful time of conversation and coffee. When I told him about my suspension for mooning the girls swim team he shook his head and looked away in a mixture of exasperation and mock disappointment, with amusement peppered on it. "Jeeze, Kid, really?"

The small room had a bed, a little desk, and a community bathroom down the hall. "If I stay here for a while and save some of the money I came back with, I'll have enough to get out to California and weather out there for a few months." He ran out of the room to the bathroom.

I sat in silence at the little desk by the window and looked around the room. Dad's bed was made with tight corners, from his Marine days. His things were always aligned and organized, but one item was askew on the bedspread next to his shaving kit—his passport.

I leaned over, picked it up, and start thumbing through it. His photograph in the front captured an image of him in a dark and mysterious pose. His thick hair parted on the side and the angle of his shoulders made him look like Barnabas Collins in *Dark Shadows*. I smiled.

As I flipped through the pages of the passport, my smile turned into a tight wince when I saw the stamps and the dates on them. He had been all over the world in the past nine months. Several entries into Bogotá, Columbia, then leaving a week later. A few weeks later arriving in Frankfurt, or entering Luxemburg, Germany, then Zürich, Switzerland. Another one into Columbia and arriving seven days later in America through LAX, all in short spreads of time. A stamp from Heathrow, then Mexico City; the dates were jumbled around. The customs agent had just flipped the pages and pounded the stamp randomly in the book.

Dad has been very busy doing something.

Later in my life, that passport would come into my possession and remain locked in my safe until a time ago when

I was in a state of paranoia, certain that some government agents would be raiding my house, so I destroyed it. To this day, it is one of the regrets in my life.

Dad came back into the room and saw me looking at his passport. He stopped all his motion, slowly turned to face the door, then shut it. He sat down gently and poured the coffee from the thermos I had brought. The sound of the rich, hot, bitter liquid filling the cups was loud in the quiet room.

I set the passport down just as I had found it, at the same angle, and picked up the plastic cap of the thermos that served as a coffee cup and took a sip. It was coming together: the Jeep, the wads of cash, the dysentery in Dad's gut. He had been doing some criminal stuff with shady characters.

CHAPTER 3

If you are thirsty, come to me! If you believe in me, come and drink! For the scriptures declare that rivers of living water will flow out from within.

John 7:38

Reflection is the beginning of reform.

Mark Twain

October, 2019 Merrill, Wisconsin

Though the box of Shawn's notebooks and writings had been in my possession for decades, for the first time I took it out and looked through it. I found a small blank-page notebook in hardcover entitled *The Next To Nothing Book; Wanna Make Something of It?* Shawn had scrawled notes on the blank pages, and I saw stubs of paper where he had torn out some pages.

Inside the book cover was Shawn's first notation: Entries by Shawn Patrick Finucan, United States Marine.

Then inside the next page, a note from when he was stationed in Panama:

Panama City

A dirty town smelling of machinery, sweat, automobile exhaust and American imperialism all rolled into one.

In a folder I found a description of five pages of his mission trip to Europe when he had smuggled Bibles behind the Iron Curtain. He had typed it up on onion-skin paper, even used white-out on some mistakes he had corrected.

Shawn's mission notes
A Sojourn for Christ
13 July – 29 August 1984

While in Vienna we stayed with an organization of European Christian Missions. We stayed overnight with Pastor Hastings—a missionary who lives near Koblenz, West Germany. We doubled our Bibles with another suitcase full, donated by believers. I wonder how to compensate for this at the border. Scott, my partner and student from the school , was mainly my partner throughout Europe. He went behind the Iron Curtain with a load of Bibles, delivered safely and we met up again in Greece. He is calm and confident.

Fall, 2019 Merrill, Wisconsin

When the manila envelope arrived from the Marinette County Sheriff's office, I took it up to my study and placed it tenderly on my desk. As it was the middle of the workday, I had to get back to the office. I spent time with my wife and grandson in the bliss of family moments and set aside the agony that I would need to relive.

A few more days would pass and the envelope would occupy more of my mind. Knowing that I had to have the energy and focus to be able to concentrate, I delayed more. As even more days passed I realized I was seeking the false comfort of time.

Finally, in one early evening, I closed my study door and opened the report.

Marinette County Sheriff Department Investigation Report Case Number 35-393

Statement given to the Marinette Sheriff's office by Scott Meisenberg—student at Northland Baptist Bible College:

On January 30th, 1985, Shawn asked if he could use the rifle the next day. I told him to get the key from Mr. Schneider, the dorm monitor—all weapons are locked in a closet. Shawn asked me how much ammunition I had and wanted to pay for it. He also had a target made on blue paper. The next afternoon on January 31st, 1985, about 5:20 PM, my roommate came in and asked if I'd seen Shawn Finucan. He told me he hadn't been seen since 4:30 AM.

I went and got the keys to the closet to check and found my rifle was gone. I went to the main office and called Dr. Ollila.

Statement given to the Marinette County Sheriff's Department by Leslie J. Ollila, President of the school

On Thursday 31 January 85 at approximately Noon, I had a conversation with a student in the lunchroom and he indicated that Shawn Finucan had not been in classes today. Later between 3:30 and 4:00 PM I contacted Dennis Steinwand (maintenance supervisor Northland Bible College) and asked him if Shawn had shown up for work and he replied: No that he did not and had not seen him. I then talked to my assistant Marty Von who had a conversation with Dave Schneider (Dorm Monitor) that he had not seen Shawn Finucan since 4:30 / 5:00 AM Thursday morning. At approximately 4:00 PM, I and several other members searched the immediate area with negative results.

The file was heavy in my hands. Shawn had been gone for twelve hours before anyone even noticed he was missing. I looked up the weather for Pembine, Wisconsin, at the time Shawn went out shooting on 1/31/85.

Weather for Pembine, Wisconsin, on 1/31/85 according to Weather Underground:

Sunrise 7:12 AM/Sunset 5:01 PM
Wind speed 18 miles per hour
Low temperature -28°F

MARINETTE COUNTY SHERIFF DEPT
Case No 85-391
Complaint memorandum

Complainant: James Morgenroth
Address Northland Baptist Bible College
Offense: Lost Person
Phone 324-5254
Report received by: Diane
Date: 1/31/85 Time: 7:43 PM
Place of occurrence Pembine–Dunbar area
Officer assigned: Information

Nature of complaint: Called and stated that a man that goes to the college was out target practicing earlier today and hasn't returned yet. Does not need to see an officer—just wanted to inform us that snowmobilers will be out looking for this man.

He also stated that this man was carrying a gun, which was to be used for target practice. They would like to be informed if we hear anything on this guy, and they will inform us if they have located him also.

Fall, 2019 Merrill, Wisconsin

There is a room in my basement filled with hunting gear. Bow hunting equipment, gun cases, gun cleaning gear, boots, camouflage clothing, stools for sitting in the forest, and thousands of small items that I may need to climb a tree, fix a hunting stand, or adjust a bow.

It's the room where my wife puts things that I leave laying out that she doesn't want to look at anymore as she cleans up. There is a bookshelf in there with books on hunting, books I have read throughout my life that I just couldn't let go of because they were so good that I may want to read them again. Some of these books impacted me so much that they earned a place on the basement shelf.

"Those books are all just going to be ruined because they smell like mildew," my wife Jamie would say with her voice of reason. I keep them dry and hope for the best. Once when she was at the height of her war on my hoarding of books, I was taking the garbage out to the curb and looked in one of the black bags to find it half-filled with books! This caused me to look at the garbage a little more when I took it out.

In the basement gear room, there was a box on one of the shelves that I looked at from time to time but only seldom had the courage to touch. In the stillness of a wistful morning when time was my friend and memories were like small children that want to be picked up and held, I reached in and let my fingers pick up an item from within it.

I become transported back in time in those moments.

The box that contains Shawn's notebooks and Bibles is one I have been visiting, finally. There is a leather pouch containing letters he had written and scraps of papers that captured thoughts of things he wanted to accomplish as well as prayers he wanted to focus on. I found a stenographer's notebook scrawled with scripture study and outlined thoughts. There were index cards with scripture quotes he was trying to memorize and live.

My hands intrusively picked up and unfolded a love letter to a girl that he hadn't mailed yet. I recall him telling me about her red hair.

Inspiring to me is the goal-setting notebook he kept. I have been a goal setter for years and have kept boxes of these through my life.

Shawn positively charged his mind with affirmations, directions, and character development accomplishments. He was working a spiritual program that is like the 12-step program

I am embracing. He was noting his character defects in detail and asking God to remove them.

I went through the material, handling the pages with delicate hands, and followed the mental trail of thoughts that my older brother left for me.

I felt amazed at his development, his conviction to his beliefs, and his selfless dedication to other people. He seemed to have written this record for me as a reminder to forsake anger and discipline my speech, to think thoughts that are righteous and noble, and to focus on God.

I wonder why God would have taken him from this world where people such as Shawn are a rare treasure.

January, 1984 Merrill, Wisconsin

Outside the window of Dad's room, fine, dry snow was falling in the cold air and blowing around like dust. The winter sunlight smeared illumination over the streets under the perpetual gray overcast sky of the Midwest.

"Dad, what's the job that got you this money?"

"I've been doing a few different things. I have been setting up tax shelters for people that have a great deal of money." So far, that sounded good. Dad had been a brilliant lawyer. I have been told that before he had his breakdown and was homeless, law students from Madison would come and watch him try a case, just to learn. He was skilled in argument, legal tactics, and research.

I had seen him pick up a subject that he wanted to learn, acquire a mass of books on it and become an expert in a particular field of law in a matter of weeks.

Cousin Mike Talbot told me Dad had an IQ of 190.

I waited for more details to Dad's story, knowing he was holding out. There were two types of people who sought out Dad: regular people with legal problems and career criminals by trade, who had chosen to live outside the law, and who were looking for an ally to involve in their crimes.

"What kind of money, what kind of people?" I probed. Someone walked down the hallway outside the door, entered the room across the hall, and shut the door. It was possible someone in the hallway could hear our conversation. I had heard that these upstairs rooms above the bar had been a cathouse back in the early days.

"These people have bales of cash, and I mean bales, like a hay bale. They have them wrapped in sheets of plastic and buried in the ground or stacked behind false walls in their basements. They got the money by moving drugs and it can't surface because it will draw attention. So, I set up these offshore tax shelters and invest it in numbered bank accounts in countries where the questions regarding money are few. There are tax havens in this world and if you know how to use them, you can earn a great deal of legitimate money on the return of your investment."

"Is it illegal? Establishing bank accounts out of the country?"

"Well, you can invest money in offshore or international investments."

"Is it a crime—what you are doing?"

"Not as far as you know." He lit up a Marlboro 100 and instantly stunk up the room.

"Wow. You mentioned a few things…what you mentioned earlier…."

"I've smuggled cocaine into the US," he said looking me in the eye. He wasn't proud of it but he wasn't going to lie to me.

"What do you mean?"

"I mean I carried a golf bag out of Columbia and into the U.S. with a hollowed-out bottom, stuffed with keys of cocaine. I've done it more than once. There is a drug cartel in Medellin that is moving incredible amounts of cocaine. I'm with a team that makes runs."

I looked down at the wooden floorboards and took a deep breath. The wind almost whistled on the window, brushing against the glass, trying to get in.

When I raised my eyes and looked at him, he appeared to be a different man.

"You could have gone to jail for a long time. What the hell are you doing?"

"Jamie, my options were to stay in my ex-wife's basement and live next to a clothes dryer or take a chance. The team I hooked up with has a need for my services. I can do this. I'm earning money again. I have money to give you kids. I'm helping people. I'm not a bum anymore."

"You told me once that before I did a crime, I should look up the maximum sentence for the penalty of committing such a crime, and that if I did that, it would deter me from doing it."

Dad took a long drag on the Marlboro 100, reinforcing his courage to explain. "I'm already living out a life sentence—a sentence of poverty. I'm so sick and tired of being poor that I'm ready to do anything."

I looked him right in the eye. "Anyone can say that. Excuses come printed on the wrapper of bad decisions; you know that. How's it going to be if you go to prison doing this stuff?"

"I am in a prison. I'm mentally ill, destitute and broken." The cigarette smoke he had pulled into his lungs would come back out in four short breaths, rolling out of his mouth and nose in voluminous amounts.

"That's a hell of a mental condition to be in while facing prison in a foreign country," I countered.

"Then I use that time to pray and build a relationship with God, like a monk would," Dad answered.

I shook my head. This was madness. He had it all thought out.

I took the envelope with the coffee stain out of my jacket pocket and extended my hand out to him to take it back. "Listen, I can't take this." I was thinking of Shawn. He was right. This was blood money, and I wanted no part of it. "You can have this back. I've still got some money from my part-time job last summer."

He stared at me, then down at the envelope. I was feeling him implode emotionally.

"You…what? Do you know what I did for that? I finally have some money and now my kids won't take it? What is going on here?" The thick, solid envelope hung in the air off my hand.

"Take the money, Kid. Not all the work I do is illegal. Consider that you got the part that I earned giving sound legal advice." His face fell in despair and rejection. His eyes moved off me and around the room, perhaps seeing ghosts as he searched for…compassion?

I felt confused. I really didn't want this money now. It would encourage him to do more stupid things, but I didn't want to hurt his feelings either. I saw no solution in the moment. I set it down on the table between us. Dad picked it up and handed it to me. "Take it. Money has no memory. You're going to need it. Everyone does." His voice had dropped to almost a whisper.

My hand went out slowly and my fingers closed on the paper. I took it for his state of mind. I took it against my better judgment and the surrendered my principles. With my innocence eroding even more, I took the envelope.

I tried to fold it once but it was so thick it only bent. I could no longer claim that I was a mere spectator to the crimes Dad was involved in. At that moment, I participated in my own aging process. No longer inculpable, I felt a piece of my youth had left me like a sparrow flying off a dying tree branch.

I was not as strong as Shawn was.

I accepted the money and a few days later used some of it to purchase an Olympic weight set that would stay in the basement of Judy and Bob's house for years.

I had a girlfriend that I was smitten with. Her name was the same as mine, Jamie. When my friend's dad, Roy Lang, found out what her name was, he said, "Now, if I was a psychologist,

I would say that has significant meaning, like you really wanted to get it on with yourself."

The first time I saw her was when I tried to crash a party at their house put on by her sister, Chris. My friends and I didn't get in the door because Jamie had answered the knock, taken one look at the three of us, narrowed her two-tone blonde eyelashes under her red hair, and slammed the door in our faces.

It was a rude introduction, and it was only for a moment, but to the question of "Is there love at first sight?", there most certainly is. The door slamming mimicked fate in my life. With that door rocking the frame of the jamb, the door of my heart slammed to the possibility that there could be another love that would pull me in a different direction.

I hadn't been introduced, hadn't said a word to her. She hadn't noticed me in those seconds, but I fell hard for her.

Later that summer I would see her again. I was riding in the Volkswagen Rabbit that Greg Ball drove around town. He would crash two of them, pissing off his Dad. We were high school students on the loose in Merrill. My enthusiasm for life was hardly contained in the bucket seat, before the dashboard of German engineering. I belted out vocals to songs on the radio and worked hard at keeping Greg laughing. I knew that the measurement of how good a friend was, is distinctly connected to how much you laugh when you are with that friend. All else is secondary.

With the square window rolled down, the summer air moved through the car with Dire Straits on the radio. It was then I saw Jamie walking down the streets with her friends. I remember shouting out the window that I loved her and would marry her. She smiled at the catcall, and we rolled on.

A few weeks later at a party at Francie Woller's house, I finally got a chance to get next to her. We went outside and made out in the bushes while a raging party of high school drinking went on in the house.

I latched on to her tight and went to her house a few times a week to watch television while her mom and sister went about their business. *Caddy Shack* was on, and I laughed so hard at the movie that her mom thought I was nuts. I *was*, for this redhead gave me a sense of purpose and something to fight for.

There was a distance between Jamie, her sister and, her mother that left her isolated within her family. I connected with her isolation and shared it. Her far-away Dad visited their male-less household sometimes, and when he did, he asked me so many questions I wondered if I needed a lawyer. That direct inquiry perhaps made up somehow for all the miles between him and this family he had created—just like my own father.

Jamie and I were young and in love. From any angle, no matter what was going on, she was always beautiful to me.

I drove my 1974 Hornet over to her house a few times a week and lost myself during the early passionate embrace of the relationship. It offered me fulfillment that would empower me with a feeling that I could do anything, and that this is where I belonged.

CHAPTER 4

"Jesus answered, Neither hath this man sinned, nor his parents: but that the works of God should be made manifest in him."

John 9:3

MARINETTE COUNTY SHERIFF DEPT. Case No. 85-393
Complaint Memorandum

Complainant: Harold Patz
Address: Duplex 5 Northland Mission Camp
Offense: Suicide
Report received by Diane
Date 1/31/85 Time: 9:01 Pm
Place of occurrence: Dunbar
Officers assigned: Jerue, Brzoza, Mattison

Nature of complaint: Re: 85-393. Harold called and stated that they found the body of the person that was lost earlier. The victim was found dead 1½ miles from the camp. He will meet officers at his residence located at the camp duplex #5 and will take them to the body. The party apparently shot himself.

We pursued the footprints in the snow that we had observed earlier. We had also received information from Mr. Dubrow, that he had observed fresh footprints in the snow on the road and into a field next to his property. We then went to the area indicated by Mr. Dubrow and followed the footprints. We then shined our flashlights and observed a body lying face down in the snow and a gun case by a tree. We had discovered the body between 8:00 PM and 8:30 PM. We then returned to

the college and contacted the Marinette County Sheriff's Department.
Statement given to the Sheriff's Department by Leslie J. Ollila

August, 1984
Ministry in Europe
A Sojourn for Christ
Our team was separated for some time in Europe because of separate ministries but we met up in Greece. We stayed overnight in various places in Europe including hotels, 2 pensions in Vienna and Salzburg and I even slept in the back of a car. I also had the opportunity to stay in a missionary couple's home in Greece. The risk of moving Bibles over the border was discussed. I am not afraid.
Shawn Finucan

1984 Merrill, Wisconsin

The change that overtook Shawn was a transformation of character and focus that I had never witnessed in anyone before. Having been in the Marines and stationed in Panama, he came home an entirely changed person.

Shawn had always been gentle and kind, quiet and introspective, and those qualities were still there after he "got saved." Now he was more confident. He had more peace about himself wanted to share it with others.

The four of us kids had been raised Catholic. We had all attended a Catholic private school but that aspect of his religion he had shed like a wet sock. In fact, he treated the Catholic religion like heresy and gave me a tract that portrayed how the Church had tortured people in the old days to enact God's justice and convert people from what the Church perceived as evil.

He would tell me that I needed to be saved and to accept Jesus as my Savior and that my Catholic beliefs were not going to get me into heaven. When he told Dad this, it caused a big rift between the two of them and they argued bitterly.

Shawn no longer went to movies or swore. He got up early and studied the Bible for hours. He had new friends who shared his belief structure and spent hours donating his time to causes and working programs that benefited others.

He was a "holy roller" now, and when my friends came over, he would look for an opportunity to share the gospel with them. Some of them at first thought he was kidding. Shawn was a guy who had held a backyard boxing match that dozens of people had attended to end the reign of a bully in his life.

Now, he had no qualms about telling people that didn't know Jesus as their personal savior that they were not going to be admitted to heaven.

"You mean my relative that died last summer isn't in heaven because he didn't know Jesus?" one of Tim's friends asked Shawn. Shawn paused then affirmed that this was true in his opinion.

Shawn stood patiently by his statements even if they provoked anguish or anger. He took the business of saving souls seriously.

Back in Dad's flop room, Dad and I drank coffee and the heat felt nice in the small room. The day was bright and the snow reflected enough light to shine in your eyes if you looked out the frosted window.

"How many days of suspension do you have?" Dad asked me.

"Tomorrow I go back to school."

"For drinking during the school day?"

"No, I got cut from the swimming team for drinking. I got the suspension for mooning the girls' swim team."

"So, how often are you drinking?"

"Not too much."

"What's not too much?"

"Well…not enough to be a problem."

"Enough for it to be a problem in your studies, enough of a problem that got you suspended, that's a sign of a drinking problem. If you are drinking, and it affects your life in a negative way, you have a problem. I know—I'm an alcoholic," Dad said as he cleaned the items in his shaving kit. He was going over his gear, packing it and repacking it. Deciding on what things he might get rid of and what things were essential. He was getting ready to leave in a few days.

"Are you drinking every day, Jamie?"

"Not…every day."

"But you can't get through the school day without going to the bar?"

"I didn't say I couldn't get through the school day…"

"You're young to have to deal with this. How often are you going to that bar?"

"I don't know. Do we have to do this?"

Dad focused back on what he was doing, but I could see his eyes had the drifty unfocused look of concern. It was time to change the subject.

"Oh, I got a call from the police department," I interjected. "They want me to come down and fill out a statement for changing money that came from a theft last summer."

"What?" Dad stopped moving and turned toward me.

"This guy in my class, Hans Gruber—he steals money and stuff like he thinks it's cool. He robbed the Laundromat several times. I think he got caught each time. He's a real case study in pathological behavior. Anyway, I guess he broke into the Laundromat yet again and robbed the machines or something.

"Last summer at Harry's Drive-In, the burger joint in the sixth ward, where I was working, he shows up with maybe fifty bucks in coins wrapped in paper. The dude is shady as hell, so I go get the manager. Shotzie is her name—nice older lady who manages the joint. I tell her, 'Shotzie, there's a character up here at the window, got a bunch of coins and wants me to change them into paper dollars. What should I do? She comes up, wiping her hands on her apron, looks at it and says fine, go ahead, so I did. I guess the cops came back later and said that money came from the Laundromat, and they knew Hans had done it because he did it several times before."

Dad sat down carefully. He was thinking. "And now the cops want to talk to you?"

"Yeah."

"Why?"

"I don't know because I was working and changed the money at the window. They want a statement on what I saw or something."

"They don't need that. The manager saw the kid at the window. She could identify him."

"Yeah…"

"You laundered stolen money," Dad said.

"What? No. Like hell, I did. I took the coins and gave him paper money, with the permission of the manager."

Dad was quiet for a moment. Then replied, "They are going to try to wrap you up in this shit. This is trouble. You are in danger here."

"Nonsense, what are you talking about?"

"I mean you are in the strike zone and they are looking at pinning something on you. Believe me, I know. I'm a lawyer and with you being a Finucan, they are laying for you. They are excited about this opportunity. They have a regular hard-on about this."

"Naaa. You're reaching here."

"Jamie, this gets at me, through you. I've been pissing off the power base in this town for years. I've made powerful enemies here and the way they work is they go at the kids when they can't get to me. Trust me. I know what I'm talking about."

"Why would they want to do that? I didn't do anything wrong."

"Doesn't matter. The jails have plenty of people in them that didn't do anything wrong."

"Jail?"

"Well, you know this guy. Sounds like you knew he was a thief. It doesn't matter what you did or didn't do. What matters is what they can insinuate. This is a big opportunity for them. That DA is a real asshole and he is salivating thinking of this."

I was starting to get uncomfortable.

"Listen, the legal system is very good at victimizing people who didn't do anything wrong, but got ground up in it because some authority figure got a hard-on for them or the family. Don't think for a moment that they wouldn't do such a thing. They do it all the time. It's business as usual when they do."

I would remember Dad's words later in life when my own son would have a party at the family cabin and a foreign exchange student would die of a brain disorder. A local DA would charge my son with a felony to make an example of kids who wanted to drink while underage. The *Wausau Daily Herald* would parade the incident through the pages for weeks, like we were the James Gang.

A few minutes passed in the room while someone staggered down the hall to his room from the bar downstairs. Dad, deep in thought, continued smoking.

"I've been calling them out on their corruption, and making known all the dark, underhanded deals they are doing and exposing their insider games since I got to this town. I've been standing up in the courtroom speaking for the oppressed and complaining in church against the oppression of the poor here for years. Now the DA wants to talk to you. Put it together, Kid. We are targets. Make no mistake. You're standing in the strike zone."

A car went by outside on the street. The buzzing of the motor and the wheel on the road grew louder and faded away—like chance in life.

"We have to get you out of here," he said with finality. His face showed it. He had a plan.

"What…what do you mean?"

"You should come with me to California. You're in trouble, and you're drinking too much. Have you considered the fact that you may be an alcoholic, Jamie? It runs in the family. I can teach you how to live sober, live without drinking. I can get you out of here and we can hang in California until this all blows over."

"I'm in my senior year in high school. The second semester just started…."

"Yeah, well, forgive me for saying that it doesn't seem to matter much to you anyway. You're screwing off at an all-star level. If there were a sport for not-giving-a-shit about academics, you would be earning a letter in it. You're sitting here in suspension for showing your ass to the school's authority and some trouble is looking you up from last summer.

Do you really want to stay here in this shitty town another winter? Wouldn't you rather hang with me in the California sun—live on the beach with the sun and sand?"

It was hard to argue with that. I walked to the window and felt the scarce shaft of sunlight on my face and my whole being drank it in. I felt it thaw my soul, warm my skin, and feed me vitamin D in its ray of heat from space. There would be sun in California.

"Some issues you want to deal with early, or you can end up meeting yourself coming back on the road in life."

"Meeting myself…what do you mean?"

"You're a writer! You need to live the writer's life, full of adventure and exploration, and you don't get that by following the desperate, neutered herd into the field of the mundane."

That kind of talk spoke to my soul, and maybe he knew it better than I did. The only thing I knew about myself: *I was a writer, damn it!*

Stories were always rampaging in my mind, spinning off comments someone would make, or building on interactions I witnessed at sporting events or store lines. Boredom of any kind triggered it into a frenetic overdrive. My imagination leapt about like a cougar during the day, creating, escaping, feeding on situations and asking "what if?" It might spark a fiction storyline that could rub on the reality of any situation and thrash about in the world between fantasy and reality, sometimes blurring the defining lines.

"Blow off getting a high school diploma?" I stammered.

Dad sat down and rested his elbows on his knees, his cigarette between his fingers and a Zippo lighter in his piano-player-like fingertips, spinning it end over end.

"Listen, Jamie, do you think if you ever write down on a job application that you are a high school graduate that anyone is going to challenge that? You read more books than most adults I know."

My spirit of adventure lit like a fuse on a firecracker. I started to hear the James Bond music playing, the riff of the base ripping in the background of my mind. California, I never had been there....

Back home in my bedroom, I selected a duffle bag and began deciding what I would take with me to California and what I would leave here at home. Dad said I would need my passport, so I placed it on the dresser.

The radio was playing a song called *Owner of a Lonely Heart* by the rock band Yes.

I got out "The Snake," a stainless steel, Ruger 357 Magnum Security Six revolver that had a pistol scope mounted on in. I had named it "The Snake" as a reference to the movie *Escape From New York*. The character Snake Plissken, played by Kurt Russell, had carried something similar. I flipped out the cylinder to make sure it was unloaded, then wiped an oil rag over it, and quickly zipped it up in its travel case because I heard Mom coming down the hall.

She hated guns.

She pushed open the unlatched door and carried in a laundry basket of clean clothes she had washed and folded for me. Her face was troubled. She looked over the stuff that I was laying out.

"This is not a good idea. You should be finishing your school year. You can run around all you want afterward, but finish what you start. You're not even eighteen-years-old yet."

"I will be in a few days," I countered, and smiled.

"I've said this before, and I'll say it again. I know you love your dad, but he doesn't always use good judgment. He has a tremendous amount of influence on you kids and his decisions are not always rational. Do you understand that?"

"Dad says you say that because you don't really like him."

"That's not true. He took Shawn with him and traveled all over, putting him in one school after the other. Shawn was alone a lot and with your Dad, who is not in his right mind most of the time. He has depression very bad. It's not good for you kids to be exposed to that. I don't think you comprehend this." She set the basket down next to my duffel bag of partially-loaded gear and looked around at what I was laying out. She looked at me for a long time. I looked away and when I looked back she was still looking me in the eyes.

"He can be very manipulative and he doesn't want to be alone."

"It's not like that. This is my call. I'm responsible for my decisions. I'm nobody's puppet. You raised me smarter than that." She sat down on the edge of the bed deflated. Her eyes misted up. I sat down next to her.

"You know I love you, Mom." I put my arm around her.

"Yes, I know that. There is always a place for you here when you want to come home. You'll always be my beloved youngest son."

"Just what every guy wants to hear." She leaned on me. I knew that my mom was the greatest blessing God had ever given me.

The band Yes was singing on the radio—"Don't deceive your free will at all!"

A few days later I got out of the passenger side of John Purcell's lime-green AMC Comet that his grandpa, Romie, had given him. It was the ugliest paint job a manufacturer could ever put on a car. The green was the color of puke, but the engine ran smooth and fast. The car was filled with my buddies.

It was my birthday party and it was my job to go get the beer, because I was able to grow a big Sam Elliot mustache at age fifteen. I had been buying the beer for years from Third Street liquor store.

I would act nonchalant, setting the liquor on the counter and asking about the game on the radio. Or, I might make a comment about the weather and try to look confident, maybe even bored. Mr. Goldie, the storeowner, hardly gave me a glance and rang up my purchase. But this night I didn't do any of that, for I was eighteen.

I selected two twelve packs of Pabst beer in cans and a bottle of 50/50 MD wine and went to the check-out and placed them in front of Mr. Goldie. To me, at the time, he was an old man with an accent who owned a liquor store. I had no idea who he was.

Later in life, after his passing, I would read the book he wrote, entitled *Rag Dolls*, about his experience as a prisoner in a concentration camp.

Mr. Goldie was an immigrant who had arrived in America after World War ll. He was from Plock, Poland and, at age eleven, the German army invaded his country and imprisoned him and his family in concentration camps. Mr. Goldie spent five years in nine different concentration camps, having even been held in the dreaded Buchenwald death camp.

He described atrocities like being lined up by the Germans and made to watch as the dogs were turned loose on a prisoner that had tried to escape. They were forced to watch while trained German Shepherds tore live victims to pieces.

He witnessed numerous people shot by guards, and men, women, and children being marched into gas chambers, while

SS guards hacked at them with swords. He saw people throwing themselves on the electric fences to escape into death the horrors of the camp. Mr. Goldie endured being forced on a death march for days while a Nazi soldier in the rear of the column shot people who fell behind, couldn't keep up, or just felt like it at random.

I had no idea that the quiet man who owned the liquor store on Third Street in Merrill, Wisconsin, survived days on end in train rides through Poland and Germany, packed in with other prisoners with standing-room-only, while having no nourishment, latrine, or fresh air as they were transferred from one prison camp to another.

On one occasion he escaped being shot by lying on a pile of dead bodies. He was almost executed on numerous occasions.

Mr. Goldie's parents and brother were killed in the death camps, and when he was finally liberated, he had no family left and nowhere to go. He was a war victim who had forged a heart of courage, determination, and fortitude in extreme conditions that I could not imagine enduring. When he gave me change for the beer I purchased, I had no idea who he was.

The most significant testament to his character was what Mr. Goldie did with that experience. Rather than living his life bitter and angry, he shared his experience as a guest speaker to community groups and schools to make known the realities of the dangers of fascism and hatred, and he delivered a message about love. I have often mused to myself that if he could endure that and still love, then can't we all?

Mr. Goldie now looked at me like he hadn't noticed me before. "You have an I.D. to show me, young man?" he asked in his thick Polish accent.

"Mr. Goldie, you've seen me in here before."

"Yes, I have, and if you want to buy that beer and that wine, you will show me an I.D."

I shrugged and pulled out my driver's license and presented it, like it was as important as a mathematical solution to a problem NASA was facing. I watched as he looked at the date of birth on my license, then he turned his short, stocky frame with his balding head and glanced at the calendar on the wall.

"It's your birthday today," he responded.

"Yes, Sir, it is."

"You little son-of-a-bitch! All year you've been coming in here buying beer, and tonight you are eighteen years old," he remarked with one eyebrow raised.

I smiled, only openly, friendly. I put the ten dollars on the counter and waited for my change. He shook his head. "Well then, happy birthday anyway, James," as he handed me the change.

"Thanks, Mr. Goldie." I pulled out one of the Pabst and offered it to him. He smiled and waved me away. If only I had gotten to know such a man, I would have asked him more questions and, if I could, have drawn out his knowledge of history.

I left the store and jumped into Purcell's Comet. We tore off into oblivion and the reckless abandonment of teenagers in the winter night of America.

The next night it was cold, and Jamie and I went ice-skating. The winter night was pretty. It had snowed and the frost had clung to the trees around the rink of Normal Park. The white, frozen precipitation looked like it had been spray-painted on everything with a giant can. The humidity somehow hung in the air so that it frosted our jackets and made our breath visible in the black, night air. Glowing orbs of winter precipitation hung around the lights of the rink and the sound of our conversation seemed to be soaked up in the chilly air until Jamie's sweet laughter broke through when I caught her from falling onto the ice.

As the night breeze moved the cold, it seeped into our clothing until we went into the warming hut. I got two cups of hot chocolate from the lady who worked at the counter. She was reading a V.C. Andrews book entitled *Flowers in the Attic* and seemed enthralled by it. I walked carefully with the Styrofoam cups of super-hot liquid on the blades of my skates to keep it from spilling on my hands.

As we sat in the corner of the hut on the benches, far from the door, Jamie was cold, and her sadness returned. Her blonde-tipped eyelashes were cast down and it was breaking my heart. I had told her earlier I was leaving and, at first, she tried to enjoy the evening we had together, but we had stopped moving now. The reality of my departure was settling in for both of us and we shared an inevitable lovers' sorrow.

"Will you be coming back?" she asked softly.

"I'm sure I will…someday." I didn't like the way "someday" sounded coming out of my mouth, but I really didn't have much of a plan other than to leave.

"You're just going to drop out of high school?"

"Yeah, well drop out is too harsh. I have a chance to travel—to see the world, and I want to take it."

"Where are you going in California?"

"San Clemente. I'll live on the beach. There is this park there, I guess. I'm going to quit drinking. It will be good for me. I feel like I have to do this. You're the best thing about any of this. I can send for you when I get all set up doing something." I was making it up as I went along.

Tears rolled down her face and landed on her nylon snow pants. She lifted a hand away from her cocoa and wiped her face.

"Well, if you're not going to be here, neither am I. I'll move to Reno, Nevada, where my dad lives. I'll enroll in school out there. He's got another wife and they'll let me live with them."

The summer before, her mother had left for Australia with her boyfriend and sent Jamie to live with some people in the city of Marathon that Jamie didn't know. Nor did her mother know them very well either. A few weeks into it, she called me whispering harshly into the phone, and told me where to pick her up. I found her crying while walking on a country road twenty miles out of town. She spent the rest of the summer living at my house. Jamie was resilient and self-reliant and knew how to roll with life when the storms came in.

"Well, Nevada is closer to California," I replied. She raised her eyes and forced a smile toward me. The holes in our lives seemed to line up and make a sight, like looking through a ship's sexton and giving us each, with each other, a compass reading on the sea of life.

Her smile drooped into a frown and crinkled up like it did when she fell apart. I put my arm around her, and she silently cried. We leaned against each other in the corner of the warming hut, like two broken vases on a shelf in a thrift store, while Prince sang "Purple Rain" on the radio. Even now, when time I hear that song, I remember that night.

The warming hut lady turned a page in her book, her attention fixed far away in another world.

CHAPTER 5

"Blessed are the pure in heart: for they shall see God."
Mathew 5:8

"Reflection is the beginning of reform."
Mark Twain

Statement given to the Marinette County Sheriff's Department 1/31/85 By Leslie J. Ollila
...we then went to the area indicated by Mr. Dubrow and followed the footprints. We then shined our flashlights and observed a body lying face down in the snow and a gun case by a tree. We had discovered the body between 8:00 / 8:30 PM. We then returned to the college and contacted the Marinette County Sheriff's Department.

MARINETTE SHERIFF DEPARTMENT SUPPLEMENTARY INVESTIGATION REPORT
Report of James E. Jerue, SGT. Invest., MRSO
We crossed the fence, and while walking toward the victim, I observed a rifle, a gun case, and a blanket on the ground near the victim. I observed a trail of blood from just south of the item leading to the victim. There was also a trail in the snow, as though the victim had crawled about 15-20 feet. He was lying on his back, with his head downhill. I checked the body and observed that the victim was frozen, obviously dead.

13 July – 29 August, 1984
Ministry in Europe
A Sojourn for Christ
Shawn Finucan
I was glad to have met the head of E.C.M. in Vienna, who co-worked with Don Kyre in the U.S. for much of our ministry. On our first trip into Yugoslavia, Scott and I brought funds, Bibles and food to two contacts.

September, 2019 Merrill, Wisconsin

I read the reports from the Marinette County Sheriff's Office that came in the brown manila envelope in my study with the clock on my desk ticking, reassuring me that time was passing. The world was unfolding as it should.

I cut back between the two statements and envisioned what they had seen. Leslie Ollila states that when he found Shawn's body it was face down. When Deputy Jerue finds Shawn's body he wrote in his report that it was face up.

My initial thought was he was alive between the time when Ollila found him and managed to turn himself over before the Sheriff got there? When I consider the temperature and the amount of time he spent outside, all day and into the evening, I realized that it was not possible. It's more likely that the initial party that was with Olilla possibly turned him over to identify him, or see if he needed help.

I reread the part about him crawling in the snow for twenty feet with a 30.06 bullet through his chest, and my heart broke as my vivid imagination took a painful flight over those moments in the dark, early morning, sub-zero winter conclusion of Shawn's life.

He wanted to live. He was fighting for his life. He was trying to get help. He was surprised by what had happened. It took him a few moments to figure it out. Once he did, he knew the situation was critical. I was confident that his faith was a great comfort to him in those moments.

March, 1984 Merrill, Wisconsin

I was in the basement, just outside of my bedroom, stinging the heavy, leather Everlast punching bag. My stepdad, Bob Weaver, is a master carpenter and had built both Shawn and me bedrooms next to each other in the subterranean workshop and gym area of the full basement. When Shawn had left for the Marine Corps, I had found a crowbar and knocked out one of the walls between the two rooms to extend my bedroom room into a Presidential suite.

The particle-board walls were full of sports posters, like Bruce Lee holding his nunchucks with three bloody scratches on his left pectoral from the movie *Enter the Dragon*, Mohammad Ali punching Joe Frasier, and Farah Faucet in a bathing suit.

My stereo was rocking to Van Halen or Steve Winwood and weapons of any variety were hanging on the walls. When it rained hard, the walls leaked, and the carpet got wet. It stank like mildew until I set out fans on it, but that didn't bother me.

The door was a mess. Year's back I had read the *Fellowship of the Rings* trilogy by J.R.R. Tolkien and had been swept up in the intoxicating fantasy world that would allow me to escape my own. I had asked Dad to use his attorney knowledge to change my name legally to Frodo Baggins, but he wasn't having any of it.

"No, that would be tremendously disrespectful to the whole Finucan clan for you to drop our name. It damn well might be the only thing I leave you."

I had wisely refrained from making comments about that being the point.

Undeterred, I then tried to cut my bedroom door into a circular shape so it would resemble a hobbit door. My carpentry skills were such that anything I tried to make in shop class turned out to be a cutting board, so it didn't work out so well.

Bob is a patient and kind man with a high threshold of tolerance, but my construction project disappointed him. He looked at it exasperated and said, "Do you know the value of something like this?" He shook his head in frustration and walked away.

My basement domain had its own side door entrance, making it super cool and accessible for friends to drop by. The leather Everlast punching bag was absorbing my pent-up frustrations and when John Purcell threw the side door open and came in, he didn't waste any time.

"What's this I hear you're leaving?"

"Yeah." I took off the gloves and started unwinding the hand wraps. "The wind is calling my name, and I got that old feeling, feeling like this one-horse town can't hold me," I added while looking beyond the basement walls like I was looking at a far-off horizon. John didn't think it was funny.

"So, you're not joining the Marines with us? I just signed up. So did Kyle Kolka, Dave Hoffman, Greg Ball, Erik Lange and Jim Grund. We leave right after graduation. This was your idea."

Shawn had been a Marine and so had my dad. They were heavy influences in my life and that was the plan, originally.

We had all gone down to the recruitment station and talked to the Sergeant that day together. I had come home with a poster and some bumper stickers. The allure of having a destination after high school seemed to have emblazoned them all with a sense of purpose. As for me, I was cooled to the idea the more I thought of it.

"I realize this was my idea. And it's true. And it's a good idea. Just not for me right now. I need to take an adventure. Some different plans came up and I'm going out to California with my Dad."

John looked at me like I was going to take off a rubber mask and reveal myself to be someone else.

"But…this was your idea. You've been talking about this for the last two years."

I set down the gloves and stopped the bag from rocking. I pushed on it gently to stop it, the chains in the ceiling rafters stopped creaking, and the basement fell silent.

"Come on in." I pointed to my room, and we went into my suite-style bedroom and sat at the big, wooden-spool, conversation table, where I had set lawn chairs around it. I found two warm Pabst Blue Ribbon beers under my bed and offered him one. We cracked the top on them, but John didn't drink his, only stared at the warm foam that came out of the can.

"Here's the thing. This is an opportunity and I must take it. I leave the day after tomorrow…"

"Wait, you're leaving before graduation?"

"Yeah."

"Why in the hell would you do that? You're going to throw away your diploma?"

"Well, I prefer to think of it, like…sidestepping it."

"You know this is a bad idea, right? Is this your Dad? Is this his idea? I just have to ask."

"Well, no…it's mine, really." But after saying it, it just didn't feel true. I didn't like how everyone was putting this on Dad.

"Ok, listen," John said and set his full beer can down on the table. "As your friend, I'm going to ask you to reconsider your plan: finish your high school education and come with us in the Corps. We can all go to boot camp together. I worked it out with the recruiter. If you're worried about passing the math part of the entrance exam, we can tutor you through it."

"That will not happen, Old Buddy. This charter is set. That old, gray wind is blowing and I'm moving down the road."

John stewed in it a few more minutes, then lifted the full, warm beer and guzzled it down in one lift. He crushed the can in his hand and belched loud from the top of his gut. "If that's that, then that's that," he said and wished me well. He would remember forevermore that I had talked them all into joining and then ditched out to California. He still brings it up.

John went on to make a career in the Marines and at his retirement party, Colonel Minick gave a speech that mentioned that, as a career recruiter, John Purcell had recruited almost a battalion of men and women into the Corps.

At that retirement celebration, John got up and told the story of how I had talked them into joining the Corps and didn't go. That had gotten a laugh from the attendees. He inferred that my influence had a hand in the outcome of all those recruits who had joined under John's signature because of my influence on him. True or not, I don't know. But that day in the basement, I had let him down.

The gray sky over the white snow blended around me like I was living in a black and white photograph. Snowbanks didn't set off against each other, they layered so it was difficult to tell where streets ended and another block began. Yards looked like sinks full of dirty suds in the tired, old snow cover.

I drove my 1974 AMC Hornet with the big, descending scuba divers stickers on each side, into the staff parking lot. The car was the victim of rust at the front fenders, so much that when it rained, water sprayed up through the holes in the left front fender and doused the windshield with muddy rainwater spinning off the front tire.

When the switch broke on the windshield wiper, I had to lean out the window and move the wiper blade with a stick as I drove. The decaying metal, with blue paint on it, was offering a skeletal cut-away view of the internal workings of a car as it disintegrated. "I think you put those stickers on your car to keep it from falling apart," Nancy Olivotti had said to me.

I was thinking about calling the car the Blue Diver, but it never shook its original name of the Hornet.

The engine ran like a cheetah. The interior dashboard had an air conditioner with a dramatic setting on the dial that read 'desert only.' I would warn people when they reached for it. "Be careful Robin, that's the desert only switch."

I slid the Blue Diver into Vice Principle Strand Wedul's parking spot. He was the guy who cut me from the swim team, then gave me the three-day suspension. I turned off the engine, cutting off Led Zeppelin's "In the Evening," playing on the tape deck. I walked in, not caring who I might encounter, because I wasn't going to class. Not now, not ever, I thought.

When I got to my locker, I spun the combination, looking over the dark lenses to read the numbers in the indoor lighting. A pretty girl from my English Lit class walked by me and gave me a smile. I drank it in and felt elevated in a powerful boost from her fantastic gesture. A woman's smile has always been a kiss of sunlight to me.

I took out my notebooks on several subjects because they had continuing stories in each one. When a class got dull, my pen flew over the paper. It might even look like I was taking notes. I slid from the stifling rooms and monotone lectures into my imagination and rolled in the elixir of creative escape like a dog on something dead.

My geometry notebook, second time through that class and I was fixing to fail it again, had a story about a kid who was bow hunting a monster like the Hodag to save the family of a girl he was dating, though the girl's family didn't like him. He would save their lives anyway and then she would dump him for some dumb, football jock with a behavior disorder, because he had big hands. In the dialogue, I find this:

"I'm sorry, Frank, but I just love the way Roger looks in his football jersey, and I love his big forehead, feet and hands, they make me feel so feminine," Becky said with her eyes fluttering in titillation. Her Dad's front porch had grown darker in the shadow of the setting sunlight. The remaining red rays were sitting on the horizon over the woodshed, shining in Frank's eyes, giving him a headache. He had just ended a fight for his life against a mythical beast that was set on killing Becky's family for sacrifice and they would never know.

No one would ever know.

"Great. You know what they say about a guy with big hands and big feet?"

"Well…," Becky responded, looking like she was about to gush something inappropriate.

"They're clowns," Frank said, spitting the words out in disgust. He turned to walk to his claw-shredded AMC Gremlin. He cranked on the ignition and worked the gas pedal, praying that it would not flood and that it would start so he could get the hell out of her Dad's driveway with some imagined level of human dignity.

I closed the notebook and smiled, putting it in the backpack. That needed further development. Maybe a screenplay take as well.

My Physical Science notebook at first was all about the study of matter—its motion through time and space, and related concepts of energy and force. On and on about how atoms formed chemical bonds in chemical reactions to form new systems and blah, blah, blah, but the word chemistry and attraction had my mind wander to thinking about Sue Wendlan, the varsity gymnast girl, perched in the desk next to me with eloquent posture and a strong, lower curve in her spine. Her legs were perfected through the discipline of exercise, and she wore snug dress pants that could have been tailored. She moved into the room like a caged lioness, until she poured herself slowly onto the lucky chair just three feet from me.

I would forget to breathe when she walked into the classroom.

I started kind of falling for her in the way I can before I get a chance to talk with a girl. I started writing this cute, summer camp story about her falling in love with a quiet kid that she doesn't notice until she falls off the dock, hits her head, and he saves her from drowning. She feels this need to pay him back using her sexual prowess, but he plays hard-to-get because she was kind of a bitch before he saved her and it really tears her up. The law of attraction and chemistry is working in this tug-of-war teenage story of back-and-forth, emotional tension and release.

There was lots of sexy dialogue with her revealing her intimate fantasies and desires, and they finally start making out on the beach of the remote Northwoods lake.

Anyway, I had to take that notebook because I had used Sue Wendlan's real name in the pages. Then I thought, so what? Wasn't I leaving town forever?

My biology notebook had a story in it about a kid who was a pacifist and transferred to a school where some of the students were trained martial artists with black belts in Tang So Do. They were running a crime ring of scalping tickets to the football games. The new kid was given a choice: he could join them in their crimes or get the crap beat out of him every day.

He had just started learning how to fight and formed a friendship with a Chinese girl who knew Kung Fu, when Mr. Jensen, the biology teacher, started calling on me every day with some stupid question that I had no clue what the answer was. So, that ended the development of that story.

I threw that notebook in my backpack and felt the potential of that idea with its weight in gold. The story was full of fierce fighting and would be a good *Kung Fu* movie. If I could find a way to make this writing thing pay, I could write my own ticket. I remember feeling that promise and wondering if there was a spot in this world for someone who wanted to just sit at a typewriter and create worlds that did not yet exist.

I gently handled my beat-up copy of William Faulkner's *Light in August*, the book that had been getting me through study hall. I recalled the story of Joe Christmas, who didn't know who he was, what his purpose was, or where he should fit in. I could relate.

I grabbed a few pens and a rock-hard piece of Bazooka Bubble gum. I unwrapped it and popped it into my mouth—that flavor always reminded me of little league baseball games. The little comic showed Bazooka Joe walking by his buddy.

"Hey, Mort," says Bazooka Joe, "what did your dad say when he fell off the ladder?"

"Want me to leave out the swear words?" Mort asks Joe from behind his turtleneck that covers his face.

"Of course!" Bazooka Joe says.

"Nothing," replies Mort. The quotation marks of expression show Joe exasperated to hear this. I threw the little comic strip back into the locker, like it was a monument that said "I was here."

I shouldered the backpack, feeling the weight of my decision cut across my collarbone and slammed the locker door. I wondered if that sound was like a jail cell closing.

The increasing isolation with each year I had felt in these halls haunted me as I moved toward the exit. I let human relationships drift from me here and bore loneliness like a rite of passage, a self-obsessed martyr doing something honorable and proud. A sense that I should be feeling nostalgic about leaving these halls for the last time haunted me, but instead, I felt like I was walking the plank of a pirate ship with no land on the horizon.

In my mind, I saw the school administration dressed in pirate gear, jabbing at me with sabers and cradling blunderbusses.

"Aye now, ere's a suspension for ya, Jamie, that you'll enjoy! Walk the plank of a dropout, rather than waste yer life in a boring school!" Strand Wedul might yell from behind an eye patch.

I didn't run into anyone as I left. I hoped for another smile from a pretty girl as a goodbye, but there were only the familiar smells of dusty halls and stale Pine Sol.

Who was there to care? Would anyone miss me here? Who was I kidding? But as I descended the stairs of Merrill High School that day, one thing was certain: in my senior year, in the second semester, I was a high school dropout.

CHAPTER 6

"And ye shall know the truth, and the truth shall make you free."
John 8:32

Marine Soldiers
Combat Boots
Bloused Fatigues
Gone to war
Thoughts… Soft warm girl, tender touch caressing…touch
NOW
Adrenalin…Fire!
Frag Right 10 O'clock
1st fire team prepare to rush—Rush!
Rapid weapons fire
SpfffttTHUD
Joe's brains on
Barbed wire
1 Arab per BBL. Of Oil
Crazy Speed
Ending Quick I'm
Downed Blood
Medivac Me Home
"Finuc"
Dec 26th 1979
L/CPL USMC

(From Shawn's Next to Nothing Notebook, one year before he was "saved")

MARINETTE SHERIFF DEPARTMENT
SUPPLEMENTARY INVESTIGATION REPORT

Case Number 85-393

Date: 31 January 85

Title: Death Investigation

He was lying on his back with his head downhill. I checked the body, and observed that the victim was frozen, obviously dead…I observed footprints leading from just south of the tree, going southeast and downhill toward a blue object by a fence. We followed the footprints, and observed that the object was blue construction paper, on which a target had been drawn. There were three holes in the target. Mattison then photographed all objects and the victim.

Sgt. James Jerue

October, 2019 Merrill, Wisconsin

When I got to this part of the statement, I flipped back through the report to find the statement given by Scott Meisenburg that stated Shawn had approached him to ask if he could borrow his rifle. Shawn had shown him a target that he had made on blue paper.

Shawn was skilled in crafts. He had outfitted his hunting knife with a one-inch piece of deer antler on the leather retention strap. There was a time when he was using deer antler to dress up items of outdoor gear. After his spiritual conversion, he had painted a Psalm from scripture on a big, sawed-off stump top of beautiful, grained wood. It had read:

"He lifted me out of the pit of despair, out of the mud and mire. He set my feet upon the rock holding fast my steps secure."

Psalm 40:2

The target Shawn had drawn was not part of the filed report and I didn't find it in the possessions that I had. He had set up the target and shot at it three times before something had occurred. These were not the actions of someone who had gone into the woods to kill himself. I was certain of this.

March, 1984 Merrill, Wisconsin

A snowstorm came in as Dad and I packed the Jeep for our trip. We loaded our gear into the back of the powder-blue Jeep through the unzipped, plastic, cover top with the wind wicking away our body heat and swirling the flakes over and around us. When the snowflakes touched any exposed skin, a needle of chill pierced that spot.

I had packed light as instructed. I had a "grip" as Dad called it, a medium-size, soft-sided duffel bag containing clothing and gear, footwear, shorts and other summer wear, and a pair of dress clothes for any business I had to do.

In case life got ugly, I had packed The Snake, my Ruger Security Six 357 magnum revolver with a scope mounted on the six-inch barrel. I included its custom, cut-leather holster that let the scope mount slide in unhindered. I packed it in the middle of the gear with a box of 357 Magnum hollow-point shells. I had also packed my Puma hunting knife in the metal scabbard.

Dad kept his Browning Hi-Power 9mm between the seats. We hoped for peace but we both understood the evil that stalks this world and knew that if evil was armed with firepower, we needed to be as well.

I climbed in and latched the soft-sided, thin door against a winter storm that would pummel us with white fury and stay with us almost across the entire country. Dad wore his Irish cap and leather driving gloves and smoked his Marlboro 100's as he drove. The big, loose, steering wheel had some play in it and the snow tires gave the impression that we could climb over anything in our path.

We switched roles driving. There was no real way to doze off in the passenger seat of the Jeep because the door was set in the frame of the vehicle too far away from the seat, so it was coffee and navigation in the shotgun seat.

The winter storm gave us about twenty feet of maximum visibility and the spiraling snowflakes moving onto the windshield hypnotized me into focusing on them when I drove for hours. The winter asteroid simulation tempted me like a siren song to leave the highway and follow a space track of white stars into a road of oblivion while I craved and fought off sleep.

The highway was buried in snow and then buried some more, but the fat tires of the Jeep kept climbing over it. We would come upon a plow traveling slowly and I would have to make a death-defying pass in the slippery fast lane and then blaze a trail over six inches of the fresh, slick, white, gloppy element.

I watched cars trying to pass us break into a spin just after getting out in front. A businessman in a suit locked eyes on me through his windshield as his car whirled around in a 360-degree spin, the front end facing us barely clearing our hood. He slid off the road into the deep ditch of immediate despair as the treacherous storm system closed tighter and tighter on us with each passing hour.

I was enthralled with the sense of adventure before me. When a passenger, I made notations in a notebook jammed under the seat with a pen that I had to keep scribbling with to prime the freezing ink. I wrote: "Meet yourself coming back on the road in life? What does that mean? You can't because the road is different. The road changes every day, as does the man." Beneath that, I scrawled a poem by Stephen Crane:

A man said to the universe, "Sir, I exist!"

"However," the universe replied: "That fact does not fill me with a sense of obligation."

I had written and submitted a few pieces to magazines in my high school years and had already begun getting what would be a long list of rejections. "Appreciate it, but it's not what we are looking for…" was the world's response to what I wanted to believe was my talent.

Could an accomplished writer be a high school drop out? My stomach fell as I realized I was going to find out. I looked at my watch. Some of my friends were in sixth-hour geometry class right now.

"Are you an alcoholic?" Dad asked me one day while driving, jabbing a glance at me, then back to the road before him. The question confronted me at the doorway of my mind like a knock by a vacuum cleaner salesman.

"Do you think I am?" I retorted.

"It doesn't matter what I think. It only matters what you think." He glanced away from the road at me. I let silence permeate the cab of the Jeep.

"Yeah," I heard myself answer from the halls of truth within. Dad looked at me again now with despair and sympathy. He understood what I would face in life as a challenge, because he was an alcoholic as well.

"You're young to face this. Jeeze, Kid. This drug—it's the worst of them all. It stripped me of everything I had. It destroyed all my human relationships and transformed my personality into a wrecking ball of trouble for anyone who encountered me.

"'The man takes the drink and then the drink takes the man, I've heard said and it's true.' When you tell me you're an alcoholic, that tells me a lot. Perhaps you have a feeling inside that you just don't fit in, or you are never really happy with your situation; you feel unsettled and restless in life at a deep level that's hard to describe."

"Doesn't everyone feel that?"

"I can't speak for everyone, but I don't think normal people feel the displacement and discontentment and depression I always did. With me, it's depression. I have mental illness from depression."

He said it to me like it was going to shock me. Hadn't I been watching him live in the parks of our small town homeless for years? The subject was serious, but I had to look out my side window to hide my slight smile.

"One of the ways we treat these feelings, or maybe it's part of the origin of the disease, I'm not sure- but we drink. Drinking offers a temporary solution, but the effect shows up fast. Alcohol destroys your ability to connect with people. The disease immediately begins to isolate you, so that it can…kill you."

My eyes opened wide as my eyebrows raised. "The disease wants to kill me?"

"Yeah, really. It's a disease of the mind—a mental disorder, a psychosis." His fierce green eyes shot over at me a glance of intensity to underline his point. "We obsess on drinking and soon can't think of anything else but when and how we are going to get loaded. We stop feeling, doing anything to not think and experience life and only crave the buzz of getting loaded, at the expense of everything around us.

And it's progressive. Do you know what a progressive disease is?"

"I can guess it grows."

"Right, it grows, like a tumor, so this disease grows within you, even after you quit drinking. It's waiting for you, all the while slipping thoughts into your mind that try to make you believe you don't have it. It worms into your subconscious and makes little suggestions. See, your subconscious is the engine room of your mind. It takes commands and doesn't argue. Your disease doesn't sleep and waits inside your head for you to get tired, so it can make its play."

"What? Like…it's alive?" I asked.

"That's right. It's like…a method of demonic possession," he said drifting away in analytical thought.

My mind went to memories of *The Exorcist* movie that dad had taken me to at the Grand Theatre in Wausau when I was seven years old. The movie had kept me up with nightmares for weeks. My mind flashed over the image of Linda Blair's head turning all the way around on her neck, then projectile vomiting out split-pea soup from under her demonic white eyes. I shuddered.

Outside our plastic cover, the snowstorm raged, following us out of Wisconsin like a specter in pursuit of our escape, across Nebraska, then Colorado, and through the mountain passes. We passed signs that told us we needed chains on our tires, ignored them, and powered through the frozen, swirling element.

Throughout that trip, Dad preached to me about the perils of an alcoholic taking to drink, and I listened. I quit drinking on that drive, and it would be twenty-three years before I started drinking again.

The storm abated when we got to western Colorado and the sun shone on our trip. The western air was dry, soft, and smelled of sage. The people dressed differently; the sub-zero temperatures from arctic winds that blow down across Canada did not reach here and dictate their fashion. The sharp beautiful teeth of winter had no bite in this region.

San Clemente was a picturesque surfer town. The streets were clean. The people were young and slim, wearing Ocean Pacific styles, waxed haircuts, and parachute pants. The women were beautiful like they had migrated here from all over the country, like geese.

"That's the house where Richard Nixon used to live," Dad said and pointed to a mansion with an iron gate around it.

We drove into the campground, and with no reservation, we were able to get a campsite for only a few nights. I looked out the zipped-down window of the Jeep as we wound through the rows of trailers, recreational vehicles, and tents to reach our tiny spot. I got a glimpse of the blue ocean and smiled.

We took a few moments to unwind on the picnic table of our small campsite. We were sandwiched between surfers to the right, and a family of a mother and dad with two little kids on the left. Dad started unpacking the Jeep to get to the tent. I tried to help him.

"Why don't you go explore the beach and look around. I'll take care of this," Dad said. He looked tired but determined.

He would need rest soon. The drive had been a strain on us both, and if he didn't knock himself out soon with a nap, I knew from experience that he would suffer a strong attack of depression that would overwhelm him for days.

As I walked away, I saw a man who knew Dad come over to say "Hi." I remembered that this was his winter hideaway each year. Dad lived homeless in the parks in Merrill for the spring and summer, but late in the fall he flocked here to weather out the winter.

I walked down to the beach, saw the late afternoon sunshine on the ocean, and took off my shoes to feel the sand. Some surfers were out in the blue water waiting for a set on their boards, out past the breakup. I felt the seafoam break on my feet. Seeing the coastal bluffs meeting the sea, feeling the sunshine, and smelling the salt air was an elixir to my awestruck, restless mind. I was here.

We made it!

Dad crashed for the next few days. He stayed in the tent and slept, and when he didn't sleep, he smoked on the picnic table and stared at the empty fire pit. He talked about how much he screwed up his family life and how his life sucked. Then he went into the tent and stared up at the nylon ceiling. There was no way to reach him in that world and it was all I could do to keep him from pulling me into it.

I stayed busy exploring the lay of the park. I walked down the bluff trails to the beach and watched the surfers. They bobbed out in the sea in their wet suits, sitting on their boards waiting for a set of waves. When a set moved in, they lay down and paddled the board hard to gain some momentum, then popped up and rode in this amazing force of God's creation toward the beach.

I wanted to get out there with them. The ocean was beautiful, vast, stretching out to an endless horizon. The seagulls that made their home on the beach replaced the cardinals and crows that I would see and hear back in

Wisconsin. I swam in the salty water and felt the torrent of the waves and the crust it left on my skin, like a sodium shirt.

The people here were less likely to acknowledge a stranger. They lived in private mental islands and seemed self-absorbed and inwardly focused. They were used to the invading transients, so they looked through me, yet another Midwesterner with nothing to offer. So, I moved about in the isolation I had developed before I came here.

I took the keys to the Jeep and went to a grocery store to get some supplies, but it was a challenge to purchase things that needed refrigeration, so I bought a cooler and some ice.

After a few days, Dad had pulled himself together and we went to Mass on Sunday. I remember stopping at a small store off Pacific Coast Highway and purchasing a rich, flaky pastry, called baklava, that weighed a pound and was made with diced-raisin filling. It was very satisfying to my recently-awakened sweet tooth, and I ate about three of those a week for a stint.

In one of my excursions into San Clemente, I got pulled over by a city policeman. He told me I had committed an offense of failure-to-yield at the turn a few blocks back. He handed me a ticket. When I got back to the campsite I showed it to Dad, who looked at it. "This is another form of oppression, Jamie. The cops are just government thugs who shove around the poor to keep us in line."

"Well, it's a hundred-and-twenty bucks…" I was saying.

"No, it's not, you know why? Because we aren't going to pay it." Dad snatched the ticket from my hand and threw it into the fire. The flames cradled the thin paper for just a moment, then blue flames engulfed it and turned the cop's ticket to ashes of defiance as I watched. "That's the way we handle that bullshit," Dad declared, and sat back in his lawn chair, like he had just served up an ass-kicking on the whole system that had victimized him.

"Is that your advice as my attorney?" I asked, watching the evidence of my infraction go up in smoke.

"You're damn right it is."

CHAPTER 7

"The world cannot hate you; but me it hateth, because I testify of it, that the works thereof are evil."

John 7:7

The Alcoholic is an extreme example of self-will run riot, though he usually doesn't think so.

Alcoholics Anonymous (the big book)

Case Number 85-393
Date: 31 January 85
Title: Death Investigation
MARINETTE SHERIFF DEPRARTMENT
SUPPLEMENTARY INVESTIGATION REPORT

...I then checked the rifle, which was lying on the ground just to the south of the tree. It was pointed toward the target, with the barrel in the snow. I picked up the rifle and noticed the safety was in the "fire" position. I opened the bolt and there was an empty, "spent" cartridge in the chamber. There were no other cartridges in the magazine.

SGT. James Jerue

2019—Notes Merrill, Wisconsin

Sgt. Jerue knew his way around a firearm. He was perhaps a military man, or someone who had training and field experience with weaponry. I recall that something unsettled me about the sentence that he wrote about checking the rifle that was lying on the ground.

Sgt. Jerue picked up the rifle to check it. If I move quickly to do something, do I notice all other details that might be relevant? Has my examination of the location and placement of the weapon ended when I exercise my action to pick up the rifle? There were no other bullets in the gun, the weapon was set to fire, so there was no malfunction with the safety, because it wasn't engaged.

Shawn had shot three shots at the target, went down to check the target, came back to the rifle and something happened. What happened? I thought of a hundred scenarios of carelessness that a Marine could make handling a loaded 30.06 rifle.

13 July -29 August 1984
Ministry in Europe
A Sojourn for Christ

We returned to the security of Vienna and there was discussion about the response when going into Romania about what to say when asked by a communist official for being there. In my own heart, I could not say "tourism' for being the primary answer. Before God, I did not have a peace and would respond in a general but closer to the primary purpose, which was God's work. This causes great consternation among the team.

October 2019 Merrill, Wisconsin

When I read Shawn's sentence about going into Romania, my mind flashed back to my trip that I had taken there in 2010. I was thrilled to travel with members of my family. I studied up on Dracula and wanted to tour his castle. I had steeped myself in who the real Dracula had been, not the Bram Stoker version from his novel in 1891, where Dracula was depicted as a vampire.

Stoker had certainly heard some of the legends of the real Vlad Dracula. Vlad the Impaler, as he was known, who impaled people by the hundreds and once sat in his yard eating breakfast amidst dozens of people impaled on long stakes. It was written that he had dipped his bread in blood and ate it, and this must have been what Stoker had heard and embellished on to make Dracula a blood-drinking monster of the night.

But the Romanian people saw Dracula as a battle hero who led his army from the front and stopped the Muslim hoard from killing the people and forcing the eradication of Christianity in Eastern Europe.

Shawn's "Sojourn for Christ" essay, making reference to smuggling Bibles into Romania, caused me to breathe deeply. I had an idea of what he was concerned about specifically, and certainly he knew the danger he faced as he approached that border.

I had seen what happened to people who fell under the suspicion of Nicolae Ceauşescu, the dictator of Romania, who ruled the country as head-of-state from 1965 until 1986. His reign ended when he ordered his secret police to open fire on some protestors in the city of Timişoara, triggering the Romanian Revolution. The army turned on him, and Ceauşescu and his wife were arrested and executed on Christmas Day of 1989.

Ceauşescu's reign was totalitarian, and his rule is considered the most repressive in the history of the Eastern Bloc. His secret police, called the Securitate, were national henchmen who used harsh treatments of torture and execution on the population of the country, or any who came under suspicion—man, woman, or child. Ceauşescu's dictatorship would be known as one of the most brutal regimes in the world.

Anyone sneaking in religious literature would have been deemed a severe threat.

Shawn was illegally carrying Bibles into a communist dictatorship and, as he prepared, his diary gave me indication that he was struggling with lying at the border-crossing as to why he was there.

I looked up from the paper and out the window. At the time Dad was smuggling drugs, most likely from Pablo Escobar into America, Shawn was smuggling Bibles into Romania.

The contrast in their simultaneous operations astounded me.

As my mind went back to what Shawn was facing for his Bible smuggling, I reflected on the insight I had gained.

In 2010, I had visited a terrible prison called Sighet in the city of Sighetu Marmației, Romania. It was only one of over a hundred prisons for political prisoners to disappear into. Over two million people were arrested, executed, or left to die in terrible jail cells from starvation, torture, and neglect. These people were ministers, journalists, economists, politicians, scientists, priests, army members, and even children who faced this fate with or without a trial. Some were forced to labor to death in projects like The Danube—Black Sea Canal, said to have been built with the blood of thousands of unfortunate detainees.

In my tour of Sighet, at the prison now made into a memorial of the victims of Communism, I had seen cells with big rings concreted into the floor. People were affixed there for torture. The rooms were windowless. People were thrown into them and left to die, like rats in a forgotten trap. And, there was a yard where some were dragged out from their cells and executed.

The place still smelled of blood, urine and rotting flesh.

The designers of the memorial had framed pictures of the victims, and displayed them high on the walls, one after the other. They lined the entire infrastructure of the massive building. Some photos were black and white, perhaps taken during indoctrination into the prison. Others were professional glamour shots of women wearing minks, dresses, and jewelry. I saw a picture of a child about eight years old staring into the camera lens with a hopeless fear in his eyes that I will never forget. Who would throw a child into prison? Some victims were men in business suits, work clothes, women in street clothes, and aprons. People from all walks of life were captured and sentenced here. Now their faces hung in frames on the walls of this murderous place so they wouldn't be forgotten.

On a concrete wall hung a big map with electronic pins that lit up in red to show the locations of other prisons for political prisoners across Romania. There were at least a hundred throughout this small country.

This memory went through my mind as I read Shawn's essay and wondered when he crossed the border with his Bibles, just how close he might have been to become one of those faces on the wall. I imagined what it might have been like to recognize his face in a picture when I made my tourist visit and felt the shock wave as though it were real.

At the last Christmas I saw Shawn, in 1984, he was relaxed and happy. He had just returned from his mission trip. He would have just over thirty days to live. Mom snapped the last photo ever taken of us three Finucan boys that day. We stood shoulder-to-shoulder for her as she took the photo. We are smiling in hilarity at some funny remark. Shawn was laughing from his belly with the wool scarf around his neck that I had just given him.

I wished I would have asked him about his trip and learned more details of what it was like. My brother had just returned from a Bible smuggling trip to dangerous places, and I didn't even ask about his trip.

In my study, staring out the window into the gentle, fall sunlight that caressed the trees, I released the time machine of my imagination, and went back and played it out. I see him standing by the Christmas tree and I turn to ask him some questions. In my escape mechanism, I hear his voice again from the precious vault of memory, where deceased loved ones voices are kept. They are accessible only on certain rare occasions when memories are sharp and blessed—or in dreams that awaken in tears.

I asked him questions, which he answers gently with his pleasant smile. He looks confused and concerned when tears fill my eyes, and my nose runs. My voice cracks and I give him a hug.

Then I have to come back home. I must make the re-entry before staying too long, or the door could close and leave me there. I've never done it, but Gross Joe, the detective in my imagination, has warned me: "You keep screwing around in your head and you're going to end up in the loony bin, Kid," he says from his chiseled jaw and steely eyes.

1984 San Clemente, California

When our time expired on the campsite in San Clemente, we moved into another campground just outside of town, called San Onefre. It was more remote, less populated, and still offered a great bluff-top view of the ocean. There wasn't a nearby gas station to walk to for milk and baklava. The bikini traffic was less, but it had advantages of being quieter at night.

I pitched the tent on the flat, hard ground where countless other tents had been. The powder-blue CJ 5 Jeep was parked in one of the slots, and when I looked at our setup, it had a nomadic flair to it.

We were up early at the campsite. Mass was at eight o'clock and it was important to Dad that we go each day. This posed a problem. Nothing that we had was capable of being locked, so we had no security measure against theft.

The CJ 5 soft-side, plastic doors had a latch that closed and twisted to open. We had no key for the door handles. The tent certainly offered no protection against theft. That left vital items of wallets, passports, and our two firearms that could not be out of our sight. We placed these items in my duffel bag and this became like the 'football' that had to be protected. If we left the campsite, the duffle went with us.

"What's the law on carrying around this weaponry? Isn't this concealed?" I asked.

"I'll start caring about the law when it starts prosecuting the people who try to kill me. When someone can rip off ten rounds through a window at me, walk away, and go about his business while the law couldn't care less, I get an idea of where the poor stand in the eyes of the law."

"Yeah, but…"

"'Yeah, buts' live in the woods. You can go 'Yeah, but' hunting on your own time. If you're going to live your life fully, you can't worry about every little law on the books. I'm a lawyer and I can tell you the law doesn't care a wet damn about you or me."

So, we went to Mass with the duffel bag containing The Snake and Dad's Browning Hi-Power 9mm, along with the passports. People in San Clemente, California, who attended St. Mary's by the Sea Catholic Church each morning, drove beautiful BMW's, Lexus, and Buicks. We slapped the CJ 5 right next to them in the parking lot and walked in through the big, double doors with a bag of guns like we owned the place.

Dad led the charge right up the aisle. His clothes were clean but tattered. He wore items that had holes in them. I didn't know if he had become unaware that these items of clothing were old and breaking down, or if he wanted to openly display poverty on his sleeve. I had noticed that part of his illness caused him to lose touch with the way others might perceive him. I became aware of that when he would not get a haircut for extended periods of time or trim his facial hair to a presentable length.

Was it that mental illness had broken down his ability to gauge the perception of how others might perceive him, or did he just not care?

We stood out in the parish community, and they were pretty accepting, if only in the way they ignored us. Dad would go down the middle aisle with a swagger of defiance, wearing his Patagonia sweatshirt and cut-off shorts with the holes in the back of them, sometimes showing the white of his ass. We walked right past the rich folks in their suits, sometimes right to the front row. I would be trailing behind with the duffle of weaponry.

I was tempted to blush and feel ashamed, but I had learned long ago that if I understood how infrequently people thought of other people, I wouldn't care what they thought.

"I don't care what these people think. That they think at all, is of question in my mind," as Dad had put it.

For Dad, it was an important hour of prayer and meditation. But my eighteen-year-old hormones kept me glancing at the pretty, California ladies, in their summer dresses. I struggled to focus on my devotions at Mass.

After Mass, a pretty, blonde lady of my age looked me in the eye as I walked alongside her a few steps. Her daddy noticed and gave me a hard stare. I smiled. I wondered if she was entertaining a bad, poor-boy fantasy for the purpose of pissing off Daddy.

Having grown up in a tough Northern Wisconsin River town, I compared this phenomenon to one when a girl flirts with you when she's already on a date, just to see if her boyfriend would fight someone for her. I called this "Let the games begin!" I was once in a fistfight for my life in the hallway of junior high school with one of the Gleason Gang, a few rough rural boys who flunked so many years of school they drove to junior high. Mr. Korpi, a six-foot teacher whose shoulders could fill a doorway, finally broke up our mutual slugfest by yanking us apart by our hair.

My head snapped back from his yank and my feet almost left the ground. In the front row of the spectators were a few girls who liked the blood sport. I saw Sonja Benson biting her lip while looking at my blood-smeared face and split-lip mouth as if she wanted to ride me like a dirt bike. The look in her dark, shark-like, dead-pan eyes, crossed the elements of lust and revulsion.

The raw hunger in the way she looked at me in that moment left more of an impression on me than the fight I was just in.

Moving toward the door of St. Mary's by the Sea, her daddy put his arm on his daughter's shoulder and ushered her down the lush, carpeted aisle toward the church door. He quickly moved away from the transient young man standing next to the old man with holes in the ass of his shorts and wearing no underwear. I stepped up beside her, letting The Snake in the duffle bag swing against my leg, hoping the scope wouldn't be knocked out of true.

"Hi," I said to her light blue eyes.

She smiled and said "Hi" back.

"I'm Jamie."

Her Dad pressed on faster. She glanced back at me.

I watched her tan, masterfully shaped legs, adorned with high heels, move like swaying corn stalks in a slight breeze from under her short, flower-print sundress. I felt the Catholic guilt for doing so in church, after Mass and all. Sister Laura, my fourth-grade teacher at St. Robert's, would have slapped my head with a stinging swipe of her hand. That would have to happen before I got kicked out for macing a bunch of kids with dog Halt, but that's another story.

I filed out with the congregation and stored her smile in the lonely vault of my imagination for later.

I didn't fool myself, other than a keen interest in her personality and wild tales of adventure, I would have nothing to offer to compete with her probably boring, self-obsessed, narcissistic, Southern California pretty boy, academic, all-star boyfriend. As I made my way across the parking lot, I realized all these gorgeous California ladies should have a Midwestern, real-guy fantasy.

I wanted to drive the Jeep in case Blondie was watching from her Daddy's Beamer, but my dad was already in the driver's seat, keying the ignition while a Marlboro 100 hung from his lips. The morning sun was warm and intense, and an ocean breeze moved over me as exotic to me as Kimchi.

We stopped by the post office to check the box and I received two letters. One was from John Purcell. He stated that graduation was some weeks away and, before they were to get on the bus to report to boot camp, four of them had planned to take a motorcycle trip out here to California and would stop and see me.

Arrangements would be up coming. That letter lit up my heart. How great it would be to see my old friends. My sole companion for the past few months was my dad, who suffered from depression. It would be great to get some buddy time.

I folded the letter, put it back into the envelope, and flipped to the next one. It was from the Los Angeles County District Attorney's office. My mood crashed back down to earth like a space capsule. I tore it open and was informed that because I had not paid the traffic ticket that Dad had thrown into the campfire with great bravado, nor had I appeared in court, there was a warrant out for my arrest.

I climbed back into the Jeep, held the warrant straight up, and looked forward out the windshield as Dad started the Jeep.

"What is it?"

He took it from me and pulled out his glasses.

"It's a warrant for my arrest," I said calmly.

He sped read it and handed it back to me.

"Hmm," he grunted.

"That's all you got to say? You're my lawyer. And, I've heard tell, quite frequently by many people, a brilliant one at that. How is this brilliant?"

I held up the letter like a prosecutor's exhibit in a trial. He threw the Jeep into first gear, feathered the clutch, and we lurched forward into traffic.

"I mean, this wasn't that hard to predict, really. I don't pay the fine. I get a warrant out for my arrest. It really doesn't take a Perry Mason or a California psychic to estimate that outcome."

Dad played it like he was deep in thought. He didn't say anything, so I felt the need to go on.

"Now, if I get pulled over for any infraction, or surface for any reason, and I have to show I.D., I'm going down to county lockup to make the L.A. County Jail Boxing Team."

"Yeah, well, we'll have to be careful until we figure out how to handle that," Dad answered dismissively. A sense of vulnerability settled over me, mixed with impending doom. I had the feeling that the Pied Piper of Hamlin was on the edge of Jamieville, and he was saying "It's payday, Motherfucker."

"Anyway, you are a damn good boxer," Dad smirked.

I took out a piece of Bazooka bubble gum from the glove compartment. In the comic, Mort was purchasing a ticket at the train station from a smiling clerk. "One ticket to Cleveland," Mort says through his turtleneck pulled up over his face.

"Do you want to go by Buffalo?" the clerk asks him.

"Of course not, I want to go by train!" Mort yells back in exasperation.

I folded up the comic and felt the sweet, familiar flavor fill my mouth with a sensation that replaced drinking Mad Dog 2020. I started wondering if it was time for me to catch a train to someplace like Mort was.

Back in Wisconsin, the ten thousand citizens of Merrill were impatiently waiting on the promise of spring in the late April daylight, while shoveling snow and wearing goose down-filled jackets. Sue Wendlan was sitting in Physical Science class in her panties and dress pants stretching the bubble gum out between her lips with her fingers and twisting it.
Maybe...wondering where I was.

CHAPTER 8

Precious in the sight of the LORD is the death of his saints.
Psalm 116:15

Humility is the result of getting honest with ourselves.
Basic Text of Narcotics Anonymous

13 July-19 August, 1984
Ministry in Europe
A Sojourn for Christ by Shawn Finucan
God then opened the door to Greece, which I enjoyed. I was left to myself while arrangements were made. I visited numerous tourist sites, which occupied a good part of my day—then prayer, reading and meditation. Our team then assembled in Thessalonica and we left Greece and transported Bibles into Yugoslavia to a contact. The contact was thrilled to receive them and said he had waited two years for them.

'Every word of God is pure: He is a shield unto them that put their trust in Him.'

(Proverbs 30:5)

MARINETTE SHERIFF DEPARTMENT 2/1/85
SUPPLEMENTARY INVESTIGATION REPORT
The victim was then examined further. There was an opening (tear) in the front of the outer shirt. There was also a round hole just to the left of the tear, which was located midpoint between the second and third buttons from the top, on the button line. Both were frayed around the edges. The three shirts the victim was wearing were then raised, and I observed

the front of the torso. There was a penetrating wound about 1.5 inches left of mid-line, and about the same distance above the nipple line. The victim was then turned on his side, and a large hole was observed in the coat, in the area of the upper left back.

Sgt. Jerue

October, 2019 Merrill, Wisconsin

I put down the report of the Marinette County Sheriff's Office and felt my own chest, and with my fingers, measured where Jerue was describing. The bullet wound was straight through the body. Shawn was leaning over the weapon, picking it up perhaps. He would have had big gloves on. The coat he had been wearing was a big rabbit fur coat that Dad had gotten him. It was heavy and warm.

I imagined the scenario like a scene being shot in a movie. I played it out one way with Shawn picking up the rifle after walking downrange to check the target and accidentally discharging it into himself. Then I changed the scene in my imagination. I added someone with Shawn in the woods, a friend from the Bible school, someone who wasn't exercised in rifle discipline and unfamiliar with handling a firearm. I saw Shawn put the rifle down on the blanket and walk down range to see where he hit the target. The guy or lady would pick up the weapon and begin to look at it.

The loud crack of the rifle reverberates through the still, dark woods…

But there was only one set of tracks mentioned in the snow by the people who found his body. What if someone followed him out into the woods? Someone who knew he was going shooting. Why? Shawn became aware of something at the college that he shouldn't have. Some piece of information came to his knowledge that put his life in danger.

I shoot another scenario in my mind. A shadow stalks through the woods, watches Shawn shooting, and raises a rifle. I change perspective—looking through the scope of a 30.06 rifle like Shawn had. The cross hairs of the scope move over trees, brush and then find Shawn wearing the big rabbit fur jacket. They line up on his back as he begins to walk down range.

I had to know more about this entrance and exit wound to understand what happened. Evidence didn't lie. Sometimes it was the only thing that didn't.

1984 San Clemente, California

After daily Mass, sometimes we would go to Charlie's Diner on the main drag in San Clemente and have bacon and eggs. We watched the parade of traffic as we ate. Little Toyota pickup trucks with the net air-gates across the bed of the trucks and hot rods, like Mustangs and Chevy Nova's with no rust on them driven by Marines from the base in Riverside, rolled past, mixed in with an array of expensive vehicles from all walks of life.

Sometimes Dad and I joked or read the paper if someone left it on a nearby table. I recall the undercurrent of anxiety and displacement within me. I felt confused by it. It was comparable to being a step behind in the beat of life. I felt out of pace from what I should be doing. It was like I had missed a bus and didn't know which one to get on next. That moment and this sensation would haunt me for my life.

As we were leaving the restaurant, a surfer approached me with a surfboard under his arm.

"Dude, I'm strapped for cash, will you buy my board? I'll take eighty bucks for it right now." His sun-dyed, blonde hair looked sandy. He was barefoot, wearing a long pair of shorts and had a desperate look in his blue, blood-shot eyes.

The board was lime green, had some wax on it and looked all right to me, for what I knew about boards.

"All I got is forty bucks," and pulled out the two twenty's I had from Dad's smuggling windfall. He looked at it, then around, like he was hoping someone else would be coming along. He took two steps away from me, but I stayed still, kept my hand out with the money extended. He circled back like a dog to a dead crow and took it while shaking his head in defeat. He handed the board off to me like he was selling his mom's cat.

My hands felt the waxed fiberglass and I noted the weight of the plank. It balanced in my hands like a fighting staff to a Kung Fu monk. There were a few dings in it, a scratch on the side, but it was intact.

Dad regarded the board thoughtfully then gave it a nod. "Keep it. It will give you some recreational activity in the park."

"Right on," I smiled back.

"Good. I could use some room and some privacy."

We unzipped the back of the plastic cover of the CJ5, put it in, and left it sticking out the back.

We rolled through town with my new purchase hanging out the back and a sensation that I had bought into living in California. I had moved from observer to participant. I felt like I had purchased a key to the door of the ocean. With this tool, I would have access to the waves and the tide and gain ingress to an activity that would challenge me and help me grow. A few surfers went by in a Subaru Brat and one gave me the hang-five, hand sign of extended pink and thumb.

I gave it back. Was I a surfer? To do is to be. I was in a brotherhood now. Now I was a native transplant. I just had to learn the moves of this new culture.

Whatever one man can do, another can do. I was stoked.

The campsites out of town in San Onofre were cheaper, more remote, and less populated. There were no showers or hot water access. So, every few days when we needed to clean up, we drove into San Clemente at night and parked outside the wall of the city campground. We waited until no one was walking by, then got out of the Jeep.

We took a towel and a shaving kit, and tossed it over the wall, then jumped up to catch the edge with our hands and hoist ourselves over. Dad and I had been jumping the fence of the Merrill swimming pool in the evenings, since I was a kid. This was easier. Once we dropped to the ground, after clearing the wall, we walked to the bathrooms like anyone who had a campsite reservation and blended. It was a blessing to have hot water, soap up, and clean the gritty saltwater out of my hair.

A clean shave and tooth brushing made me feel civilized again. Something spiritually cleansing happens when I shower. The water washing over me renews me like rainfall on dry soil. We were getting ready to leave the community bathrooms when dad found the Rip Curl Dawn Patrol wetsuit hanging on a coat hanger from a showerhead.

A surfer of my height and weight had taken it off, rinsed it out, and forgot it.

"Most likely forgot it after he got stoned on some good pot." Dad presented it to me with great enthusiasm. I was elated. The value of the suit was hundreds of dollars and here it was in my hands for free. It wasn't stolen, it had been abandoned and rightly mine.

That night the moon was full, and I lay on my ground pad with the sleeping bag over it. I stared out through the zipper flap at the night and listened to the ocean bust waves on the beach below the bluff. Dad was incredibly, not snoring.

My imagination drifted down to the beach, out over the ocean, and I thought of fish swimming around under the surface of the waves. Beneath those waves, in the night, the sharks were coming in to feed on the seals off Catalina Island. Their dark shapes rocked with serpentine motion through the water, sensing any movement.

Up top ships moved cargo and freight over the swells. I reached for the expanse of the ocean to take hold of my mind and drift it off to peace, and then sleep. But again, I thought of

Jamie, my girlfriend, and wondered where she was—if she had moved to Nevada or had finished the year at Merrill High School. I had written letters and popped them into mailboxes, addressed to a condo in Reno, Nevada. They were going unanswered. I would later learn that Jamie's dad's wife, Karen, was throwing them away before Jamie could receive them. And her letters to me that Karen had promised to mail for Jamie were also going into the trash.

I was like a ship that was out there on the ocean, traveling with no destination.

I thought of my friends in school, getting ready to go into the Marines after graduation, my mom and stepdad, and brothers and sister. I felt my connection to them all, though I was thousands of miles away. I sent my imagination out like a nighthawk to find them and bring back a report to me in a dream. A moonbeam was shining on my shoulder, the same light that would be touching whales surfacing to spout water and dolphins jumping in the waves a few nautical miles out in the dark sea.

I drifted off to sleep with a prayer to God in my mind for protection and guidance.

The next morning, I woke up before the late, spring light broke over the eastern horizon. I worked into my new Rip Curl wetsuit and was delighted to find it fit like a glove. With my board under my arm, I picked my barefoot steps down the bluff trail to the beach in the growing light.

I stood on the sand for a while watching the waves breaking near the beach. Surfers paddled out to others sitting on their boards beyond the break. They had paddled out before daybreak. They were the cool kids that I wanted to be.

Like swallows on wires, they lined the ocean break and called out to each other, laughing, watching, and waiting. When the right waves came in, they went into action. After about twenty minutes of watching, I was ready.

I attached the board to my ankle with the leash and walked out with it into the surf. The sea showed me its power, knocking me down and washing me up on the shore with my face grinding in the sand like a rubber tire making a skid mark. As the salt water slid away from under me, I found myself choking on sand and gasping for air. It was going to take some determination just to get out there.

I clutched the board, headed into the surf again and learned how to bust through. I got out past the breakup and mounted the board. I looked down the line and saw the other surfers, politely ignoring me. Didn't everyone have to learn at some point? The shoreline went down for miles in either direction. With the sun shining on me, I was a part of this magnificent blue playground. A smile of joy stretched across my face.

Though it took most of the morning, I learned by watching the others. When I recognized a sizable wave rolling up behind me, I started paddling. I popped up at the right time, pulled up my legs, planted my feet on the fiberglass board and balanced.

When I got it right, I shot forward in the wave, feeling its force catch my fin on the inside curl and I rode this incredible force generated from the gravity of the earth. I moved forward like a torpedo from a sub, becoming one with the sea. I immediately fell in love with this sensation. I stayed out the whole day, skipping lunch. Soon I was popping up faster and moving more easily around in the curl of the wave by my own choice. The sea accepted me.

I had broken a barrier within myself. I was in California, surfing, and my friends were in third-hour chemistry class.

Dad's smuggling money was dwindling, so I took the Jeep and went into San Clemente to find a job. The first place I stopped at was a car wash on the corner of the main street. I watched the attendants wipe down cars, vacuum them out and clean out the interior of the expensive Cadillacs, Buicks, sports cars of every kind, and even a Delorian and a Porsche. The work was simple, fast-paced and there was a chance to earn tip money.

The owners were a Chinese family: a man and wife who knew how to run a business to maximum efficiency. A loudspeaker blasted directions to employees in their accent a few times an hour. "Jamie, upfront for car wipe down." The wife of the owner would call because I ran to get the job done. Working in the Midwest, if you had a job you were grateful, and you worked your ass off to keep it. I found myself hustling past my California workers as they leisurely strolled to get to the task like they were above it.

I cleaned the inside of cars with a vacuum cleaner, wiped down the interior with an Armor All-type of chemical, and shined the water off them when they got through the washing machine. When the manager called for someone to report to the drying station with a rag, I ran to get there. When a call came over the speaker for an attendee to report to the vacuum to detail a few cars, I ran to get there.

My California co-workers didn't much like the way I operated and, though they were well dressed, they wouldn't last ten minutes in a factory job in Wisconsin. Most of them would have been fired. On my third day on the job, I got a quarter-of-an-hour raise.

I understood something they didn't. No one owed me a damn thing. If I wanted any job, I had an obligation to perform it well, or I would be replaced.

There was a tall guy with an expensive haircut and a tailored shirt, who wanted to stand around and describe what a great guy he was. I moved away from him to polish up a lady's Cadillac. She complained afterward that there were streaks on the windows and wanted me to do it again. I did it, without a fuss. Tailored-shirt followed me over to the car and chatted at me while I worked.

When he leaned on the car, I motioned with my hand to move so I could dry off the door. The lady watched me work with a bitchy expression on her face, but gave me a ten-dollar tip. Cool.

The day went by faster when I worked with intensity. It was an honor to be employed, for not all could be. Dad wouldn't admit it, but I felt he had envied the worker who could routinely get up and grind out a day.

I did see three car wash slackers go to work, like never before, when one of them said he sucked up a big bud of some red-haired pot into the vacuum cleaner from the floor of a Cutlass Supreme. The three grown men tore the vacuum cleaner apart and sifted through a weeks' worth of dust, debris, and Kleenex—never finding what they were looking for. As I passed by them, they looked up at me from their project, their faces brushed with dust like zombies eating a brain.

Back at the campsite, I pulled in to find Dad sitting at the picnic table pouring over some big books. He had his big study glasses on and a highlighter in his hand. He dragged the pink highlighter over a paragraph and completed the task before he looked up and greeted me as I climbed out of the Jeep.

He had one of his legal tablets next to him on the table as well with pages of notes in ink penned out. I had moved enough of our gear to know that the big books in front of him were nothing we had brought with us. I turned one toward me and read the cover. It was a law book on setting up offshore tax shelters. I flipped it open and thumbed through it. The pages had Dad's highlighter marks and notes in the margins. It grated on me when he did that.

"Where did these books come from?"

"The San Clemente Library," he responded, with his finger on a paragraph, then picked up his pen to scrawl a note on the legal tablet.

"They won't let you check things out without a card. And I couldn't get a card with my Wisconsin driver's license," I said, flipping through the boring pages. Dad stayed focused. I waited for a while. "So how did you get them out of the library?"

"I threw them into the briefcase." Then he highlighted another sentence and wrote with his pen in the margin of the book.

"So, you stole them?"

"No, I didn't steal them. I'm going to return them. That's what you do at a library."

"But you're marking them up."

"Yeah, well…they happen to be brilliant study notes. It will save someone reading them time to figure out this law."

"But it's public property…"

"What are you, a library cop? I have to make a call. I'll be back. Why don't you get the bread out and make us a couple of peanut butter sandwiches?"

He drove off in the Jeep toward the ranger station of the park. I flipped through the notes he had made. It was all gibberish to me but Dad doing this legal work for an international crime syndication made my stomach roll up like a window shade.

The next morning, I got up before Dad could drag me off to Mass, grabbed my surfboard, and hit the ocean. I paddled out past the break of the waves and sat up on the fiberglass plank, while I watched the sunrise over the sandy bluffs and deep blue of the ocean around me.

I kept my mind off the sharks and allowed no thinking about how I might look like one of the seals that played off Catalina Island, twenty-two miles away. The other surfers would look more inviting, I was sure.

The waves were just right, and I rode the morning away, catching one that carried me all the way into the beach before I had to bail on it. By late morning, I was exhausted and stroked in to dismount the board and walk up the wet sand. I got out of the wet suit, rinsed off in a cold-water spigot, and sat on the sand next to the board, soaking up the sunlight. I heard some pleasant giggling behind me and noticed two ladies in swimsuits sitting on towels not far from me. The one on the right was the blonde girl who had given me the smile after Mass at Saint Mary's by the Sea.

I was lonely for conversation with young people, and I was feeling out-going. I picked up my gear, moved next to them, and started a conversation. They were smiley and pleasant, and I was feeling that I was in rare form, telling short stories and making what I thought were funny comments, while riding a wave of spontaneity.

At the first lull in the conversation, when I looked away and then looked back at them, they were French kissing each other passionately. I was just beginning a story of sorts and started stammering into a stream of thoughtless murmurings. They weren't listening to me anyway. The two of them wanted to be alone in fact, and I wondered how long they had been waiting for me to leave. I got the "third wheel" message after I waited for them to break, but they didn't, so I ambled on. I made my way up the bluff to the campsite with my trusty surfboard, who seemed to understand how I was feeling, though I wasn't sure I did.

Coming from a small town in Northern Wisconsin, I had not seen anything like that before. I had the "long way from home" feeling again.

I reported to work for my afternoon shift at the car wash. Some of my co-workers were just out of prison, transients running from something, or people lost in the carnival of life, like me, perhaps. We joked and I formed some friendships. I enjoyed moments in this life where I realized that I had carved out an existence in this world. I was a surfer in the early morning, sometimes going to Mass with Dad; I was an employee of a company, car wash or not; and I was a writer at the picnic table, where I found myself crafting stories.

It was different and better than being a drunken screw-off in a high school. But, there was an impending sense about it all—that time was running out and I still didn't really fit in here. This was not where I was "meant" to be. The feeling of displacement hunted me down like a bloodhound, closing in with each passing day.

Back home, my closest friends were going into the Marines. John Purcell would forever remind me it was my idea, and then I was the one who didn't enlist. In a few months, they would be doing their boot camp at the Marine Corps Recruit Depot in San Diego, just down Pacific Coast, where my brother Shawn had done his training.

Their lives would be meticulously planned out for the next four years, while mine was in the air, dancing like a tin can getting shot by a pistol, fast-draw, sideshow exhibitionist.

With the checks from my near-minimum wage, part-time work, I purchased bananas, bread, peanut butter, instant coffee for the portable gas stove, and Sara Lee pound cakes for special occasions. After my shift, I would swing the Jeep into the library and spend a few hours reading any book that might grab my fancy. I found for the first time a popular writing magazine. I was in awe that there was such a publication that could teach specifics on creative writing.

I read books on alien abduction, by J. D. Whitney. I read about the investigation into the Hillside Stranglers. I read Mickey Spillane's *I the Jury* and Jack Kerouac's *On the Road*. I "got it" when Truman Capote said about that book, "That's not writing, that's typing." I read Raymond Chandler, more Mickey Spillane, Dashiell Hammet, authors of hardboiled detective novels, and Joan Didion, as well as books on surviving in the wilderness. That library still enforced quiet, so I could study for hours without interrupting my bliss in growth.

CHAPTER 9

If the Son therefore shall make you free, ye shall be free indeed.
John 8:36

"We made a searching and fearless moral inventory of ourselves."
Step 4 Alcoholics Anonymous

13 July 29 - August, 1984
Ministry in Europe
A Sojourn for Christ
Shawn Finucan

I talked with a pastor from a certain country who was put into prison for handing out tracts (information on the gospel of Jesus Christ) and said it was a "wonderful experience." It gave him opportunity to preach God's word in prison.

God gave me the opportunity to see the fallen remains of Philippi, who were once the caliber Christians esteemed in Paul's eyes ... "My joy, and crown..." (Phil.4:1). The marble ruins, fallen colonnades are a special treat to observe.

Seeing many things in Europe I recall when the train I was traveling on stopped in a small town in Yugoslavia. A very poor, thin child came up to the train car and begged. "Whoso stoppeth his ears at the cry of the poor, he also shall cry himself but shall not be heard" (Prov 21:13). The boy's shoes looked like they had once been discarded. On the long train rides, the Lord gave me the opportunity to meditate on His word and pray at times. I've found that meditating cleans my mind, and calming my mind has a general positive effect with my entire well-being in as much as I am content with it. "My son, attend to my words: incline thine ear unto my sayings. Let them not depart from thine eyes: keep them in the midst of thine heart" (Prov. 4:20-21).

MARINETTE SHERIFF DEPARTMENT
SUPPLEMENTARY REPORT

Case number 85-393

Mattison then photographed all the objects and the victim.

Report of Sgt. James Jerue Investigating officer.

November, 2019 Merrill, Wisconsin

I highlighted that part of the report and ruminated on my next action. I needed to get my hands and eyes on those photographs.

As I read the file before from the Marinette County Sheriff's Office and reread it, I prayed and asked God to reveal to me what had happened to Shawn. I had enough prayer life to know that God doesn't often answer with a thunderous voice, but one that is a soft breeze.

Scott Meisenburg had mentioned that the first time Shawn had asked Scott if he could borrow the rifle, Chuck Heyza was going to go with him. There was no indication that Chuck had gone with him that morning. There were no other footprints going out to the scene.

From this, I discounted Tim's theory that someone had been with him, handled the weapon improperly, and caused the death of Shawn by way of gunshot to the back.

I could read clearly that officer Jeru's report believed that initially the shot had gone through the chest. I would need to read on to see what he found in the autopsy.

1984 San Clemente, California

As holiday weekends came along, they presented some problems to park life. With Memorial Day just a few days away, our lack of ability to plan became apparent and forged an obstacle. The park campsite we were in, number thirty-seven, was reserved, thus dethroning us from our claim to our beach front real estate and casting us out of the park with no place to go.

Every campsite in the state had been claimed as the weekend approached. So, we packed up our tent, sleeping bags and cooler, and stuffed the gear into the Jeep. We went to morning Mass with the duffle bag of pistols and offered up prayer as to where we would sleep that night.

I recall thinking that if there would have been an armed attack on that parish while we were there, Dad and I would have been the only two members of the congregation prepared to stop the slaughter. I can just see the headline, "Homeless father-and-son team stop church mayhem!" However, upon thinking it through and realizing that no good deed goes unpunished, it might have been more that we would have been vilified for breaking the law by not having the weapons in a proper gun case and carrying them concealed.

The media might have splayed the headline to read: *Homeless father-and-son team unjustly shoot mass murderers with illegal weapons*! Splashed across the front page, pictures would show us being hauled off in handcuffs—me looking confused and Dad looking pissed.

We frittered the day away. As evening approached, we prepared to sleep sitting up in the Jeep. We were looking at the prospect of spending the Memorial Day weekend in such a dreary manner. Even parking somewhere inconspicuous was going to be a challenge. I was becoming aware of how difficult it was for Dad to just find a place to lay his head and sleep. We drove back to the church and talked to Father Lavire, who agreed to let us sleep in the church rectory for the night.

We parked the Jeep under a light in the parking lot and found the key where Father Lavire said it would be. The building was attached to the luxurious church and inside was an office. We settled in and I found a newspaper to read as Dad rolled out his bedroll. I hoped he would crash fast and hard away, providing relief from the stress of wandering.

In the quiet of the room, Dad started spiraling from the fatigue.

"What a life! I wander around like a bum with nowhere to go. Any place I sit down, people want to move me out and I never have any peace. I screwed up my life, my marriage, my career, and at this age have nothing to show for any of it."

I turned the page of my paper and looked around for a radio I could turn on—anything to stop this drivel. Tonight, I just couldn't listen to it.

"If only Judy would have listened to me and not divorced me. If only I had taken a different path, maybe I could have lived a life where I could have provided for you kids. Your mother thinks I live like this because I'm a screw-off, and it's just not true." His voice resounded with pain.

"Ok, listen. She divorced you because you were having an affair with another woman." I braced for repercussions when I heard the distinctive sound of a radio crackle at the door. That sound always meant police. Who else carries around a two-way radio?

The door flew open and a Sheriff's deputy came in with his semi-automatic handgun leveled at me. I was looking down the barrel of a .45 single stack 1911. The hole in the end of the barrel looked as huge as a twelve-gauge shotgun.

"Hands up!" he yelled. Another Deputy entered the room behind him and swung a Beretta 9mm on Dad.

"Damn!" I wondered if it was going to be the last word out of my mouth.

They entered the room tactically, glancing around for any further threats, while snapping back their attention to us. They moved low. The first one was tall and side-stepped around the office, lifting his legs a little higher than he needed to, like he didn't want to trip on something, all the while keeping the .45 aimed at my head. The other one looked at Dad like he wanted to kick his ass. He keyed his mic on his shoulder and tipped his head to speak into it. "We're inside. Two occupants, and we are questioning them now."

"Hey, hey, hey, it's alright. Put those guns down," Dad said calmly. "You could hurt someone." They didn't respond. I thought of the bench warrant out for my arrest from the traffic ticket that Dad had thrown in the fire. Then I became aware of the bag on the floor next to my sleeping bag with the firearms in it. A search of our gear would pose a problem here. Of that, I was certain.

Our situation had gone critical in a moment.

"What are you guys doing here?" the deputy asked.

"We have no place to stay tonight. We attend church here and Father Laverie let us stay here tonight," Dad explained. They finally holstered the weapons but kept eyes on us. The lead deputy looked at the gear I brought in. His eyes settled on the duffel bag for a moment.

"Yeah? What are your names?" asked the deputy as he pulled out a pad of paper and a pen. The other deputy looked at both of us with disgust and kept his hand on the butt of his holstered Beretta.

"Patrick Finnegan, and this is my son, Jamie, same last name."

"Spell that for me."

"Finnegan." Dad deliberately misspelled it. I remembered he was a genius and hoped it would work.

"You have any I.D. on you?"

"No, I don't," Dad lied.

Then the deputy looked at me. "How about you?"

"No," I lied as well.

He cocked his head sideways a bit.

"Well now, that's a hell of a thing isn't it? Two men without I.D.?"

"We're homeless. We don't have much of anything," Dad informed him.

"Is that your Jeep out in the parking lot?"

"I'm borrowing it from a friend. I have to get it back to him."

"What's his name?"

"Joe Corrigan," Dad answered.

The other Deputy glanced at the lead Deputy.

"That registration checks out," the second Deputy said. The first Deputy went to the phone on the desk and opened up a phone book lying next to it. He flipped through it until he found a number. We all sat in the silence. I prayed to God for protection.

He called the number of the church and got Father Laverie on the phone. "Hi Father, this is Deputy Carlson of the Orange County Sheriff's Department. I'm here in the rectory and there are two men staying here. They say they have your permission to be here. Is that correct?"

In the silence of the room I was able to hear what the priest was saying in response.

"Yes, that's correct."

"What are their names?"

"Pat and Jamie Finucan," Father Laverie replied. There was a moment of silence as I watched the deputy process the name he had been told and checked it off against what Dad had said. It was close enough to Finnegan that he accepted it as legitimate and didn't question the pronunciation difference.

"Okay, thanks." He hung up the phone. Then he radioed into the station to do a background check on our names of Finnegan and nothing came up as a hit. He bid us goodnight and the two left the rectory as Dad and I exchanged looks of relief.

"That was close," Dad whispered.

"We don't pay traffic tickets," I commented and laid down on the floor. It had been a long day. It had almost been longer with a trip to county lock-up. I wondered if it wasn't such a bad idea to be shoveling snow in Wisconsin.

We were back in the park after the holiday weekend and things were normal again. I drove through San Onefre campground after my shift at the car wash and pulled into the parking spot that I was sure was ours, but then again, not so sure because

Dad and I didn't have a camper. As I shut down the big V8 motor, Dad opened the small half-door of the Jayco camper and stepped out. He was smiling like a new father.

"Isn't she lovely? What do you think, Jamie?" He stepped aside and gestured to the camper like he was presenting it at a game show. It was used, but there didn't seem to be any tears in it. It was oddly familiar, and then I realized I had seen it before, down at the south end of the park with a "For Sale" sign on it.

"It's…great." The tent was still pitched, though the flap door was unzipped and snapping in the salty sea breeze of the ocean. Dad must have been in transition of transferring the gear from the tent to the camper.

"It's our new home. We get to sleep in beds tonight. You got that side and I have this one." He said it like the two pop-out shelves with zippered canvas over them were master suites in a mansion. "And get this, it locks! We don't have to take the bag of guns to church anymore. And, now, one of us can leave camp without us worrying if everything is ripped off when we get back. We can have some peace of mind. He took a key out of his pocket and fiddled it in the door. He stopped and looked back at me, then asked, "How much of the two grand do you have left?"

"About two-hundred-fifty bucks," I answered.

"I'm short two hundred for this, so I need two hundred back."

I took it from my wallet and handed it to him.

"I'll get it back to you. The camper was a big investment."

I smiled at him to show it was all right. He was out of his smuggling money and I was down to fifty bucks. I had a paycheck coming from the car wash on Friday.

There was a small propane tank under the gas burner in the camper, so we had a stove to cook on now. Cooking was easier than over the fire pit, so Dad was making olive oil pancakes for breakfast after Mass. They were pretty much like any other pancake, but for some reason, Dad poured copious amounts of olive oil in the pan to fry each one so that they became heavy, weighted masses of greasy cooked batter. Anything tastes good with the seasoning of hunger and syrup poured over it, so I ate them.

To wash dishes, we had a scouring pad with a small bar of Ivory hand soap wrapped in it. That evening we were frying burgers and making a salad. Dad chopped blue cheese to put in the combination of lettuce, tomatoes and olives. Somehow, the Ivory soap bar got chopped up and thrown in the salad.

Thinking it was blue cheese, I ate it, noticing it tasted very odd, but thinking it was a strong cheese. Moments later I was puking in the bushes behind our campsite. I tasted the soap coming back up and vomited soap bubbles on the sandy soil. It burned my throat and then loaded my shorts with diarrhea. I did some deductive reasoning between purging and retches, and figured it out. I got more active in the cooking process of the camp after that.

Dad's grilled chicken was the best I've ever had. He used a whole stick of butter on a few pounds of legs and wings, and peppered it hard, adding Old Bay, seasoned salt, lemon pepper and barbeque seasoning.

He flame-scorched the skin and kept turning it to cook it through, while constantly slathering it with butter. The flames would jump up through the grill on the fire pit and lick at the butter and chicken legs. Dad worked the tongs, moving pieces around from hotter areas to cooler until they were all done at the same time. He expertly seasoned and charred the skin, resulting in a delicious, crispy, pleasing texture that was succulent to eat.

We had to pay up on the campsite or run the risk of having our slot rented by someone else. We kept up on it as far as we could, but money was running slim. We were sustaining on my paychecks from the car wash.

After a shift, I stopped to pick up some supplies at the grocery store, picked up a paper back on the impulse item rack and read the back cover as the items were rung up. It looked good so I threw the copy on the checkout counter—*Red Dragon* by Thomas Harris. When Dad unloaded the supplies from my bag, he threw an angry fit about wasting money on such a frivolous expense.

I read the book and left it lying around. Then he read it and we talked about what we liked about it. He offered his comments about how much he enjoyed it, then apologized for his outburst.

I was lonely and wrote letters to Jamie, my red-haired girlfriend, but got no response. I can recall the devastation of week after week, going to the post office to find no letter from her.

I surfed in the afternoons or mornings until my black hair got bleached to a light brown and started turning grey early, like Dad's. I entered a writing contest with a piece I wrote on the picnic table at our campsite. Though the requirements said it needed to be typed, I wrote it on a legal tablet in cursive.

It was a fictional short story about a guy who gets sent as a punishment to a Colorado Outward Bound School where he hikes through the Rockies and learns mountaineering. He gets a new perspective on life. When he comes home, his friends want him to participate in a crime with them. His rock-climbing skills save his life. He has changed his perspective and heads into a bright future.

It was based on the experience that John Purcell and I had when we spent a month in separate patrols in Outward Bound the summer we were sixteen.

I had seen the ad for the contest in a writing magazine at the library and had glanced around to make sure no one was watching. Then I quietly tore the page out that listed the submission requirements. A few weeks later, I got a letter in the post office box from the contest's judging panel, stating that I didn't win but they would be interested in reviewing more of my work.

I threw the letter away, thinking it was a scam, and even got perturbed when they sent several letters as follow-ups, asking if I had received their last letter and did I have any more material to share with them? I threw all of them away, except for an actual telegram they had mailed to the post office box that ended up folded in my notebook.

Years later, I would find that letter and realize it was from a huge publishing house and signed by the senior editor. An opportunity to be published had literally knocked on the door, and I had slammed and locked it. For years to come, I would think of that letter many times when I got numerous rejection letters for work I had submitted.

Dad would get depressed and sleep, leaving me to tinker away evening hours in loneliness. I sat on the bluffs of the park and watched the sunset, then struggled to find something to do when the sun went down, because it was difficult to read or write by flashlight.

I made endless fires in the pit in our campsite, silently observed the people around me moving in and out of the sites next to us, and listened to KLS radio—a rock station that got the Led out and played lots of Led Zeppelin, the Scorpions, Van Halen, Ratt, Yes and The Cars.

I came home from a shift and found Dad lying in his bunk staring at the canvas ceiling. I set a small bag down on the Formica fold out table.

"Hey, I stopped off at the Safeway. Check out what I got." I pulled a Sara Lee pound cake out and set it on the table, like it was the severed head of a defeated and revered enemy. Dad didn't look. "But wait, there's more." I pulled out a quart of milk and a bunch of bananas. "These items go together like a quiet room and big fart."

He glanced over.

"That's nice, Jamie. I don't feel hungry right now."

"You haven't eaten in a few days. Come on." I took the cardboard lid off the pound cake and picked up the big survival knife with the hollow handle that contained a sewing kit in it and a compass on the pummel. I cut two big slabs of the yellow, moist goodness and put them on paper plates. Then I put the teakettle on the stove to make hot water for instant coffee. I held out the cake on the paper plate until he looked at me.

"Come on, let's go outside and eat this in the sun." I knew that was important, the whole lighting had to change. This camper was dark. "We'll have coffee in a few minutes."

On the picnic table, he took a half bite of the cake and chewed it slowly. His eyes didn't move off whatever he was staring at on the ground.

"We'll be out of money soon," he said softly. "We won't be able to pay the rent on the campsite."

"I got it covered. I got a part time job, remember?"

"That's not going to be enough to get us by, Old Buddy."

I went inside for the coffee and came out with two hot cups.

"It all seems so pointless. This struggle, the endless worrying, no one caring, the isolation, the useless internal fight in agony just to get by—it makes me wonder why I bother. I live a life of failure. Nowhere to go, living in a park with my back endlessly against the wall, I get run out of everywhere I happened to go. My kids don't write. My own family treats me like I'm a disease. What the hell happened to me? I'm a bum and no one wants a bum around. And can you blame them?"

I had to get him to break this dangerous pattern of thinking, fast, or I would start to follow. It's that deadly and contagious.

"What are you talking about? We're having a ball."

"Everything I've ever touched has turned to ashes."

"God gives beauty for ashes. Look where we are, in California in the summer sun, eating cake and drinking coffee. You're hanging out with me. Look at where your feet are right now." I turned on the little radio I had left out on the picnic table when I left for work, glad no one had stolen it. Led Zeppelin came out of it singing "Hey, Hey, What Can I Do?"

"Turn that off will you?" he said slowly. I did. It was too much stimulation for him at the moment.

"I saw a beautiful lady downtown in the store. She had a summer dress on, wearing these high-heeled sandals. She looked dynamite. She had blonde hair, pinned up on one side, showing a nice neckline. Great legs, too."

"Yeah?" That got him looking over at me.

"She moved like music when she walked."

"Like music?" He took a bigger bite of the pound cake.

"I'll tell you, these California women have a great deal of vavoom going for them. Knockouts—every one of them. They're in shape because they exercise."

"They do have an active lifestyle out here, don't they?" Dad said as he raised his head.

"They smile a lot, get tanned, have a great sense of style, and carry themselves with an elegant poise."

"Yeah." Dad looked around, like he might see one any second. Looking externally, that was good.

I knew I had his attention, so went on, "Just getting within five feet of these women brings out the man in me. I just want to start talking to them, ask them a million questions just to watch their mouths move and hear their minds working. The distinctive tone of voice each one has, the way they express themselves, it's so alluring, isn't it?"

"Yeah, they could impact a guy's life in ways that are unimaginable."

"Oh, it's imaginable. What we need to do is get you a date out here."

"Oh, those days are over for me. That part of me, being able to maintain that kind of relationship with a woman, it's over."

"Nonsense. There are women in Southern California that would love a lawyer next to them. You have a great sense of humor, you're in shape, and you're still a good-looking chap, Dad."

He put his hand on his thick, gray hair and smoothed it down, pushing down a cowlick that stuck up in the back. His shoulders pulled back and he looked up.

"I am a pretty good-looking guy, aren't I?"

"It's in our Irish genes." I thought of my red-haired girlfriend that didn't write me and felt a stabbing sear of pain in my heart. I looked around me, at the table, the ground, like I had lost something. Then I realized I had. It was the relationship with the girl who had my heart. Wherever she was, she had a piece of it with her. In that moment of emotional collapse I gained a new understanding of the pain Dad carried within him.

"I could be good for a woman," he said thoughtfully.

"Heck yes! You're smart, could handle any problem she has, and you're a marginal cook." There was a pause as he took in that last crack. I let it work its magic.

"What are you talking about? I'm a great cook."

"Well, your chicken is great, but your pancakes are horrible."

"What's wrong with the pancakes?" He was turning toward me slowly now, like a gunfighter on a western, dusty street.

"You use a quarter cup of olive oil with each cake. It's too much. Back that off. Before I ate one of those pancakes, I could rub it on my hair to grease it down for the day."

His posture straightened up. He leaned back and looked at the camper, at the Jeep, and then at me.

"Listen, Kid, you should just be grateful you have anything to eat."

"Your pancakes are so greasy I could butter my popcorn with them." That got a slight smile from him. "Your pancakes are so slippery and greasy that a carpenter couldn't nail them." We both started cracking up. "If one of your pancakes was second base and I slid in, I would end up in Milwaukee."

I wanted more humor and reached for it, but the reaching itself dried it up. Dad wanted more, too, but neither of us had any. Sometimes we could go on for an hour, laughing, but this moment had ended. Later in life, in the silence of problems, alone, after Dad had left this world, I would cherish the memories of the humor we shared and feel warmth in my soul, as a gift from God.

I finished my slab of pound cake and cut another, a little thinner this time. The moist balance, heft and texture of the yellow, sweet bread graced my hand with a promise of satisfaction. Sara Lee delivered the culinary bliss from a simplistic combination of ingredients that knew how to deliver flavor, although not much in the way of nutrition.

The wind blew the ocean's salt smell over us and I heard a seagull cry. Dad went into the camper and came out with a banana. His mind was working on something as he ate it. He looked away, then at the fruit, then away again toward the sea. His distant expression told me the mental tumblers were turning, clicking, and fitting together with some kind of plan. And that wasn't always a good thing.

"I have to go down to the ranger station and use the pay phone," he blurted out.

"Who are you calling?"

"Tom. I'm going to see what work the team needs done."

"Don't do it."

I swung my legs around from the picnic table to face him. I thought of all the stamps in his passport and him smuggling cocaine in the bottom of a hollowed-out golf bag through two border crossings. Yet he had never played a game of golf in his life. A bogey to him was a line from the movie *Casablanca.*

I pictured him wearing a wrinkled suit, flying into Luxemburg with smuggled gems to establish tax shelters for drug lords, so they could hide their illegal gain for a Jeep and ten grand.

"We need money," he responded, looking up toward the sun. "I am so sick of this shit, living like a dog. This is what it means to be poor in spirit. To be endlessly broke, not knowing where your next meal is going to come from, looking down the road and seeing nothing but despair along the trail of life."

A seagull sang its song of praise in the distance.

"Poor in spirit?" I asked.

"Yeah, it means experiencing the pain of failure of all your most important human relationships in your life, and then watching them wither. It means watching your dreams strangle slowly through your life, like a cat caught in a downed clothesline. I live life on the fringe of society. Being poor and poor in spirit, means you live a life where no one wants you around because you're unable to bring any value to anyone, most of all yourself.

It's to know the crushing sorrow of hopelessness and to know that it is of your own making, so you can only look at the travesty you have made of your life and know you will live out your life in this mess."

His tone was distant and final.

"To us, the poor in spirit, there is only God to cling to, and His mercy. With nothing else to keep us afloat, we wait on Him. He is the only remedy."

"If God is the only remedy, why go smuggling and risk your freedom? You think God wants that? We don't need money that bad. I'll get more hours at the car wash." The air around us seemed to thicken as my lungs pulled it in. I breathed deep and swallowed the last bite of pound cake; it was ruined now. My stomach turned acidic.

"We need bigger money than the car wash pays to live out here. Stuff is expensive. We have to survive." He got in the Jeep and drove off.

Two days later, I drove him through Los Angeles to the airport. The traffic on the 405 accelerated, then stopped. It would start crawling along, then speed up to eighty miles per hour with a few feet of space between cars, then slow down fast to a crawl. We ran behind schedule, but neither one of us showed the tension. We were both in operators' mode.

We knew what was in our control and what we were supposed to do. The tension was high. Our actions required us to perform the task-at-hand without either of us adding or detracting from them. Words were few, carefully chosen, and not wasted. Every movement was performed in an economy of scale.

When we got to security at LAX, Dad broke his protocol by giving me a hug and then went through the gate. I watched him as he moved along—a lean, hard man of fifty on a mission, in dress pants and shirt, with a suntan and a mop of thick, gray hair. He did that thing where he leaves and doesn't look back, like he left everything behind him on fire.

CHAPTER 10

The LORD preserveth all them that love him: but all the wicked will he destroy.
Psalm 145:20

This above all: To thine own self be true, and it must follow, as the night to the day, Thou canst not then be false to any man.
William Shakespeare

MARINETTE SHERIFF DEPARTMENT SUPPLEMENTARY INVESTIGATION REPORT
Case Number 85-393
The victim was transferred to the rear of Messar's vehicle, and transported to Wausaukee. Mattison and I then drove back to the duplex. Brzoza was just finishing the statement, and Mattison contacted the District Attorney. He also contacted the Merrill Police Department to assist in notifying the victim's Mother. Then we left the area.
Sgt. James Jerue

November, 2019 Merrill, Wisconsin
When I read that part of the statement, I recalled how I had been sleeping upstairs in my room. I had returned to Mom and Bob's home from my trip to California and other points of the world with Dad. I had just begun to finish high school—a year after I had dropped out. I would finish with the underclassmen.

I recall that I had been sleeping very soundly that night. Mom later told me she had as well, as though God was preparing us for the change that we were about to face in our lives. I woke up to Mom sobbing hysterically and shaking me by the shoulders. I sat up in astonishment. She told me that Shawn had died. She reported that the police and a pastor had just left the house from delivering a death notification.

We clutched each other in shock and grief, experiencing a tempest in life. We absorbed as much as we could, like hanging onto a boat in a hurricane as the course of life changes.

We made phone calls to my brother, Tim, and my sister, Deirdre, to share the tragedy in our lives. The kitchen phone, with its long cord, became the communication center and headquarters for the halls of the broken.

13 July – 29 August 1984
Ministry in Europe
A Sojourn for Christ
Shawn Finucan

The Ministry in Europe included witnessing to others of Christ, stamping tracts for the churches of two missionaries, helping move all the possessions of a missionary in Vienna, passing out many tracts to people on the street and I helped work on an engine from a church van in West Germany.

I wish I would have studied more language.

1984 San Clemente, California

The next few weeks I was stationed solo at the campsite while Dad was on his mission. I kept to a routine of working my shift at the car wash and surfing. I put on my wet suit, grabbed my board and barefoot treaded down the bluff to the ocean. If I worked the afternoon shift at the car wash, I was up early. It was great to watch the sun come up while out on the board and feel the power of the ocean beneath me. I got better at it daily.

At the campsite, I found a yellow notice on our campsite number post. Site fees were due. I would have to pay the rent or hook up the Jayco camper and get out of the park. I had until the next day. My next paycheck from the car wash wouldn't get issued until Friday. I had a quarter tank of gas in the Jeep and if I had to move out of the campsite, I would be mobile with the camper and with nowhere to land it.

I had eight dollars and fifty-three cents to my name.

The next morning, I tied the surfboard on top of the Jeep, went to Mass and prayed for our situation and for my future. My internal compass was spinning, with no bearing. I was lost. I was a bum, like Dad. The ability to develop a plan didn't seem to take shape in my mind. It would be a few years before I was able to plan. The future was something that just poured out of me like a urine stream, with about as much value. My brain didn't seem to be able to grasp a concept of the future—how to prepare for it and project a living in it.

I went to Mike's café and ordered bacon, eggs and coffee, and splashed Tabasco sauce over all of it. That left me about two bucks. Just like how I acquired the board, I waited for someone to walk past and asked if they would like to buy the surfboard. The first two sales pitches got nowhere, but the third guy was interested. I got my fifty bucks out of it fast. The board had a new ding in the side from when I had piled up on the beach a few times that first day, but it was still a deal for anyone.

It broke my heart to watch the piece of equipment that had brought me so much comfort, be loaded into a pickup truck and hauled off. I wondered what I would do with my time at the campsite now. But, I had money. In the interest of enjoying the simple things, that Dad had taught me, I picked up a baklava, the Greek pastry, and gallon of milk, and ate it for lunch in the afternoon sunshine on the beach.

I squared up with the park rangers and had money to buy a few cans of ravioli, canned corn, a loaf of bread and some peanut butter to hold me over. I could stay in the park here at San Onefre for a little while. I thought that if Dad wasn't back by the following week, I would start to worry, but that was all I would be able to do. I had no idea what he was actually doing, though I knew it was ethically questionable and probably illegal on an international level, and certainly dangerous. I prayed for Dad to be able to escape the situation he had gotten himself into and asked God to remember His mercy toward us, and to take pity on us.

I hung around the campsite the rest of the afternoon without my board, as blue as hell, and wished I could talk to my friends. I wondered where my red-haired girlfriend was and why she wasn't answering my letters. I imagined she had moved on with some other guy and realized I couldn't really blame her. What did I have to offer for a future anyway?

I felt isolated and alone, a feeling that would haunt me through life, until I realized it was put there by God to draw me to Him.

Warm Santa Anna winds blew up from the south that night, bringing stifling hot air that pushed across the land with a negative psychic element to them. Those winds had an electrically-charged spirit of restlessness in them that agitated me internally and infected me with hot discomfort. Arguments broke out down the beach between lovers, and heated voices carried in the wind, like shouts of ghouls from another dimension.

Even the firelight from my pit seemed angry, crackling and dancing in the winds of discontentment over the logs whose coals appeared to glow with resentment.

I wanted to sleep on the picnic table in the hot wind because the camper was too stifling. To a Midwesterner, it is confounding that wind cannot bring with it a cool relief.

"What the hell? Am I standing in the door of a blast furnace?" I yelled to no one and whipped a marshmallow into the fire. I felt an open wound within me that I couldn't explain, and wanted to start bawling like a four-year-old.

I lay down on the table with my sleeping bag beneath me and tried to hear the ocean below the bluff. But all I could hear was the fucking wind. My heart was racing and I didn't know why.

I tried again. As my heart rate descended and I carefully stepped down into the realm of sleep, I guarded my thoughts. Any disruption at the early phase of dropping off to sleep could mean a long night. My unfettered creative mind could turn poisonous on me in these hours and cause me to suffer a long, lonely night of emotional and mental turmoil. I could be plagued with thoughts of worry, paranoia, wrongs, offenses and slights that should be forgotten. A night could turn to this if I kicked a single mental stone as I drifted off.

Before sleep, I remember staring up at the stars and thinking of the sharks swimming off Catalina Island, a few nautical miles out from where I was at that moment.

They weren't concerned about their future. They just went around biting stuff and hunting, because that was what they did. There was no expectation of them to be anything other than a shark, and their instincts told them what to do. They didn't have to figure it out.

I wondered what I was supposed to hunt, what I should be biting, what I should be swimming after, because, unlike those sharks out in the dark, deep sea, I didn't have a clue.

The idea that there were freaks and murderers, like Charlie Manson and the Hill Side Stranglers, roaming around in Southern California, crossed my mind, and if one walked by the campsite and saw me sleeping on the picnic table in the hot wind, he might come over and cut my throat.

I considered getting The Snake out of the camper and sleeping with it under my pillow, but then I wondered how that would help me to wake up to my throat being cut. I envisioned myself waking up with my throat cut, clutching the gash together with one hand and running after some California freak. I would blast away at him with The Snake, while he sprinted off into the night, laughing maniacally with a big knife in his hand.

Then I imagined the ranger taking a statement from me, writing on his little notepad while I bled profusely from my throat and tried to explain what the hell I was doing with the gun—like that was the issue here. Then I got pissed off at the ranger because that's what he would be worried about. Forget the fact that some sick asshole just cut my throat. "By the way, Ranger Rick, you think you could call me an ambulance or something, or are you entirely incompetent?"

Then I sat up on the table and drew in a breath. The hot Santa Anna wind moved through my hair like air out of a volcano. Dust got in my eyes. Sparks whisked out of my fire pit and bumped the camper.

I wondered why I was thinking about such morbid shit and remembered my writer's mind needed to be corralled sometimes. Then I thought of the book *Twenty Thousand Leagues Under the Sea.* A league is a measurement on top of the sea and a fathom is measured in depths. It should have been Twenty Thousand Fathoms Beneath the Sea. I wondered how that screw-up got past an editor? I mean, you think they could get a title correct if it was going to be a classic novel. Then I wondered why I was thinking such nonsense.

By then, I didn't give a damn who might come by while I was sleeping.

I was tired of holding my guard up all the time. I needed to be more like a shark. I needed to hunt, to go on the offensive. I shouldn't be afraid of danger in this world. The sick predators should be afraid of me.

The thought stuck. I lay back down and drifted off into a deep sleep of oceanic dreams filled with calls of whales, creaking boats, foaming waves, and underwater storms that stirred up sand against brilliant-colored coral creatures. Images of lonely moonlight cutting through the saltwater, touching on fins that moved to propel fish forward, drove my descent into rest, replenishment, and restoration—the beautiful healing world of sleep.

The next day I swam out past the surf break and tread water in the rolling cresting waves. I watched the shoreline light up with morning sun but an infectious thought of circling sharks below me ruined my peace of mind and again I missed my surfboard. Then I went into town for my shift at the car wash. I hustled around doing my job because the day went faster. But I was distracted. I worried about what Dad was doing, and about what I was doing here. I wondered if I was doing the right thing and if I was where I should be in life. I missed Jamie with a big piece of my heart.

She was the cool breeze in my life, the only sweetness I had really felt and known in this world. She enthralled me like nothing else. My mind was circling concerns, like a crow over a dead animal on the roadside, not landing, and only flying in a circle because the cars were scaring it off. There seemed to be no answers to the unexpressed questions on my mind, no completion, and no way to put the thoughts to rest.

Back at the campsite in the sunshine of the afternoon, I reread Thomas Wolfe's *Look Homeward Angel.* The voice of the writer somehow hit me hard inside, where I was lost, and caused me to hold up the tattered paperback for hours until my neck got stiff.

Or, I watched the pretty girls in swimsuits walk past the campsite, feeling like an alien who couldn't speak the language. I was like so many members of the transient population in Southern California that had nothing to offer. I couldn't get past the perception that none of this around me was for me. I felt like an extra actor on a movie set, waiting to give my line, then going to the cafeteria for a sandwich and eating it next to a guy wearing a Genghis Khan costume.

The following day, I drove home from work in a sour mood. I made sure I stopped at the stop signs and knew that if I got pulled over, the arrest warrant would be triggered, and I would be in the pokey with no one to bail me out. I could spend the weekend making the prison boxing team because

Dad had thrown my ticket in the fire to express his revolt against "The Man."

When I got to the camper, the campsite next to me was occupied by a guy with a daughter who was close to my age. She was only about twelve feet from me, so when I wrote in my notebook at the picnic table, she sat there putting on makeup for a long time while listening to country music. When she spoke to her dad, she had an adorable southern accent and, with a glance, I saw she was cute.

I figured she wanted to sell Mary Kay cosmetics or something, because she had this big case and was brushing on stuff and painting her eyelids with a thin type of pen. In the later part of the afternoon, her dad put on some chicken that smelled good. I laid on the picnic table and started reading a copy of *Les Miserable* that Dad had.

I recalled that Victor Hugo penned his first draft of his books while naked at his desk, so he didn't get up and walk around. He had submitted the manuscript of this classic book to a publisher with only a question mark, rather than a query letter. The editor of the publishing house responded with only an exclamation point. I paused in the reading to dream about being a published author of a book one day.

"So are you going to notice me or what?" she said over the small plant that separated our sites. I smiled and looked over at her. I liked her already.

"Oh, I noticed you right away. I was wondering if you were going to want to paint my nails or sell me a highlighter or something."

"It's called an eyeliner. You got something against make up?"

As she walked into my camp, I sat up and swung my feet around to put them on the bench. I slid my Bazooka Joe gum wrapper bookmark in where Jean Val Jean was requesting from Inspector Javert three days to search for the girl while Fantine died.

I looked into the eyes of my new neighbor and saw wholesome, brown peepers that stared back at me under light brown hair. Her features were sharp and pretty, with a little too much blush on the cheeks. Her lips were pouty and smiled easily. They would feel good pressed against mine, with the smell of her hair in my nose.

"A pretty girl like you doesn't need makeup," I grinned with that stupid smile spreading across my face that I could never seem to control. James Bond didn't smile when he said stuff like that.

"Well now, he's a flatterer too." She sat next to me and tossed her hair back over her shoulder perfectly. Some of it brushed on me, the first contact I had with a woman in months. It fell like corn silk over her shoulders, and I drank in the sensation like rain on desert sand. Her legs were fit, tanned and looked oily smooth. I stopped myself from imagining them gently drawing up, brushing on each side of my rib cage with her underneath me.

She had an aroma of delicious frosting about her that made me hungry. With her hair flipped back, her neckline looked like it needed to be nuzzled, kissed and lip bit. I imagined her feminine nature enfolding me, her long hair falling on me as we rolled around together, and her soft hands feeling my shoulders.

She would find them firm from the hours of surfing and she would respond biochemically by pulling me more toward her and moving her hips toward me.

"It's not flattery to state the facts," I replied, trying to snap out of it. "Besides if you're at the beach, you don't need to be made up. If you're going swimming in the ocean, all of that is going to wash off anyway." She looked sideways at me. "That is a swimming suit you have under that skirt thing, isn't it? A yellow bikini?"

"You do notice after all."

Her smile lit me up. Her dad turned some chicken with a pair of tongs, having the decency to pretend he wasn't listening.

He changed the radio station from country to pop and turned it up. The Thompson Twins were singing "Hold Me Now" on the little radio.

"I'm Jamie."

"I'm Tammy Killian." She held out her hand and I shook it gently. "Jamie, isn't that a girl's name?"

"Not if your Irish, Ms. Killian. You should know that. Want to go down to the ocean and go for a swim?" She checked with her Dad and he mentioned the chicken would be done in twenty minutes. Her Dad invited me to eat with them and I was delighted, as the only thing I had to eat was a banana and a lousy, stale, granola bar.

We ate off heavy-duty paper plates and I made conversation with the Killian's as I devoured their chicken and potato salad. He had grilled avocados, as well, that had a seasoning salt on them. Tammy had cut up a watermelon that was red, juicy and sweet, and offered the taste of summer. I smothered the chicken and potato salad with Tabasco sauce as they watched, stunned.

Then Tammy took it from me and did the same, looking at me as she did.

Mr. Killian liked my Irish name and asked me if I was alone here at the campground. I explained that my Dad was off on a job, working. That felt fresh to say since he was usually known to be homeless in my hometown. Out here, things were different. So, I told them about Dad, how he was a lawyer that set up tax shelters for people in places that were tax havens and was an expert in doing so. Mr. Killian was a salesman for a tech firm or something. I had a vibe from him like he was hoping to have some daughter time and I had interrupted it, but I was so lonely for someone to talk to that I kept chatting and asking questions.

After dinner, Tammy and I walked down the bluff to the ocean and went swimming. She knew how to swim out past where the waves broke, and we enjoyed the activity in the warm sun. Afterward, she shared her towel. We sat on it and she told me about her life in Corpus Christi and how she was going to beauty school to help women become empowered.

She wanted to go back to camp when it got dark. She sat with her dad by the fire while I frittered away the evening in the camper, trying to look like I was doing something.

I went to work early the next day and looked forward to getting to home base to talk with Tammy. I stopped at the post office and found a telegram sent by Erik Lange, one of my friends who had embarked on a motorcycle trip out here before going in the Corps. Sent from Huntington Beach, it read:

WE CAN'T COME TO SEE YOU (STOP) JOHN ARRESTED FOR CARRYING A KNIFE (STOP) HAVE TO GET BACK TO BOARD A BUSS FOR THE CORPS (STOP).

Huntington Beach was only about fifty miles up the coast from where I was. They would go back to Wisconsin, get on a bus and arrive in San Diego for boot camp, just down the coast from me.

When I got to the campsite the Killian's were gone. They had packed up every trace and the father-daughter duo vaporized without even leaving tire prints behind. It was like Tammy was never there.

I wondered if she had looked for me before they left, or if she had knocked on the door. She likely saw the blue Jeep was gone and knew I was as well. I wished I had called in sick to the car wash that day. The other guys did it all the time. This was one of those occasions when it really sucked to be on time and dependable on a stupid job.

I sat there on the picnic table feeling abandoned by everyone I knew. From my girlfriend, who didn't write, to my Dad, who took off to do crimes, and even this pretty girl in the next campsite. Everyone just seemed to walk away from me when they got the chance. I felt a hollow emptiness awaken and sear through me. I had started noticing this since I quit drinking.

I went into the camper, found a can of tuna and ate it with a fork in the sunshine while trying to think of my next story to write. Anything to keep my mind from spiraling into a mental abyss that might take me days to climb out of, like my dad would do. I wondered how much of the shit he faced was hereditary.

I took a piece of Bazooka bubble gum from my pocket and unwrapped it. It was soft from my body heat. The pink wad of sugar-filled resin flooded my mouth with the sensation that reminded me of a shot of Mad Dog.

I looked at the comic wrapper. Mort and Bazooka Joe are walking past some girls. Mort says through his constant turtleneck, "I can go steady with any girl I please." Joe turns to him in the next frame and asks, "Why don't you then?" In the next frame Mort says, "I don't please anybody!" with exasperation scribbles coming off him.

I crumpled up the comic between my fingers and tossed it into the unlit fire pit. That one was a little too close to home to bring me any amusement.

CHAPTER 11

In the sweat of thy face shalt thou eat bread, till thou return unto the ground; for out of it wast thou taken: for dust thou art, and unto dust shalt thou return.

Genesis 3:19

If a thousand old beliefs were ruined in our march to the truth we must still march on.

Stopford A. Brooke

I received Christ as my savior in the summer of 1980 while in the military service. By God's grace was this possible, also by the persistent prayers of a Christian girl whom I met in high school and the petitions of other Christians as well.
My direction, I have come to realize, in my 24th year, is missions work. I believe the door opening to Europe this summer to transport God's word as well as other Christian literature may influence my direction for work for our King in the future.

From a notebook of Shawn Patrick Finucan

MARINETTE SHERIFF DEPARTMENTSUPPLEMENTARY INVESTIGATION REPORT Case # 85-393

On Friday, Feb. 1st 1985 at approximately 10:00 AM, I went to the Morasky-Messar funeral home and was met by Mr. Messar. I photographed the victim, both clothed and unclothed, with the unclothed photo being of the upper part of the body. Further examination of the wound in the upper left chest of the front of the body, shows an absence of "tattooing." There was also an absence of "smudging" from burning powder.

The projectile had passed through three layers of clothing, which would account for the absence of "smudging." The length of the barrel would account for the absence of "tattooing." I also observed a wound in the area of the lower left scapula. It was approximately the same size as the wound in the front chest, except was round, had some torn skin protruding from the edges, and had a fragmentation wound outside of the larger wound.

From this, it is decided that the wound in the back is the exit wound and the wound in the front chest is that of the entry. Examination of the weapon shows dried blood inside of the barrel at the end of the barrel, at the muzzle end. There is an absence of any "blow back" on the muzzle end of the barrel, nor is there any on the outside of the barrel.

From the examination of the scene, the weapon, and the victim, it is concluded that the manner in which the victim died, is from apparent self-inflicted gunshot wound to the chest.

Sgt. James Jerue

October, 2019 Merrill, Wisconsin

When I read that last line in the report I felt an inside part of me collapse. In those moments, I felt that Dad had lied to me. I saw the whole incident of Shawn's death and the narrative I had received of it through the years as one of deception, given to me because Dad couldn't deal with the truth.

I recalled the day Dad had left to go get Shawn's things. I wanted to go with him, but he wouldn't let me. I remembered how devastated he was, but still was finding the strength to do this mission of closure of what every parent would consider—unthinkable. He had displayed an inner strength that was unimaginable.

I thought of all the times, through the years that I had been asked about the incident of Shawn's death, describing it as something odd, and was unable to tell a complete story because I didn't understand it myself.

"How does a gun accidentally go off into somebody's back?" people asked me, as though I hadn't asked myself that question enough times. And then, after being asked, I resented having to discuss it. I wondered how someone so tactless could have survived this long in this world without being punched in the mouth.

I recalled the moments of personal anguish that I had spent trying to figure out how that had happened but still, not having the courage to look into it until thirty-seven years later, only to find this horrible conclusion when at last I did.

I understood why Dad had to use deception about Shawn's death. Dad wasn't well enough to deal with Shawn having shot himself. In those moments, I was so furious with him. Though he has been long gone since 2009, I wanted to yell at him.

I was one of the few people that had understood Dad's illness. I had seen him for years sleeping homeless in the parks of our town, plagued with depression, living in desperation, and being the subject of ridicule as a man who was once a successful lawyer, who became an outcast of society. I remembered my compassion for him and our dear friendship and let it be a balm on my agitated resentment.

I sat in the silence of my study with the autumn night closing in outside like a gate on a fort. I set the report down gently. My Howard Miller clock ticked on my desk with each passing second, assuring me that the world was moving on. The passing seconds went marching by like footsteps in a hallway of a hospital until I dug them up and examined them in hopes of finding peace. But, instead, I found only a blood trail leading to a heartbreaking deception.

It took a while, an hour of silence and breathing before the anger abated, but when it did, I thought about something else.

The funeral director, Mr. Wistein, had said to my sister Deirdre that he believed he was looking at a homicide here because of the nature of the wound. Mr. Wistein didn't have any cause to lie about that or conceal anything. As a mortician, he had certainly seen his share of bodies on slabs.

I remembered what I knew of Shawn, and how at peace he was in his life of newfound Christianity. It was unlikely that he would have shot himself. He was happy. Lonely, yes, but content. Would others who have supposedly committed suicide ever have been described as being happy?

I looked over the report again, there were three bullet holes in the target. Why would Shawn shoot a target at all if he had meant to shoot himself? What would be the point in doing some target practice before turning the weapon on himself? It wasn't that unusual that he was target practicing. All of us Finucan boys had grown up hunting and shooting, and did that frequently.

I re-read the part of the report about the crawl marks in the snow, after the incident occurred, he had tried to get help; he had tried to crawl out of the woods. He was "surprised" by what had happened. His actions told me that in my heart.

I re-read Jerue's description of the bullet hole. I was unsatisfied and wanted more information. I would need to see it for myself. I highlighted the words that told they had photographed the victim. There were photographs of the scene of the incident as well.

When I called to request this report, the clerk said they couldn't find the photographs. But, they had to be there. I found a written note in Jeru's handwriting that read "for photos, see photo file #85-11."

I would take a day off from work and drive over to Marinette, Wisconsin, appear at the window and request the photographs. There was always power in being present. I would explain that I was the brother of the deceased, and this information was vital to our peace of mind. Would they help me?

I pushed out of my mind the conclusion of Officer Jerue. His report was professional and thorough. He knew his way around a weapon and knew how to investigage, possibly had military background and a high level of training. But that didn't mean he was correct.

Jerue had left me enough information from his collection of evidence to learn some facts on my own. He had left me threads to pick up.

By looking at the photographs, I would be able to examine the scene. I dreaded the thought of seeing my oldest brother dead, after having missed him most of my life, but it was time to face the truth.

I closed the report, picked up my soft-sided leather briefcase and began assembling my tools for my drive. I would need a stenographer notebook, the report itself, my Sony microcassette recorder and a few Pilot pens.

I picked up the yellow folder and yellow notebook with thoughts on how to construct my story on this—color-coding all items for this project, as I liked to do. The yellow folder had information on where Les Ollila was now—in Ankeny as a pastor of a college. He had been the president of the Northland Bible College at the time of Shawn's death and had been one of the original members of the party who had discovered Shawn's body. I believe I had met him at Shawn's funeral.

"I recall him speaking your name," he had said to me. "In fact, he spoke of Jamie often."

I wanted to ask him what he remembered about the position of the body. Was it facing up toward the winter sky or down into the cold snow? That information was conflicted in the report and statements given by witnesses. I wanted to know who had turned him over in the snow.

In the upcoming spring, I would be at the annual turkey hunt at my brother Tim's farm, not far from Ankeny. I wanted to take an afternoon off from the hunt, drive down to Ankeny and pop in on him—surprise him.

I wanted to introduce myself again, see if he remembered me, listen to his voice and feel his reaction as I mentioned Shawn. I had moved beyond thinking that anything sinister had happened on behalf of the school, but I was still fuming about how long Shawn had lain out in the cold before anyone thought to look for him.

I set the items down for now and my restless soul writhed within me, fresh yet from sobriety. I was feeling emotions for the first time since I was a kid: emotions that I didn't understand, but clamored to be felt and interpreted, because it was time to know and understand what had happened. Or maybe Shawn was trying to communicate with me from Heaven.

I prayed that God would help me find the truth because there can be no nobler thing to pursue. I asked Him to reveal what happened to Shawn, to give me the strength to interpret it, and internalize it the way He wanted me to. Then I could share it with others, so that perhaps they, too, could learn to find peace from the past, as I hoped to do.

13 July – 29 August, 1984
Ministry in Europe report
A Sojourn for Christ
Shawn P. Finucan

In Greece, I met a Greek boy who could only speak a little English but was curious about my ministry. I shared Christ with him and hopefully will see him again someday, if not in this world, the next.

The Europeans, though many of them are set in their traditional ways, listen to what you have to say simply because you are an American.

1984 San Clemente, California

Dad arrived by cab after his two-and-a-half weeks of travel. I was glad to see him for I was lonely for someone to talk to. He got out with his grip and reached in to pay the driver. When he turned to face me, I saw the trip had taken a toll on him in a startling way. His eyes were tired, his posture was stooped, and he had lost weight.

He greeted me, then went into the camper and collapsed on his bed on the western side of the fold-out camper. While he slept through the day, I poked around in his briefcase. His passport had more stamps on it—Columbia, Frankfurt Germany, Luxemburg, and LAX a week ago. I wondered what the hell he was doing in Los Angeles last week without coming to see me. There was a writing pad of paper from Grosvenor House in London with tax shelter notes scrawled across it. That pad of paper is still on my desk thirty-eight years later.

There were thick, expensive-looking business cards printed up with his name on it in fancy calligraphy, saying that he was BA LLB Juris Doctor Chief Legal Counsel, European Central Office for The Wellington Research Institute. The address was 2 Boulevard Royal, Luxembourg. I had heard Dad come up with this before and knew this to be a fictitious organization. Just part of the guise he was working on behalf of the team.

It was nightfall when he came around and wandered outside the camper with a peanut butter sandwich in his hand. He had pulled on his dress pants and a sleeveless sweatshirt, the combination of style showing the contrast in his life—lawyer, yet bum.

He was exhausted and his nerves were frayed. With the sandwich in one hand, he lit a cigarette with his other shaky hand. It was dark and I was looking at a fire I had built. The evening was warm and the sky was peppered with stars. I asked him how the trip had gone.

"As well as it could. I made a few grand for us."

"What did you do?"

"I'm working on setting up a tax shelter outside the U.S. and I smuggled some cocaine in from Bogotá." A park ranger drove by slowly in his pickup truck, checking registrations on the posts at the campsites.

"Damn." My stomach did a flip. "How did you do that?"

"It was hidden in the fake bottom of a golf bag. Joe was with me. An immigration official in the Frankfort airport, wearing a leather overcoat, came over and sat next to us. Joe talked PGA stuff like a pro. I was glad he was there because I wouldn't have known what to say." Dad dragged on his cigarette and stared at the fire. He ran his hand through his thick hair. "The customs agent took one of the golf balls and dropped it in the bag. It made this hollow sound. I could see that he didn't like that. He stared at me for almost a full minute."

"What did you do?"

"I smiled slightly, looked back at him and awaited my fate."

He took a tired breath and bit into the sandwich, letting the cigarette smoke curl from his other hand. The odor of sea salt mixed with a whiff of wood-fire smoke, then Dad's nasty cigarette.

"Do you try to forget your fear when that happens?"

"No, you must be very much in touch with your emotions and handle them accordingly. I take a Valium before going through customs. That seems to help. They stare at you from all these different angles and have one-way glass with people behind that, watching you. They are looking for signs of stress or discomfort and are trained in doing so. It's a very intense experience that taxes me to the core."

A jet went by in the night, up somewhere above us. It was loaded with people on a night flight going somewhere fun I suspected.

"Life hangs in the balance in that moment. All of my worth seems to be on a scale, teetering up and down, and I pray that God forgives me, shows me mercy."

"Were there any problems that came up on the trip?

"On the trip back from London, Tom hid sixty grand in my bag and didn't tell me about it. He thought it was funny, but that really pissed me off. Imagine if they would have tossed that bag and asked me about all this cash? What the hell would I have said?" The information brought my blood to a boil.

"We have an informant in Doyle's office—he's the Attorney General in Wisconsin. We've heard that we have come to their attention of the Attorney General and their office is asking questions about us. What that means I'm not sure, but I think the team is getting hot."

"All this shit for a few grand? You're being taken advantage of." I picked up a stick and held it in the fire. It wouldn't be long before it would glow, then catch fire. The bark rubbed off on my sweaty palm.

"I have a promise of more down the road, but I have done significant work here. I invested their wealth into a stock I picked, and it did very well, quickly. I set up a numbered account in Luxemburg and invested their money with these brilliant people who guarantee a very high percentage in return. I've also suggested they buy gems with their cash, and they have listened to me. It's easy to transfer wealth over borders in the form of gems."

He burned on his Marlboro 100 down to the filter then threw it into the fire.

"I'm working, Jamie. It's like I have a job."

"No, not really," I countered. I thought of all the compliments I had heard about Dad's legal mind in the courtroom, and tactically how he could build a defense for people out of the smallest evidence to work with. Now he was using it for a purpose that was not righteous, and my stomach was turning. I was young and did not yet fully understand the theory of consequences for action, but I was uneasy. "To every action there is an equal and opposite reaction," I had learned in a science class. What bill would come due for this?

"Is it going to be worth it, Dad, when you find yourself in a prison cell in a foreign country?"

"I'm already in a prison cell, in my own country. Just what the hell do I have to lose? I've lost my career, my family, and even my sanity. I can hardly stand to be alive in my own skin minute by minute. I've been sick for a long time now. I live on the edge of society where I have no respect, no means of making a living, and I deal with constant mental anguish every day.

"Throw on top of that, everyone, including members of my own family, who treat me like I was an animal. They act like assholes and take every opportunity to be abusive in word and deed. Add that up and you get a man who is fed up with this shit.

"I live the life of a shadow. You've seen it. For some of it, you've been right by my side. Can you imagine how a man might keep hold of his dignity living like this?" He put a Marlboro 100 in his mouth and clenched his teeth down on the filter, like he did. He flipped open the lid on his Zippo and spun the flint wheel. The flame popped up and steadied like the top of a Bunsen burner. He took the first drag hard, rinsed the smoke through his nose and throat, and the second, he drew deep into his lungs.

"I've had shrinks who were listening to my story, lean forward in their chairs, peer over their glasses and ask me how the fuck I have managed to stay alive carrying this load."

I looked away into the night and promised myself I would never wallow in this type of self-pity for a moment, for all my life, no matter what happened to me. When I looked down at the stick in the fire, it had caught, and I took it out. It went out, but the end stayed red. I put it back in the flames and it sparked right up again.

"If I pull this off for a while, maybe I can help you kids out for a change. Maybe I can finally show up in your lives as someone other than a failure."

"You don't need to give us money to show us who you are. You're my dad, always will be. I don't care how much money you have. You've made a huge difference in my life. You've given me love. Any kid only wants to know that he's loved by his dad. I don't care how much money you make. Don't you know that?" I said as my eyes filled up with tears. I hated myself when they did that. It ruined any message I might have had because I start crying like a baby.

"You don't have to do this illegal shit for these people. These people, this team, they're just taking advantage of you. When the walls come down, none of these assholes will be around to help you. Don't do this anymore. I don't ever ask you for a damn thing. But don't do this anymore. No good can come of it." A few moments of silence punctuated the switched roles of the conversation, me scolding him now.

"I have to do this. I'm committed to this attack. You don't quit on these people. Once you start playing cards with the devil, it's hard to fold and walk away before the kitty is paid out. Anyway, I don't have any respect for the law. What the hell has the law ever done for me?

"Remember a few years back when some psychopathic asshole emptied a clip from a rifle through a window at me? You couldn't pay someone to give a damn. Do you remember what the law did about that? Let me remind you, nothing. That degenerate asshole, and we know who he is, is still walking amongst us. The law is for rich people who can afford it. We poor make our own laws and our own rules. And the rule in this game is simply 'Don't get caught.'"

Down the line of campsites, a guy and girl were laughing together about something. I wished I was that guy right then.

I unwrapped a piece of gum and tipped the comic so I could read it by firelight. Mort, wearing his turtleneck over his mouth, approaches Bazooka Joe with a bunch of trophies and awards. "I won these trophies and medals at school for having a good memory," he says to Joe.

"What's that one for?" Bazooka Joe points at one.

"I don't remember," Mort says and walks away. Bazooka Joe has exclamation points around his head. I threw the comic into the fire, while my mouth filled with the sweet, gummy, bubblegum flavor of comfort.

"There is more work coming up. I need to go to Singapore. I've cleared the way for you to join me for a while. I could use your help."

"Whaaat?" I lifted my head and looked across the fire at him.

"It's a big presentation. I won't give you the details. It's a need-to-know thing. And what you don't know can't hurt you."

"What do I do?" I was feeling my spirit of adventure awaken to conquer my principles.

"You get to travel to Singapore–an exotic country on the other side of the world."

And, just like that, I sold out and joined him in the underworld of high risk, low profit.

Dad crashed down again in the camper for the better part of three days, sleeping off his jet lag and work. He snored like a chain saw that almost started with each pull on the ignition cord. I fell asleep in a dream where I was adjusting the choke, making sure the switch was on, pulling the cord again with one hand, and pushing the saw away with the other hand that held the top bar.

I worked my shift at the car wash, went to the San Clemente library, and read. I wrote in my journal and worked on a story about a young guy from Wisconsin, who enters a surfing competition and out-surfs all the California dudes, then dates their girlfriends. He outworks them in jobs he's hired for until they band together and try to kill him because he makes them look so bad.

The opposing characters are a bunch of pretty boys, who comb their hair a lot and pick fights with people who don't have the proper exhaust modifications on their cars, and don't recycle plastic properly. They whine about their jobs and like to talk about how hard they work, while they should be working.

The girls in the story are very pretty and nice. They crush hard on the Midwestern guy because he's down to earth, hard and strong like the oak and maple trees he hunted under in the harsh northern climate conditions. He doesn't expect anyone to hand him a damn thing. He knows that if he wants something in this world, he has to work for it. He knows how to make a lady feel special. The fit, supple ladies find his direct approach and Wisconsin confidence romantic and captivating. He gets a lot of action, if you know what I mean. The rating on this story is a hard "R", featuring girls who experience their first orgasm. This results in a type of awakening that leads them to be vivacious and zesty toward life from then on.

When I look at the writing from the journal now, I almost blush. My frenetic energy was dispersed in unleashed sexual tension and desire. My fast, feverish handwriting in a story was raunchy enough to make *The Kama Sutra* look like *Pride and Prejudice*.

In the afternoon, I missed my surfboard, but swam in the ocean like all the other tourists, and lay on the beach, missing home. I discovered I'm not really a beach guy.

The ocean has its beauty in a "Jimmy Buffet" style. But even more captivating is a Wisconsin swamp, covered in moss in the morning mist, during the fall. The ocean is blue and mighty, but a Midwestern field of corn, rimmed by Maple, Oak and Pine trees with a God-painted orange and violet sunset behind it, is gentle and soothing to the soul. The seagull's cry is alluring and forlorn in the salty breeze. But a caw of the crow answered by another from across a glacier carved valley of Aspen trees on a late spring morning in the Northwoods, can make you know the Holy Spirit has touched your day.

Swimming in the ocean is nice. Though, when you swim in the rivers and lakes in northern Wisconsin, the water is cool, gentle and refreshing, and doesn't leave a salty crust over you all day. And, up north, there aren't as many people everywhere. There are no traffic jams, no lines to wait in and the attitude toward strangers isn't as flaky.

I thought of Jamie a great deal. I relived the walks we took, played back her laughter in my memory, and remembered the way she smoked a cigarette out of the side of her mouth. I thought of the color and smell of her auburn hair and her two-tone eyelashes when she looked down. This brought an emptiness to my heart that nothing seemed to alleviate.

I was noticing my situation more each day. I was considering what I had to offer for a future.

Here, living in a park, far away with no objective to seize, I was starting to feel like a dog chasing a car. To provide for Jamie, I would need a skill, and washing cars was not going to cut it. I would need some kind of education. Reading books at the library was not lending itself to any accreditation by the circus masters, who set the standards of acceptability in the sideshow of the job world.

Although I had not yet developed a method of examining the future, as many people had, I was beginning to become aware of this defect in my plan, or lack thereof.

It was leaving me with a haunting feeling that I was living a life of self-deception.

Right now, I had no money, no car that was mine, no real job, and no future. My surfboard had no fin. In the sports car of life, I was going nowhere at one hundred miles per hour and stomping on the accelerator, while, up ahead of me, a storm of accountability was moving in from the Northwest.

CHAPTER 12

Be still, and know that I am God: I will be exalted among the heathen, I will be exalted in the earth.

Psalm 46:10

Satan will openly at times step forward and use instruments...people who are enticed to do wrong. Unclean spirits speak through men as instruments.

(From a notebook of Shawn Patrick Finucan)

13 July – 29 August, 1984
Ministry in Europe
A Sojourn for Christ
Shawn P. Finucan

In Greece, I was part of a ministry which played music and that drew crowds, sang songs and did pantomimes, and passed out tracts. The group was from Springfield, Massachusetts. I was handicapped not being able to speak the language here to communicate the Gospel fully, regardless it was a privilege to hand out seeds of God's word to the people, "For I am not ashamed of the gospel of Christ; for it is the power of God unto salvation to everyone that believeth; to the Jew first, and also to the Greek." (Rom. 1:16)

MARINETTE SHERIFF DEPARTMENT SUPPLEMENTARY INVESTIGATION REPORT case number 85-393

...left chest of the front of the body shows an absence of "tattooing." There was also an absence of "Smudging" from

burning power. The length of the barrel would account for the absence of "tattooing."
Sgt. James Jerue

Tattooing is a term used to describe the punctuate abrasions observed when epithelial tissue comes into contact with partially burned or unburned grains of powder. These punctuate abrasions cannot be wiped away and will remain visible on the skin for several days.

The intensity of the tattooing will be primarily determined by the muzzle to skin distance and may also be affected by the length of the barrel and type of powder used.

(National Crime Justice Reference Service)

November, 2019 Merrill, Wisconsin

As I have re-read the report of Jerue, I questioned what he meant by this observation. Why would there be no smudging or tattooing? Was it because the barrel was pressed up against his chest? Would then all the powder be blown into the wound and therefore not be peppered all over his chest or clothes? Or, was it because the shot came from a far distance, so as to not allow this result?

Smudging: when a firearm is discharged, smoke, containing soot and gunpowder is ejected from the muzzle with the bullet. These deposits around a bullet wound in cases of close-range fire are referred to as smudging and tattooing or stripping.

It is the diameter of spread and the density of these deposits that aid in estimating the distance from which the gun was fired.

(National Criminal Justice Reference Service)

Jerue wrote that he noticed no smudging. Is that because of the jacket, or the distance? That fumed in my mind as I tried to determine what this meant.

Jerue wrote that there was dried blood in the barrel of the weapon but an absence of any "blowback." Well, what the hell do you call dried blood in the barrel? Isn't that blowback?

Outside, the sunlight retreated earlier now. The autumn promise of cool nights and extended darkness started the shadows stretching out for nightfall. The trees had turned their leaves to orange, brown, yellow and amber. This colorful foliage was dropping past the window of my study like the reflective days of a paper calendar being peeled off my life.

Teach us, Oh Lord, to number our days so that we may present to you a heart of wisdom, the Psalmist had written.

I tasted my life in these memories. With fresh eyes, I felt the gold in the relationships I treasured around me—those that I knew now and held dear in the living world of real time, and those that had passed on from this life and watched me from the other side. With sober eyes, I grieved as though I never had. I can only grieve to the level of how capable I am. I only experience life to the level of how alive I can be. If I'm wasted, I can't feel emotions, I don't get to grieve. This is an honor for the brave and clear-eyed. This is reserved for those who live life on life's terms.

1984 San Clemente, California

It was Dad's idea to write the letter to the principal of the school. I can say that in all honesty. I did it, I know, and that's on me. I have no excuse, but Dad was a good salesman when he wanted to be. He could influence me in those days.

We were sitting around the fire pit in our campsite, number thirty-eight. The California evening air was dry and I could hear the ocean breaking on the beach. The darkness closed in around us, giving me the feeling that it was a wall that the world couldn't invade. The orb of firelight could give the impression that nothing existed outside this ring of illumination. It awakened something primal in our psyches. It solidified our unity against the outside darkness, making us feel in counsel with each other against the world.

Dad called the fire pit "the campfire of despair" and here we discussed tactics. Dad analyzed problems, legal problems of others, potential pit falls with our situation, often his relationship with my mother that was over years ago and anything else that came up for contemplative consideration.

"There's something on your mind tonight. You seem preoccupied," Dad said.

"They are going to graduate next week."

"Who is?"

"My friends, everyone in my graduation year, 1984." I picked up a log and laid it gently on the cabin-style fire I had built. The cabin was ablaze, like little Indians had attacked a settler outpost and shot flaming arrows into it as they circled on horseback. This log I put on lay in contrast to the structure. It was out of place, but the flames accepted it anyway and started to lick around the corners of its maple bark until they met from each side.

"I see."

The smoke drifted up into the black night toward the stars.

"Do you wish that you were also, graduating with them?"

"I don't know what I wish," I said from my restless spirit.

"The educational system is a lie. It's a hypocritical example of a failed indoctrination process that has nothing to do with teaching students but seeks to make them conform to an underlying system of values that are untrue, unethical or false. School has nothing to do with education."

I had heard this shit before. The emptiness inside me stayed alight.

"Let's write a letter to the principal. What's his name?"

"Lanny Tibaldo," I said, looking up, my eyeballs dry with heat.

"Let's write him a letter telling him what we think about his school and what he can do with it."

"What good will that do?"

"It will give vent to the frustration inside you, heal you and perhaps give Mr. Tibaldo a chance to repair something that is broken. We're actually helping him."

I liked the sound of that suggestion. I was, after all, a man of action and wanted to help anyone I could.

I picked up my Mead composition notebook, the one I never liked because, without the spirals, it didn't open completely. But, it did keep ideas in order without allowing the removal of pages so easily.

Dad waited for me to get ready, pen in hand. I leaned away from a pillar of smoke that the ocean wind was blowing in my face.

"Dear… (Name again?)"

"Mr. Tibaldo."

"First name for this address."

"Lanny."

Dear Lanny,

My pen flew over the first two words and I waited in the firelight, looking at the paper with Bic pen in hand.

I write to you from an Oceanside campsite, beside a fire—what I call, the Campfire of Despair in Southern California. I have taken pen in hand because I feel compelled to tell you something. I came into your school with a heart filled with great expectation and wonder about life. I arrived on the campus of Merrill High with a sense of victory for having made it there, to the halls of this local educational institution, alight with the possibilities of what I would learn and explore.

I expected to be shown the value of knowledge and to be inspired by scholars whose mission in life was to bring out the potential of the students in their charge and show them the possibilities of exercising their talents to their fullest. I was anticipating brilliant ideas and instruction from people who cared and were passionate about education and lighting the flame of wisdom in young minds and inspiring them to climb, excel and exceed their own expectations.

What I found was a world of oppression and tyranny and incompetence. I found teachers who couldn't give a crap about the student body and had no passion for their duties, and quite frankly wished they were someplace else. Therefore, most of their students did as well.

Dad flipped open his Zippo, lit a cigarette and looked at me for a moment without seeing me.

You have suspended me from my studies for a minor infraction, kicked me off a sporting event that was giving me healing and joy, and issued me detention in an effort to break my free spirit, and weaken my resolve toward being an individual of unique character. I have had fingers stuck in my face with endless ass chewing from so-called instructors and administration who were projecting their own defects at me, speaking from projected resentment from their own life's failures with viciousness and guile, until it has succeeded in souring my own life.

When I did the only thing I could do—act out in defiance, you suspended me from the studies that I desperately needed and isolated me further from the educational system rather than help me.

On the altar of your good conduct…

"Maybe you should spell conduct with a k—
give it a German-kind of Hitler feel."

you have sacrificed my desire for an education. You have succeeded in strangling my hunger for knowledge with rules and oppressive regulation and heavy consequence for trivial defections from stupid mandates and gutted my interest to study and flourish in any learning institution henceforth.

"Hold on…" I said, scrawling down the words on the paper as fast as I could.

I have, therefore, Lanny Tibaldo, consulted one of California's more renown practitioners of the black arts and have had the following curse put upon you.

That each morning, when the sun rises and shines its eastern rays on the soil where you are, and each day as the last rays of sunlight fall upon the trees near you, a clutch of disorder will affect your lower intestinal tract and cause your bowels to purge without restraint and project the contents therein with great force outward, with which you will be unable to constrain.

This shall be done without regard and affect of your free will, but it will be involuntary and powered by a great force. For it is only fitting that a man obsessed with rules and order and good Kunduct…

"Use the K there again."

should, each day at the beginning of the new day, and in the end of it, shit his pants.

Signed,

In Disgust,

We both laughed and thought this to be brilliant. I thought of trying to submit it to *National Lampoon* or some humor magazine that could really appreciate it.

Since you don't write a letter unless you intend to mail it, I did just that. The next day when in town I stopped at a blue US Mailbox and dropped it in. I had a touch of a doubt, wondering if this was a good idea, but overcame it in the spirit of getting things done.

That feeling was amplified when I was back at the campsite and told Dad I had mailed the letter. He looked up from straightening his gear.

"You mailed the letter?" he asked surprised.

"Well, of course I did. What the hell would we have written it for if I didn't intend to mail it?"

Dad looked a little concerned for a second.

"I guess I was thinking that sometimes you can write a letter as a type of therapy and then you don't…actually mail it."

He shrugged it off and went back to his task.

Later, I would remember his reaction vividly. One thing Dad and I shared at that time was an uncanny sense for not understanding the consequences of our actions.

I walked down the avenue of campsites on my way to the pay phone by the ranger station. I strolled past the segmented worlds of recreational lives on display and took in the eclectic methods of existence in every ten-foot slice of asphalt that was a campsite. The human play of existence was on display with no walls around it and changed with every few steps.

I wondered where, amidst it all, I was supposed to fit in. If it was a play, what were my lines and when was my curtain call? Did I have a big part or was I an extra?

I dropped in a bunch of change in the metal phone with the steel wire cord and my oldest brother Shawn answered. We chatted for a while. He was at home visiting before he was leaving for Greece, Yugoslavia and then Romania on a mission tour.

"I am bringing Bibles behind the Iron Curtain," Shawn said. I recalled that he had mentioned this trip before, and I had seen the flier that he circulated accepting donations for the trip to support his ministry.

"Why don't you just mail them?" I asked.

"They have to be brought in; 'smuggled' is the right term."

"What? Like…they were drugs or something?"

"Something like that. The penalties are severe I am learning. People have been waiting for the word of God for years. We take our religious freedom for granted as a culture, but there are people in closed-off countries who would give anything for a page of the word of God."

"Are you traveling in a group or alone?"

"I attached to a group who has done this before."

"I'm sure there are risks involved with this…"

"Yes, there are, as with many things, but I will not be alone. Christ will be with me."

I could hear the smile in his voice. I thought of Dad smuggling cocaine in the bottom of golf bags from Columbia into LAX and compared the two of them, such different motives and actions, but both being ready and able to break the law. It was, afterall, the year of the smuggler in the Finucan family.

"Well, be careful. What else is going on?"

"Gus died. He was hit by a car going across the street to the Dairy Queen."

The news hit me like a punch in the gut.

"Oh, no."

"We had him lying here on the couch for a while, but he passed away a few hours after it happened."

I thought of the Springer Spaniel with the gentle, playful personality and soft fur coat that loved affection and had a genuine love for humankind. I felt like I had lost on old friend, because I did. Shawn and I talked more for a while and then I got off the phone and walked back down the road toward campsite number thirty-eight, my home.

I thought of how Gus had helped mark the truck of the guy who had shot at Dad when I was younger. He scratched his claw down the side of the door while the guy ate a cone and teased him. Then when the creep had thrown the cone at Gus, he had caught it in his mouth and trotted off, not toward the house but off in another direction.

I remembered how he leaned into me when I petted him and looked back over his shoulder at me with what I believed to be loving eyes. When hunting, he bounced above the cattails and tall grass, in the Springer fashion to flush a partridge while staying expertly away from the bird until I got a shot off with the 20 gauge. His mouth was always gentle when he retrieved the bird and never crushed it in his jaws.

He was a dog who brought a smile to anyone in the room and approached with a wagging tail that brushed away any blues you faced. I would have numerous dogs throughout my life, but there was never a dog like Gus who could occupy that same place in my heart.

I told Dad about Gus when I got to the site and he sat down with me. In silence, we had a moment of remembrance for him.

That night we had ring bologna cooked on a stick over the flames of the fire. I had picked up a pineapple and was cutting it up with the big survival knife with the compass in the pummel and sewing gear and matches in the hollow handle. Also, on the way home from work I had picked up a Sara Lee pound cake and was going to bust it out in surprise after dinner.

The campsite next to us had some young people playing music a little louder than Dad could handle and I saw it affecting him, agitating his mental condition. They were enjoying the new album by the Scorpions—"Love at First Sting."

The music was playing out of an El Camino with the doors open. At any moment, Dad's response could go one of two ways. He would turn into a confrontational, officious person and *chew* out these people, or just seethe in resentment until he crashed into a deep dive of depression that could last for days. I never knew what might happen.

I didn't want a scene. The new neighbors were young, like me, and with the troupe was a lady wearing a bikini that moved around their campsite like music notes on a scale. She had the legs of a dancer and a rump that looked like two bowling balls being held to the bottom of her lower back by a tiny, electric-blue, nylon swimsuit bottom. She laughed at just about anything someone said and danced like a groupie at a rock concert.

The guys she was with were motorheads and were wrenching on a Cadillac. A few had their heads under the hood of the car and a few others slid underneath the front of the Caddy on a small board with wheels on them. They drank beers and the women grilled up burgers. Skunky plumes of potent cannabis drifted over to our camp and I felt the isolation of a guy who was eighteen hanging out with his Dad all the time.

The guitar work of "Rock You Like a Hurricane" was sliding into the chorus then skipping off the baseline and jamming into another cord. I was enjoying hearing the album in its entirety.

"This music sucks," Dad said a little too loud.

With a nod of my head, I pointed out to him how pretty the girls were, and when he took notice, the blood pressure at our campsite dropped.

"I got an idea," Dad said between bites of stick-cooked ring bologna. "I think it's time we got out of here for a while. We have some money from the last job, but not a great deal, as you know. It would go further in Mexico, where things are cheaper. We could hole up down there for a few months and save some dough."

"Mexico?"

"Sure, you speak Spanish don't you?"

"Well, not really. I had a class and got a C in it."

"You've been listening to those Professor Berlitz cassettes I gave you, right?"

"As a matter of fact, I have—a bit. *Qual ese lago debajo deno sotoros*," I responded.

"What's that mean?"

"What is that small lake below us? Here's another; *Es usted no canaesada? Usted seiempre de pie*."

Dad cracked up laughing from his belly, then beckoned with his fingers in a "give it to me" gesture.

"Ok, let's have it. What was that? What did you say?"

"Are you not tired? You are always standing?" It was the only thing I could remember from the tapes at the moment. It was something you say on the plane to the stewardess. Electric-blue bikini looked over at me and smiled. I about fell off the picnic table. She was California pretty.

She started rubbing Banana Boat suntan oil on her dancer's legs. Her skin was so smooth and soft I had to remember that my heartbeat and breathing were supposed to be autonomous actions.

"Hey, Kid, did you hear me?" Dad grunted.

"What?"

"I have to go there anyway to a little town of Jimenez, over the border. The team said there is a guy with a legal question for me. I figure we'll just stay down there. Our money will last longer. Then, when I fly out to Singapore, you can hang out down there until I send for you. Won't that be great?"

"Sure."

The raven-haired lady walked with a grace of a waterfall. Her bikini danced over her oily body as she moved over to a cooler, lowered herself over into a bent position with her legs straight and lifted out a beer. The tab on the top of the can of Budweiser popped in release and hissed in ejaculation. My heart felt like it was made of grinding metal gears.

The guys worked into the night on the Cadillac but turned the music down when it got late so we had no reason to complain. In the first light of the morning, they were gone, but where they had been working, they left an engine in the parking slip of their campsite. A clean, stripped down, shiny engine sitting there where a car had been the previous night, like a monument to their hard work over the weekend.

I watched a half a dozen rangers show up and stare at it with puzzled expressions until they all squatted down by it, lifted it into their low trailer and hauled it away. I was impressed that the motorheads had come here with a plan and had the competency to change out an engine in the night and install another in the Cadillac, then drive it away.

It took skill to do that. They were just a little older than me. I wondered again what kind of skill and service I would have that anyone would pay me to do for them? My friends would be leaving for the Marine Corps in a few days. They would be going through boot camp at MCRD, just down the coast from where I was. I was going to Mexico to live on a few grand that my Dad got from smuggling and setting up tax shelters for crooks. Again, the feeling of being lost awoke inside me.

That night I had a dream that I was on a surfboard and got pulled out to sea on a riptide that spun me around so that I couldn't see the shoreline anymore. I paddled around trying to see it, but when I did, I was so far out that there was only blue ocean all around me. The sun was setting on the western horizon and night would be falling. That's when the sharks come into feed.

CHAPTER 13

Not that which goeth into the mouth defileth a man; but that which cometh out of the mouth, this defileth a man.

Mathew 15:11

It was not until Beethoven had become so deaf he could not hear the fortissimo of a full orchestra that he composed his chief oratorio. It was not until John Milton had become stone blind that he could dictate the sublime poem of the ages. It was not until Walter Scott was kicked by a horse and confined to the house for many days that he could write the "Lay of the last Minstrel."

The painter who mixed his colors with blood from his own broken heart makes the best pictures. The mightiest men of all ages have been mightiest in their agonies.

Talmage

(Found in Shawn's notebook)

Imagination is the only weapon in the war against reality.

Jules de Gaulter

October, 2019 Merrill, Wisconsin

I had learned what I could from reading the reports and the statements of the officers regarding my brother's death. I needed to know about the gunshot wound. The family information I had was that the wound was big in the front and tiny in the back.

I had been deer hunting since I was a kid and I had shot many a deer. I had seen entrance wounds and exit wounds with a rifle and had seen the damage a bullet from a 30.06 rifle could do. It was a big game rifle cartridge. A bullet enters small and expands as it blasts its way through flesh and bone, as the bullet is mushrooming open. By the time it exits, it has ripped open flesh to produce a gaping exit wound.

Jerue's report didn't really sound like that was what he was looking at.

I couldn't explain the blood in the barrel of the rifle or why Jerue said there was an absence of what he called "blowback" or "smudging," but I did read in the report that there were photographs and I had to go get them. I considered calling the Marinette County Sheriff's office again and asking them to search the files. They had been kind and had provided me what they had, but there was a part of me that didn't trust the process. Through the years, we, as a family, had dealt with this tragedy and suspected that something was afoul and that Shawn was not responsible for his own death.

I wanted to go to the Marinette County Sheriff's office and ask for the photos directly. A voice on the phone was one level of request, but a man standing at a window needing answers to his brother's death from long ago was another.

I decided I would take a day off work, miss having breakfast and lunch with my grandson that my wife was watching and do a thorough investigation to the best of my abilities.

I owed Shawn that. I needed to know the truth.

13 July – 29 August, 1984
Ministry in Europe
A sojourn for Christ
Shawn P. Finucan
In Yugoslavia, there was a psychological tension that was experienced. The Christians in that country face harassment and pressure from the government for belief in Jesus Christ. They feel the pressure on their jobs as adult Christians and the children feel it in schools.

1984 San Clemente, California

We were going to Mexico. We paid up the rent on the campsite for the month and agreed that once we got settled down in Mexico we would come back for the Jayco camper. I went to the Bank of America and took the firearms in the bag into the room with the safety deposit box and put both of them into the box. I had gotten the biggest box available and The Snake, with the scope mounted on top, barely fit in. I made sure both weapons were empty and laid the boxes of ammo next to them. Dad's Browning 9mm High Power lay on top of The Snake with an envelope Dad wanted in there. I thought it might be a will or something.

We packed the Jeep light. I wanted my knife, so I stashed my Puma six-inch blade in the metal scabbard under the seat. Dad saw me do this and decided he wanted the big survival knife under his seat. At least we had some steel. We didn't have much gear or clothing. We wore clothes till they stunk and went to a laundromat when we had to. We made sure we had our passports in our possession and headed south.

At the border crossing the Border Patrol officer asked us how long we were going to stay.

"Maybe two or three months," Dad answered. "We've had it with the states for a while," he added with a little swagger in his voice.

"Business or vacation?"

"Vacation."

"Enjoy yourselves," the Border Patrolman said as he handed us back our passports, and we were off. The roads turned to dirt and the houses looked more third world in a hurry. The road signs were unreadable, and people looked at our Jeep as we passed.

The map posed some challenges. I had to ask directions and my Berlitz cassette training would allow me to ask a question. But when they answered, thinking I could speak Spanish, I could only nod. I would jump back in the Jeep and make up something I thought they were saying, and we would drive on.

We got lost in no time flat.

Dad got frustrated and showed signs of coming unglued, so I took the wheel. The culture shock had him wide-eyed and sad looking, and I could see he was spiraling. I encouraged him to take a nap. The Jeep didn't really work well for that because there didn't seem to be anywhere to lean against. The roll bar was just a bit too far back and the soft plastic tarp doors didn't offer enough support.

I got us to the city we were looking for and we checked into a hotel, as it was nightfall. The room had two small beds in it and a TV. I turned on the TV and dad crashed hard right away. His snoring sounded like a chop-saw that I ran one summer in a factory job, while earning minimum wage and a per-piece rate.

The TV had episodes of stuff like *The Love Boat* with dubbed-in Spanish over the English dialogue. I kept watching it and wondered how they got the lips of the actors to look like they were speaking Spanish. I fell asleep imagining I was flying a small plane with the engine sputtering. The craft would descend when the engine cut, kick back to life and lift me up into the sky every time Dad snored.

Below me were lakes and farm fields of terrain that I knew and loved. One-hundred-year-old farmhouses, made of brick, and red barns that had stood for generations, passed by below me on a fall harvest landscape. I barely cleared a silo with the plane until it sputtered alive and carried me over the top with a few inches to spare.

Wind blew leaves over porches and men worked in the fields wearing Carhartt jackets and jeans with Stormy Kromer hats on. The shadow of my plane fell on a boy who ran with the energy of the young down a gravel driveway while a yellow school bus pulled away. He ran into the arms of his mother who was wearing an apron, sweeping off the porch.

The wind drifted my craft sideways, and I slipped with the northeast gale into a tranquil realm of restorative sleep that so often could evade me. I escaped a tortured night of mental anguish.

The next morning, I woke up to Dad sitting on his already-made bed with his briefcase beside him. He was looking through his notes with his glasses on. He was showered up and focusing on the task. He glanced up at me and noticed I was awake.

"Let's go, Jamie. We got an appointment to keep. I'm supposed to meet these guys about something business-related."

"What kind of business are we talking about here?" I swung my legs off the bed.

"I don't know. Joe said these guys were impressed by my work and they have a proposition for me. Not sure what it's about."

"What kind of work did you do that they were impressed by?" I asked, scratching a bug bite on my back that had occurred in the night on the nasty mattress.

"I didn't get a chance to ask that question."

He organized items in the case, snapped it shut, and then lit a cigarette. I didn't like the sound of any of it. I thought of all of our firepower locked away in a safety deposit box in San Clemente.

"What do we know about these guys?"

"Not much. Joe knows them somehow."

"We drove down here for a meeting with criminals, and we have no idea what the subject is or who they are?"

"I picked stock for Tom called Cooper Industries that made them all a lot of money. I researched it and knew what I was doing. That's legitimate business. Maybe it's something like that."

"How do they know we're here?"

"I called the number from a pay phone in the lobby. What the hell is this, twenty questions? Let's go. Get ready."

The shower was ancient, filthy, and looked like there had been blood in the bottom of it. I washed my hair and tried to rinse out the imagery of a B-grade snuff movie having been filmed in this very motel room.

As much as I turned the hot water valve, it produced only cold, but it does something positive for me to rinse in the water in the morning. Even after a cold shave that felt like the razor was yanking out my whiskers, I had on clean underwear and a fresh perspective on the day.

I stepped out of the hotel room and walked to the Jeep. I unzipped the back flap to toss our grips in the back. I glanced around the small parking lot and noticed a burgundy 1978 Lincoln Continental parked, the engine running and two Mexican men in it. They were staring straight ahead not looking at me. Their necks were stiff and they sat there like manikins.

I dropped the grip on the gravel parking lot, then stooped down to pick it up and brushed off the bottom with my hand. When I glanced at them again, both were looking at me, but then both snapped their heads in unison to look straight out the front of the windshield at the side of an old parked semi-truck.

They were so nonchalant that they were *chalant*.

I zipped up the back flap while my stomach took on the sensation of dropping into my shorts, like I was on a rocket-propelled elevator. Dad came out to the Jeep, and we got ready for takeoff. I took the driver's seat, found my Newport Beach baseball cap and my Wayfarer sunglasses, and put them on. I was in disguise. As I keyed the ignition, Dad looked at the directions he had written down on an envelope. I remember thinking that I was glad the Jeep didn't blow up when it started.

In the rearview mirror, the Lincoln moved out of the parking lot into the street behind us, letting a few cars between. The driver had a big, fat, misshapen head, like a phrenologist's dream. I considered telling Dad about the car that was tailing us, but I had concerns about his state of mind, as he was mid-stride in something shady. I had to consider what he could handle.

As I moved in the city traffic faster than he could orientate, he told me to slow down. At a light that was yellow, I moved into traffic and made a dirty-blue pickup to my right have to wait for me to go through the intersection. The Lincoln stopped at the light behind us, and then ran the damn stoplight. With my eyes on the rearview mirror, I had to slam on the brakes and take the Jeep out of gear to avoid rear-ending an old, panel station wagon full of kids with a mother driving.

Dad clutched the "oh shit" handle in the dashboard.

"Hey, Kid, watch what you're doing. Take the next left."

I worked the long stick shift and clutch, and rolled the blue Wrangler through the traffic on its big wheels.

I was sure we had a tail. What I didn't know was who they were. If they were Mexican police detectives, we may want to abort the meeting. My big, side view mirror showed the Lincoln moving up in traffic to stay with us.

Just when I was about to alert Dad, the burgundy Lincoln turned off onto a residential street. I relaxed my neck muscles. Dad was focusing on giving me directions and struggling to read street signs in Spanish. He was nervous enough about what we were doing. I didn't need to add to his tension. He was ten minutes from breaking down and mentally collapsing at any given time; I could feel it. How he handled the pressure of what he was doing, in the condition he was in, boggled my mind.

I kept the conversation light and tried to get him to laugh, but he wasn't having any of it.

Being in a land where we couldn't read the street signs, billboards, shop windows or understand the radio had me missing the US.

"I don't like this. I don't trust these guys you're working with. If things fall apart, don't you think they'll cut you loose to take the fall?"

"These guys wouldn't do that,." Dad said, looking at the directions he had gotten out of his briefcase.

"You already said Tom hid sixty-five grand in your suitcase when you went through customs. You think that was a joke? They would throw you under the bus tires faster than kitty litter in an ice storm."

Dad wasn't telling me anything about what we were doing down here and that told me it was an activity that could get us killed or, at best, I could make the Mexican prison boxing team. My fighting name would be The Gringo. I downshifted to round a corner when Dad pointed.

I saw myself in a velvet robe coming out of the corner of a third-world gym ring holding up my boxing gloved hands to three cheers and four people booing. Some gay guy in tight shorts would be the ring girl walking around the ring holding up a sign with the number one on it.

In the opposite corner El Tiburon, a man twice my size with arms like legs, would be taking his robe off, spitting in the face of his cornerman rather than in the bucket, and looking at me with hate as he chewed on his mouthpiece.

"What's El Tiburon mean?" I asked my cornerman.

"The Shark. In the second round, he's gunna bite your face after he spits out his mouthpiece."

"I can take him," I would say and knock my gloves together, giving a little jump up on my toes.

"No, you can't," Corner Man would say.

"The hell I can't. Whose side you on anyway?"

"I'm on yours, Gringo. You gunna take a dive or Pepe will pay your Dad a visit in cell block Cinco with a razor blade and cut his throat before he wakes up tomorrow morning."

The fight would deflate out of my shoulders, and I would stop bouncing up and down.

The sound of Dad's voice shattered my anxiety-riddled vision and I came around.

"I said turn there at the last block. Don't do that crap where you fade out somewhere. Not now. Stay with me, I need you in the game." I glanced at him and saw the fury mixed with horror and grave concern in his green eyes.

We finally found the address we were looking for.

We pulled up in front of a cement house with a waist-high wrought iron fence around it in the middle of a business district. The pungent odor of burning plastic filled the air.

I cut the engine and Dad looked again at the address on the building, then at the envelope in his hand.

"This is it. I need you to stay in the Jeep. Wait for me. I don't know how long it will be, but if it's a few hours, just wait."

"A few hours? What am I going to do in the Jeep for a few hours? Let me come with you."

"No, I need you out here. You'll stay in the Jeep, right?"

I didn't like this, and he saw it in my eyes.

"Listen," I reached out and grabbed his shoulder. "Just what the hell is this anyway?" He shook off my grip, worked the lever on the soft door, and climbed out. He looked up and down the street and went up to the door. After he knocked, it opened and a Mexican man in a Hawaiian shirt and a big smile stood aside to let him in.

Once Dad walked past him into the house, the Hawaiian-shirt guy stepped out of the house and looked up and down the street. His eyes rested on the Jeep and then on me. He smiled and waved. I waved back.

"I see you too, asshole," I said in the hot stagnant air.

I didn't like the way he had surveyed the perimeter to see who was with Dad before going in. He was assessing how many were in the arriving force. Now they knew I was out here. If this got ugly, I was a sitting duck.

In the hour-and-a-half that passed by, some neighborhood kids came out and started a game of stickball in the street. A woman with long legs and pants that were so tight— any tighter and she would be wearing them on the inside—walked by with a dog on a leash, some kind of mutt. The dog stopped to piss on almost every car tire it passed. This made me realize I was going to have to do the same soon.

I started looking up and down the sleepy little street and noticed a car behind me, parked along the curb three cars down. It was the burgundy Lincoln Continental. I moved the side mirror over to see the driver's seat. It appeared to be empty.

I got out of the Jeep and stretched my legs. I looked around to get a view of the passenger side of the Lincoln. It was empty as well. Both the occupants were where? I guessed, in the same house Dad was in. A piss shiver shook me to the core.

If I didn't empty my bladder soon, I was going to look awfully funny with a urine stain in my pants the rest of the day. I noticed a gap between the house Dad went in and the next. I walked up to the gate to the wrought iron fence, went in and moved toward the door. Instead of going up the little stoop, I walked around to the side of the house into a gap between the buildings. After a few paces, I started to urinate about a half-second before my bladder burst. The image of the Hoover Dam crossed my mind and I shuddered in relief.

The dirty window at my left shoulder was emitting the sound of discussion going on in the house. I recognized Dad's voice responding to a question. His tone was confident, professional, but measured with care. He was nervous. I moved closer to the window. The drape was pulled against it so I put my ear to the cloudy glass.

"I think you would be better off with a local attorney. I'm not licensed to practice in Mexico," Dad said. Someone spoke in Spanish, and then it was interpreted by a man who spoke English very well.

"Señor Ortega says that with your reputation and your tenacity, he feels that you are just the man to get his cousin out of jail. He also says there are ways around this license nonsense that he can take care of, for he knows people in government. Reynosa State Prison is a hard place for the young man to be in, and the family is concerned for his well-being. We will have local legal counsel to assist you but want you to oversee Juan's defense."

"Tell Mr. Ortega that I'm flattered by the offer, but I have some things on my plate that are consuming my time with my own team."

The interpreter related Dad's sentence. After another response in Spanish from Mr. Ortega, the interpreter relayed: "Mr. Ortega says he has talked to Joe, who says they can make time for you to help us."

"Perhaps another time. I am too busy right now, but thanks for the offer."

"Mr. Ortega is not used to people refusing his request, especially when it is known that he pays very well and there is always an assurance of more work. You see, Patrick, you get to become a member of the Ortega family."

I listened to the interpretation made by the man, but I had distinctly heard two words mentioned by Mr. Ortega that the interpreter did not convey. Ortega had used the words "mucho muerte," and no reference had been made to those two words, which I just happened to know from my Professor Berlitz course. They meant "much death."

"Also, Mr. Ortega has a package that he wishes for you to deliver to a friend in El Paso, Texas."

"I'm afraid I'm not going that way. I have my son with me, so I won't be carrying anything across the border. But again, thank you for the offer."

"It's highly advisable for you to reconsider, Mr. Finucan." He said something else that I didn't pick up, but I was certain the interpreter's words were meant as a warning. There were footsteps with the message as well. Some people were moving about in the room.

I didn't like any of this shit before, and I liked it even less now.

I walked back to the front of the house and hesitated. I went back to the Jeep and got the Puma hunting knife with the metal scabbard and jammed it down the front of my pants in the waistband, then pulled my shirt over it.

After I jumped up the stairs of the front porch, I took both of my hands and messed up my hair and put a stupid smile of innocence on my face. "I look like a kid," I said to myself aloud. I grabbed the doorknob. I was surprised when it turned in my hand. The door opened when I pushed on it. I stepped into a cement breezeway that smelled of dust, onions, peppers and feet. In front of me were two doors. I took the one to the right, stepping loudly on the old wooden floor. I opened the door fast with a smile and walked in. Four men were in the six-hundred-square-foot room. The two leaning against the wall were the guys in the Lincoln. Both were Mexican. The passenger had a pockmarked face. He was reaching into his sport coat at his waistline but stopped his movement when he saw my empty hands. I waved my right hand at everyone, thinking of Richie Cunningham from *Happy Days*.

"Hi," I said as naively as I could. The driver of the Lincoln with the misshaped head had the dead-black eyes of a shark. They flared at me in anger. He walked out into the breezeway I had just come through. He looked around, came back into the room, then slammed the door and twisted a knob on a deadbolt to lock it behind me.

The nature of the action was not lost on me. On the wall by the door, there was a red stain at waist level, the size of a pie plate, that could have been dried blood.

I moved over to the passenger who had withdrawn his hand from the inside of his sports coat. He was four feet away from me. The other two men were split—one to my left, the guy in the Hawaiian shirt, and one to my right, possibly Ortega.

"This is my son, Jamie," Dad said, the tension rimming his voice. The look in his eye was forlorn, scared. It was the last thing he wanted—me in here, but he was hiding it under a thin layer of professionalism. Ortega was confirmed when he spoke in Spanish something to Hawaiian Shirt. Ortega was a thick-necked guy with a wide forehead and wearing a tight satin shirt that covered a pot belly. He had a calm look of layered fury on his brown face. I picked up the word "carniceria" from him and they all laughed. I had learned that word and it took me a moment to remember, but I was sure it meant butcher shop.

"I've been waiting outside for hours," I said exasperated. "You said it was only going to be a few minutes. I'm hungry and you said we could get some enchiladas, then go to a bull fight. I want to go. I want to go now." I said it like a thirteen-year-old with a lot of pitch in my voice, heavy on the frustration. I moved around the room like I was bored, closer to the passenger of the Lincoln in the sport coat, who had reached for something in his jacket when I came in.

If we went for his piece under his jacket, *he* didn't have a gun, *we* had a gun. I would close the distance when he reached for his firearm. I would trap his hand as he closed on the grip before he could pull it up from the holster and I would stuff his draw. I would blast my weight into him and move in tight, pivoting, then draw the weapon with his hand on it and with both of mine covering his. I would keep moving into him, clearing the steel from whatever holster he had and level it at his buddies who would certainly be moving in toward us. With my finger over his trigger finger, I would work it like a hundred-dollar hooker, keeping the muzzle pointed at the Mexicans and off my dad. Hopefully, Dad wouldn't move. If the pistol had a safety engaged, I would need to find it. They are usually positioned for the right-hand thumb. In this gunfight with multiple attackers, boarding house rules apply; everyone gets firsts before anyone gets seconds.

I kept my hands in my pockets. I glanced around like I was bored. Hawaiian Shirt exchanged a glance with Ortega, then the other two, now on my left. There were three-to-four feet between each of them.

The Mexicans were deciding all of our fates.

If Lincoln Continental Passenger with the pockmarked face didn't pull his metal, they may instead move toward me to lay hands on me. If they grabbed me, that was it. I was done for. So I needed to deem the situation "red" and move at the same time they did. The Puma knife would come out of my waistband. (Was the strap undone at the top of the sheath?) I would need to gain the upper hand in a very, grave critical situation and maintain it. Anything goes. Play to win! It's all up for grabs. There are no second-place winners.

I prayed to God that none of this would happen. I asked Him to direct my efforts and protect Dad and me. I lingered by Sport Coat and cocked my head to the side like a bored kid. I had to hide my rapid heartbeat.

"You said we could see a bullfight," I whined. "I want to see a matador." I stepped to the side, back erect, and snapped up my arms like I was pulling away a red jacket from a charging bull. No one moved or laughed. The room fell silent. I held my position, in bullfighting pose, not knowing what to do.

The Mexican men glanced at Ortega and at each other, waiting for a que as to what to do about me. The smiley one kept his grin on showing his "I can't believe it's not butter" yellow teeth. Then Mr. Ortega looked at me with loathing. He stared me down hard with his slicked-back hair, while twisting the rings on his fingers. I gave up my position by Sport Coat, then moved around the room to a bookcase by the dirty window I had pissed under a few moments ago.

I looked at Dad and then at the door, then back at Dad. I moved around to a bookshelf and picked up a wooden egg painted to look like a lady. When I did, it opened and there was another woman in an egg inside of it. The bottom dropped away from the shelf and I caught it with my left hand.

I put it back together and turned back to the men in the room. Mr. Ortega was staring at me with steely black eyes, but a smile underneath them.

"I'm in the middle of something, Jamie..." Dad said.

"I don't care. You said we could go to a bullfight and I'm hungry. I haven't had hardly anything to eat today. Mom said you would do this—take me places and then I would have to wait a long time in the damn Jeep," I whined. I walked over and took his sleeve in my hand, like a kid might, and pulled. Dad got up and moved to the door as I did, showing the palms of his hands. He nodded and cast a look at the room as if to say, "What can I do?" But his feet kept moving right beside mine as we reached the door.

"I have to take care of this gentleman. I will be in touch. Thanks for your proposal, but I don't think I can help you just now."

The men froze. Lincoln Driver was watching Ortega, who was watching us leave out the door as though he wasn't sure what to do. The asshole passenger had locked the door and it took me a moment to figure out which way to roll the deadbolt. It stuck until I wiggled the door with my weight.

I waited for footfalls to come our way as I got it open, but they didn't. God had heard my prayer.

The sweet, hot air hit our faces and we moved fast to the Jeep. Dad took the driver seat, fired up the motor and jammed the long shifter into gear. The big tires rolled us out of there with a lurch. I pitched back in the leather Jeep seat with my stomach in my throat. I swallowed bile and burped a little so I wouldn't throw up. I pulled the metal scabbard of the knife out of my waistband and put it back under the seat.

My hand was trembling.

Dad spun the big steering wheel fast, rolling his shoulders over the leather-covered orb to dive one fender down into a curve, then the other, as we cornered streets. I grabbed the "oh shit" handle and hung on. Dad glanced in the rearview mirror to make sure we didn't have a tail.

As we drove through the city, I smelled diesel fuel burning, something cooking on an outdoor grill, and sugar from the half-eaten Banana Flip under my seat. The day was hot and the air was dry. The streets were unfamiliar, and faces looked strange and hostile. It seemed like we were on another planet.

The afternoon passed in the tense silence that rims a traumatic experience. Miles of dry road passed under our big knobby tires. We felt the hot sun move across the sky, ignoring our thirst and hunger, while stopping only for gas.

The Jeep rolled on northward as night fell like a smothering wet blanket. It brought both a feeling of escape colliding with an impending sense of doom. The small villages we drove through had few people who cared. They seldom turned their heads to stare at the Gringo's from another land.

Headlights behind us cast our shadows over the dashboard. It was hours before we spoke. Dad was the first to break open the subject of the escape.

"That was close. I didn't know how that was going to end. You took a risk coming in like that. You violated protocol and went against my instructions. It's very important that when we are working together you do exactly what you are told. You had no idea who those people were and what they were capable of."

"It looked like you were about to find out what they were capable of," I said.

"I don't ever want you to do that again." He flicked his eyes away from the road to look me in the eye by the light of the dashboard.

"You were in trouble."

"No, I wasn't, Kid. I can handle myself. What you did was get yourself in trouble."

"Oh, no, you got us both in trouble. Do you think if they decided to kill you that they would have just let me drive away after a long wait? They would have come out and said you wanted to talk to me inside, led me in and wasted me, too. We would both end up as dog food."

"You know, when you run your mouth off at your father like that it shows disrespect and no class."

"And I mean dog food! You know when they were speaking Spanish, they were talking about a butcher shop? What do you think they were planning for us?

"This is bullshit, Dad. Running with these cartel assholes is going to get us both killed. You play this like it's a fucking game. This is the land of the bandito down here. I may not be a genius like you, but I know this, down here life is cheap. And, these people you're playing with, they have their own rules. That asshole had a gun under his jacket and was fixing to use it. He's probably killed and buried a dozen people. Who knows, maybe more," I said into the darkness between us.

Dad clenched a Marlboro 100 in his front teeth, flipped open the lid on his Zippo lighter and spun the flint. He stopped his hand halfway to the end of the cigarette. The flame light showed his face frozen in alarm as he looked in the rear view mirror at the lights behind us.

"We got company behind us. These highway-hijacking assholes in this country run people off the road at night and kill them every day. Get ready."

I looked out at the side mirror. It did seem to be close on our ass, and getting even closer.

"Get your knife out and put it in the bag between the seats," Dad ordered. I reached under the seat and grabbed my Puma with the metal scabbard. It was razor-sharp.

"I got it."

"Take it out of the sheath and put it in this bag between the seats."

"It's right here. I got it." I didn't want the big blade loose in the bag without a sheath on it.

"Damn it, Kid, do what the hell I say!" he barked in the thick tension of the dark cab. I unsheathed the blade and laid it in the bag.

A few miles passed in the black inky night. The road signs told of highways we didn't know and cities we didn't remember. The car worked up tight to our tail, then moved around us and passed at a high rate of speed.

"Where is that map? I think we might be lost." Dad thrust his hand into the bag between our seats that I had just put my knife in. "AAAAHHHH," he yelled and extracted his right hand from the bag with a big slice on the middle finger. Blood flowed out down his sleeve, dribbling into the bag and onto his leg.

"AAAAHHHH," he cried out again like a gut-shot cowboy. He was giving a full dramatic performance equal to a Shakespearian actor. "You put your knife in the bag!" he groaned.

"You told me to put it in the bag."

"AAHHH, without the sheath!"

"That's what you told me to do."

"With the blade up? What were you thinking?" He said it like it was the stupidest thing anyone could do. He steered the wheel with his knees and clutched his wounded hand with his other hand, like it belonged to someone else and he was fighting to keep it off him.

"Well, first of all, don't thrust your hand into a bag where you know an unsheathed knife is," I said.

Dad shook his head, took a handkerchief out of his jacket pocket, and wrapped his hand. I had seen him blow his nose in that cloth. He groaned a few more times for effect.

We plowed through the night in deep fatigue and despair for miles before I asked, "Where are we going?"

"I want to go back—to the States." He said it like a lost child and looked at me for approval.

"I thought we were going to live off the land down here. Our money would go further and maybe we would go back in six months or so…"

"I know I said that, Jamie. You don't have to remind me. I'm tired of this third-world shithole. I want to go back to the States."

I really didn't care. I wanted to as well, but I couldn't resist reminding him of his bravado.

In the early morning hours, we reached the border. Incredibly, we had the same border guard who met us when we went across just a few days before. He looked at our passports and shined a light through the interior of the Jeep, then came back to the window.

"Back so soon? I thought you were going to stay awhile. You certainly are packed up like you are."

"Yeah, we were going to, but we decided we want to go home," Dad said like a chastened child, his swagger now gone.

"Welcome back." He smiled like he had seen this type of scenario before and handed us back our passports. Those words felt great to hear. It felt great to be an American.

CHAPTER 14

***And blessed is he, whosoever shall not be offended in me*.**
Luke 7:23

Jesus teaching his own kin…
Jesus ….marveled at their unbelief…
And he could do no mighty work
Jesus could do no important major work for people who did not believe in him or rejected him. In my prayers, I ought to picture what I am praying for to be done or standing on God's word. Unbelief is an annoyance to Him.
(Shawn's notebook)

Fall, 2019 Merrill, Wisconsin

I packed my soft-sided leather briefcase with my writing tools, pen, notebook, voice recorder, and file with the report on Shawn's death. In the file, I had notations, his obituary, and a copy of a strange news report in the paper I had found of a double-shooting in Spread Eagle Wisconsin—not far from Pembine. A guy had shot his brother in an argument, then shot himself as the authorities rolled up onto the scene.

The sheriff's office had ruled it an accident. The fact that they were arguing, and an eyewitness reported that one man had aimed the pistol at his brother and shot him, was clearly no accident. I tried to image the horror and agony the guy lived in after his impulsive act of killing his brother. When the authorities approached, he realized it was the moment where he would have to live with his regretful impulsive act or take his own life. He chose the impulsive response of escape. The sheriff's office had reported the actual homicide—suicide as an "accident'" to soften it to the community.

This told me that it was not unheard of for law enforcement in that region to fudge a ruling on a murder investigation to make it more palatable to the public.

I drove east into the sunrise on a Tuesday morning, missing breakfast with my grandson.

Now as I write this, I am reviewing the tape of my comments and I hear the emotion in my voice as I record mundane details. Thirty-seven years later the wound is still open. Some pain stays fresh through life—the loss so great there is no salve for the damage. The slice is always weeping, fresh and tender.

I remembered when Dad and I had driven over this same road to visit Shawn in the spring of '83. Dad insisted on it. I really didn't want to go.

"Come on, he's lonely there. He would love to see us," Dad had coaxed. So, I had gone along, and Shawn was thoroughly delighted to see us. It would end up being the last time the three of us were together in this world.

Shawn proudly paraded us around and introduced us to anyone we passed on the campus. We met his fellow students, teachers, administrators, maintenance people and his roommate in his dorm, perhaps the guy he would borrow the rifle from on the fateful day. We stayed for a few hours and then left.

Shawn had only been twenty-three then. Is everybody lost when they are young? Did he feel that displacement anxiety that I do sometimes? I experience the sensation that I'm not in the right place, room or company, that I have stayed too long at a stop in life, or I should be standing someplace other than where I am at that moment. How strange, to feel like you are never just breathing the right air and occupying the frame of space that you should be. Did he have the haunting feeling of existing a moment ahead or behind, living out-of-sync of life's rhythm, and not understanding why?

Life's pain is so personal, quiet, and unique.

"It was only a few hours away straight east. Why didn't I go visit him more when he was at this school?" I say into the tape recorder with the super-charged engine purring behind my voice. The trees were full of orange, red, and green colors, and the Dodge Challenger glided over the road in its low and powerful chassis. I could feel every bump in the tight, sensitive suspension.

The glacier-cut valleys to my right and left held an early morning fall mist. Like a little kid, I suddenly miss my Dad. He would have gone with me today. He was unemployed, and had no ties to his day. He looked for any reason to have an adventure with me. He would have encouraged me to do this. A second review of that sentiment has me question if he would have been able to carry it off, emotionally.

He had been a broken man in so many ways after Shawn's death, never fully recovering.

The thought of doing this would have shattered him like a wine glass on a marble floor. I pass over the Wolf River and head into Mountain Wisconsin with the sun rising in the sky. The task before me feels like I am arriving at an ongoing battle, and I am the late reinforcements.

"Shawn was so lonely," I recall Dad saying about him.

I shudder at the fact that he died alone out in the woods, crawling for help in the sub-zero temperatures. My mind soothes me to remember how beautiful the winter is and how much he loved it. Perhaps it was a perfect way for him to go. He certainly knew his fate in those last moments. His faith was strong, though, and he also would know his destination was into the arms of his beloved Savior, Jesus.

"You go asking these questions, you're going to find answers you don't want to know," my brother Tim said to me when I told him about this book in its inception. I had been stunned by his response. Had he found peace with Shawn's death, where I had not? Living sober now, peace was something I had to earn through exploration and review.

The fourth and fifth steps of the program had me digging up the muck, searching for lost artifacts of unresolved issues and defects that I would need to address.

The voices ran through my mind as I drove my fast car toward the truth. "This is bullshit that he was alone. Someone was with him, shot him in the back, and ran off." Tim had said that at the funeral, thirty-seven years ago. But the report from the officials and the statements of the searchers qualified that they followed only one set of tracks.

"Did he lean the rifle on the tree, and it fell down and went off?" someone asked me once. "How does a gun go off into someone's back?" another voice replays in my mind. The sheriff didn't seem to think the gun went off into his back but had been pressed to his chest.

I knew one thing: if I could see the pictures of the autopsy Jerue had taken, I could make my own determination.

I was sorry I didn't do it earlier.

13 July – 29 August, 1984
Ministry in Europe
A Sojourn for Christ
Shawn P. Finucan
Another Highlight of the trip was the opportunity to hand out tracts in the city of Salzburg, Austria. This was very enjoyable.

1984 San Clemente, California

We were home, in our little Jayco camper. The familiar sounds of the surf, the smell of the sea in wind and the activity of park life around us was a comfort after our culture shock. We had caved, really. We talked a big game, like we were going to live down in Mexico for a few months. "Make the money last longer," Dad said, but we had a bad experience and turned tail and ran.

I sat on the picnic table with my notebook and pen while Dad was tightening his gear, cleaning it, and organizing it.

When he was done, he looked at me for the first time since our return. I put down the pen on my notebook and watched it roll off the paper. I had lost the blue cap to it, so now it was mobile whenever I set it down.

Dad looked down in painful assessment at the bandage on his right hand where the blood had seeped through the white gauze.

"I'm just wondering if there is a James Bond movie when Bond gets culture shock and runs back to England and tells M he got scared," I said. I picked up my Bic pen and held it up to my ear like it was a phone and put on a British accent. "Ello, M? It's Bond here. James Bond. I'm aborting this mission, M. These people look different, it's scary and I don't speak the bloody language. How the hell am I supposed to know how to communicate with these wankers?"

Dad shook his head. "That's not what happened, Kid. I just changed my mind about staying there. Why do you have to be so critical? You were there. It was spooky. We almost got killed." Dad hadn't admitted that before. I wanted to emphasize it, but didn't know how to get there in conversation without coming across as an "I told you so."

"Where did you get the bullfight idea?" He started to smile. Perhaps the Bond bit had added the levity I wanted.

"It was something I was actually hoping to do when we were down there."

"That was quite a little act you threw down in Jimenez, stumbling in there like an impatient child." Dad lit a cigarette and sat down on the cooler opposite of me on the fire ring. A seagull cried off on the bluff and a car door slammed. A child laughed a few sites down and a parent said something that made the child laugh harder.

"You're a good man to have around in an emergency," he said quietly.

"Yeah? Thanks." Compliments were rare in my life, and I took it.

"I'm proud of you. I'm proud of who you have become," Dad added. The image of a cactus in the desert receiving water came to my mind. The moment passed all too soon.

I looked at my notebook, but nothing would flow out anymore. I picked up the copy of *Les Miserables* and opened it at the bookmark. I started reading where Cosette had found the love letters in the garden from the young man who had written beautiful prose about love to express his love for her. I wondered if I could write something like that and send it to Jamie. Would she write me back? I had to put the book down after that thought. I closed the paperback gently and set it on my lap, like it might shatter.

Les Miserabes—the Miserable. I certainly was. Jamie was never far from my mind. My thoughts went to her every twenty minutes throughout the day. But never was there a letter in the post box.

If my heart were an aircraft, my affection for her felt like a hole in the fuselage. I was trying to fly the bullet-ridden bomber with a wounded crew, hydraulic fuel leaking out over the Pacific, and without an island in sight for miles.

"You know, when you told me once not to meet myself coming back on the road in life?" I asked Dad.

He looked at me. "My father used to say that to me."

"What do you think that means?" Instead of answering, he got up and climbed into the powder-blue Jeep and drove off. I dozed in the sunshine and thought of my girlfriend, how her hair was sometimes red and other times appeared strawberry blonde. I thought of her smile and laughter, and how we clutched each other in intimacy in a relationship hemmed in by desperation and infected by dysfunction.

Hours passed and I missed the damn surfboard.

Dad came back from town with some hamburgers to grill, some big Kaiser rolls, a Sara Lee pound cake and a quart of milk for the small refrigerator. He handed me a standard Zippo lighter. I looked at it and noticed the engraving on it.

6/20/84 In Memory of the Mexican Disaster—Lest we Forget. He showed me his own lighter. "I had it engraved on mine, too."

He was smiling at me, and I had to laugh.

The payphone by the ranger station at the entrance of the park was my landline home. I made a call home and talked to Shawn about his upcoming mission in Europe, smuggling Bibles to Christians behind the Iron Curtain. I didn't fully understand the danger of what he was taking on, but later in life, when I would tour Romania and see the prisons for political prisoners and the torture rooms, I would realize how dangerous his mission was and that his life was at stake.

I spoke with Mom and Bob and got news of what was happening in Merrill.

Dad had stayed in touch with the team and was ready to be deployed to Europe again, this time for a longer stint, and then he would go to Singapore to establish a tax haven. He would send for me later in the summer. It was time to prepare to mobilize. The Fourth of July weekend was fast approaching, and our campsite was claimed by campers who had reserved it long ago in preparation for the holiday, as were all the campsites in the parks in San Clemente and across the state.

There was nowhere for us to go.

Around the campfire of despair, Dad and I got into operators' mode and formulated a plan. It was time to strike the camp here in Southern California. Dad would leave for Europe then Singapore. I would go to the Zen Center in San Francisco and stay there for six weeks while Dad set up tax shelters with funds from the team. I would lay low in the Zen monastery. Then Dad would send me a plane ticket in the mail that would fly me to Singapore. He would be there waiting for me. I would arrive to assist him.

We would need to fold our park-beach operation and liquidate our assets, like the Jeep and the Jayco Camper. What we would do after that, we weren't sure, but Dad was certain he would have some money.

"Maybe we'll live in the islands somewhere for a while, maybe down in Belize. Our money would go further there." He stopped his sentence and looked at me, realizing I was thinking of the Mexican Disaster. I didn't say anything.

I started reading Dad's books on Zen Buddhism so that I could pass a rudimentary exam allowing me into the Zen Center.

We put an ad in the paper the next day that we had a Jeep and camper for sale and prayed that we would get a call in the remaining days before the Fourth of July weekend. We did. A nice guy came and looked at it and gave us the money we were asking for both the Jeep and the Jayco. He would be back within the next forty-eight hours to pick them up, just before the weekend.

We worked it out that the guy would purchase the Jeep and pull the camper. I would ride in the Jeep with him to his home in Long Beach and drop it off, then jump into a rental car with Dad and head to San Francisco. Dad would drop me off at the Zen Center, fly out of LAX to Heathrow Airport, and be off on his mission. I had asked Dad why he would drive six hours all the way back to Los Angeles and not fly from San Francisco. He said the Team always flew from LAX, citing more traffic there and presumably less strict getting through customs.

This was one of the few times we had a plan in place, and it felt immensely good to me.

Dad hopped into the Jeep and went into San Clemente to get some chicken so he could grill up his legendary recipe. On the list was corn on the cob, a salad, some Oreos and a pound cake. I needed the time to be alone to catch up on my notebooking. If I didn't do that, I would never sleep.

I brought out the big survival knife we used as a kitchen utensil and a big avocado, and sat on the picnic table in the sun. I cut the avocado in half around the pit and swigged at a gallon jug of some orange drink, not juice, but more of a cheap Tang knock-off.

The sun felt good on my shoulders. Someone was grilling up steaks a few sites down.

I scooped out a bunch of the mushy, pale-green, tasteless goodness away from the skin of the avocado with the blade. The strange texture at first made me think it had turned rotten. This avocado business was so Californian that a guy from the Midwest had no business eating it. As I got into it, I decided that the people in this state might build nuclear plants on fault lines, but when it came to eating avocados, they were onto something.

Between gobs of mushy bites of tasteless paste, my imagination crawled like a spider over the pages of that notebook with my greasy hand clutching the Bic pen. The ink flew over the white paper in the form of a journal, then a story about a park ranger named Sonja who finds a body washed up on the beach and a registration form in the corpse's pocket from camp site number thirty-eight.

She remembers registering the camper and finds herself ass-deep in a murder investigation and the target of a corrupt politician who wants it all kept quiet. She falls in love with a guy from Wisconsin who saves her life from a hit-team sent by the crooked, corrupt governor.

"Not every action has a consequence," Fredrick said, advancing with the pistol.

"To every action there is an equal and opposite reaction," Sonya replied, backing away to the bluff's edge.

"Well, look who was listening in science class…"

"I was listening," Sonya added, glancing over his shoulder. "You were staring at the McCloud girl. Don't you remember the story of the Pied Pieper of Hamlin? The bill comes due for everything."

"The town should have accepted living with the fucking rats," Frederick spat.

"Hindsight is like that. It's really wise. The trick is to be wise on the front end and avoid the fallout from a poor decision-making process. Something you have yet to develop, apparently. You see, if you kill me, they'll know it was you. We were seen together." She extended her legs and arched her back. She needed him to come in a little closer...

I turn the page of the notebook fast and let the pen fly. I'll edit later.

I was feeling the excitement of the end of an era here in the park. It felt like when a barometer registers a change in pressure and the animals react; life itself has the same type of feel when change finds me. My mind becomes unsettled and agitated. I get sentimental and clingy to thoughts, instead of giving them flow, until I start getting it down on paper.

This writing experience was done in simultaneous actions: the scooping of the avocado, writing for a spell, putting the pen down, wiping hands on shorts, taking a big swig of the orange drink, and working up a scoop of the avocado. Then picking the Bic pen back up and decorating the page with the ink until the action of distraction would repeat and tease out more creativity.

I glanced up at the sound of a prowling car on the campground road. The burgundy Lincoln Continental from Jimenez, Mexico, was slithering past, then suddenly stopped. My breathing shallowed and my heart rate slammed into overdrive in a moment. I straightened my back and heard it crack between the seventh and eighth vertebrae.

I had stopped writing and was looking around because I just knew trouble was near. The big car would have kept cruising by real slow if I had been sitting in the camper, because the Jeep was gone and that was what they were looking for.

The passenger with the pockmarked face saw me and we locked eyes. He held up his hand and the Lincoln stopped. The driver leaned forward around the passenger, showing me his dented head; then a spidery smile crawled his face. They both stared at me while chatting for a bit. A fan in the front-end of the car kicked in and added to the sound of the engine.

They backed up a bit, angled the big, square front end toward the second parking spot and drove in to my campsite, real slow, like a shark approaching swimmers' legs. The pilot light of rage ignited deep within me. I closed the notebook and put away the things of a child now. For trouble had found me.

The big survival knife was on the table to the right of my hand, next to the avocado, with my pen and notebook in front of me. Just inside the camper, with the door unlocked, The Snake was out on top of my gear. It was never left out because I took great care for it not to be. Yet, here it was today—left out. I had just cleaned and oiled the .357 magnum and was planning on packing it in the bag. The magnificence of its stainless-steel finish with matching scope and rubber Pachmayr grip to help absorb recoil would be the first thing someone saw if they opened the door.

I said a quick prayer to God for strength, courage, and protection. The Lincoln shut down and a moment of silence encapsulated us all, unifying us in a potentially fatal outcome. The campers down a few sites were eating their steaks now, with onion, the wind revealed. They would be of no help, only witnesses after the fact. I had been in enough scrapes and I knew enough about this world to know that when you face danger, with the exception of God, you faced it alone, always.

The Snake in the camper was so far away. That might be a good or bad thing, depending on how desperate this situation really turned out to be. To overreact was almost as bad as under-reacting in a critical situation.

As the two Mexican men got out of the car, I took a close look at them. The passenger was tall with a big dirty-teeth smile, wearing a button-up shirt with the top button closed at the neck. He wore polyester pants that flared at the bottom. He was genuinely glad to see me. He had a scar on his forearm. It appeared to be the result of a jagged slash that had certainly cut tendons that needed repairing at the time. It had healed with a shitty stitch job that showed holes from the stitching on both sides of the cut. On his other forearm, there was a small patch of shaved arm hair. That was where he tested the sharpness of his blade. This was the telltale sign of a knife fighter.

The driver with the thick, dented head had no smile on him now. His eyes moved moved back and forth like the flicker of a snake's tongue. He glanced around as he got out of the car, looking to see who might be looking or noticing. Criminals always looked around to see who was watching when evil was in their hearts. These types of human turds are "six dozen for a quarter" in this world.

"Hey, I've seen you before," said Smiley from behind his horsey, stained teeth. "How are you?"

"Hola, Amigo. Cual es ese lago debajo de nosotros? I responded. (What is that small lake below us?) They both looked at me in surprise. Big Head said something to me in rapid-fire Spanish that I guessed was unflattering. I was glad I couldn't speak the language.

"Apparently the border patrol agents are just letting any shit bags with legs walk into this country without checking who they are," I said.

"Oh, we're hard to escape. Enrique and I, we're like crows, and we turn up around dead things," Pockmarked Face said. They moved up around the Lincoln toward me.

"Well, you are what you eat," I said. The big survival knife was beside the avocado on the table, next to my hand. I had to get off my ass and get my feet under me.

They closed the distance toward me a few more steps. They were looking around, heads on swivels, potential pre-attack indicators. Looking for witnesses for what they were thinking of doing, or looking for Dad, I wasn't sure. Soccer Head said something in Spanish, fast.

"Enrique asked you, 'Where is your dad?'" Smiley translated.

"I think he's doing a job for your boss's boss," I said. I hoped Dad wouldn't roll up in the powder-blue Jeep from the grocery store right now. I looked at their hands, waist, and eyes. The waist of the Pockmarked Man showed a form that was printed against the shirt on his left hip. If he was right-handed and that was a weapon, he would pull it in a cross draw. I questioned my guess. Would he have taken a firearm through customs?

Smiley, with his shaved patch on his forearm, would have a knife.

"Is there anyone in the camper?" Smiley asked. The passports were in the camper, along with my weapon, Dad's Browning Hi-Power 9mm and our remaining cash.

They couldn't go in the camper at any cost.

"Just your mother," I said with no smile. I made a fist and pulled it and down toward my pelvis. Then pumped my hips up in a rude gesture I had seen James Hess do when he was talking about his date with Tina Kerndt. The other man moved over toward the door of the Jayco. He peered around and then underneath it for some reason. Smiley moved toward me a little closer. I stood up between the bench and the table. I put my hands on the table, right hand next to the big survival knife.

Smiley was close enough for me to smell cheap aftershave. "You mind if I have a drink of your juice?" he asked as he picked up the gallon jug.

"Actually, I do. I don't want your lips on the edge of the carton. I don't know where they've been." His smile dropped and his black eyeballs drilled into mine. He shook his head. The mouth smiled again but the eyes didn't. A steely expression of hatred crossed his face. He reached in his front pocket and pulled out a knife handle. He pressed a button and a long, thin blade snapped open. It glinted in the sun for a moment.

He picked up my jug of orange drink by the handle and thrust the stiletto-style blade into the plastic. Then pulled it out about halfway down into the jug. Then he lifted it, the stream of orange drink spouting out from the puncture he had made. He held it up over his face. The flow of orange drink went over his brown dress shirt. Then he corrected the stream's flow to reach his mouth and drank from it like holding a wine flask.

When he had had enough, he set it down, closed the blade on his knife, and put it away in his right pocket.

"Now you don't have my germs, eh?"

Enrique was looking in the window of the camper and said something in Spanish.

"Enrique says you come with us, we'll buy you lunch at a nice place, come back and maybe your Dad will be here then."

"How do you say 'fuck you' in Spanish?" I responded. He just stared at me. "Since I don't know, I'll just say it like this, 'Fuck you in Spanish'." Now I smiled a big, toothy smile, like his, in mockery. "Tell Enrique that." He didn't tell him, but Enrique seemed to figure it out.

Enrique turned toward me and lifted his shirt. He showed me a gun on his belt, a little automatic in a leather holster made of a thin strip of shoe leather. The band held the weapon to his belt around the trigger guard and barrel. He put his hand on it and pointed to the Lincoln, then said something in Spanish.

So, he had come over the border with it.

I let my imagination dance over the situation and loosed my grip on reality. There was no way I was going anywhere with them. They intended to take me to a secondary crime scene and kill me after torture. I was certain of that. It would play out here; whatever would be would end here.

As an adolescent growing up in my house, my stepfather Bob Weaver had built me a room in the basement.

Not long after he had replaced the door I had destroyed trying to make it into a circular hobbit door, I trashed another one.

I had some throwing knives and some metal throwing stars. When some rowdy friends were over, we started throwing them into the door of my bedroom. We got pretty good at sticking them in the wood, and I learned how to judge distance and throw it hard to penetrate the hollow, wood door. I learned success in knife throwing was about distance, and whether I held it by the handle or the blade when I released it.

When Bob saw it, he was pissed. I wasn't there when he discovered what I had done to the door, but he let me know his displeasure by leaving an ad from the newspaper with a picture of the very door that was now destroyed on sale for fifty bucks at the lumber yard. The next time I saw him, he was working in his woodshop and turned off the jazz on the radio to let me know how much my juvenile behavior was unappreciated. He was right and I felt bad about it.

But I had learned a skill.

The big survival knife that I had used to cut the avocado was four inches from my right hand. The closest opponent to me was Smiley with the pockmarked face, three feet from me; he had a switchblade for sure, maybe a gun. The driver was in front of the door of the camper at a distance of twelve feet. He had a pistol.

If I snatched up the big-handled survival knife and slashed the throat of Smiley, I would need to whip the knife the distance of twelve feet into a soft tissue area of the driver's throat before he could pull the metal on his belt. At that range, the knife would spin one-and-a-half revolutions, so I would need to flip it after the slash of Smiley, so the blade was in my hand and whip it in a chopping down motion, hard and fast.

The throw would take everything I had, and the steel would need to fly hard and fast.

Would Soccer Head at the camper door still be able to pull his piece and fire at me with the blade hilt deep in his throat? I envisioned him stumbling with the handle sticking out just below his chin, then pulling his pistol and cranking off a few rounds in my general direction—hitting Smiley, staggering after the slash. I would dive away from the table and roll, while rounds cranked off in my general direction. The campers a few sites down would be screaming, as all of Hell was breaking loose.

Or, if I threw it hard enough from this distance, could it penetrate the throat and chop through the spine, knocking out his chances of pulling the piece on his belt?

"You…you got a look in your eye, Kiddo, that I have seen in men before. You're not a simple as you were back in Jimenez, are you? That was some little play you put on, young Gringo." He glanced down at his orange-stained shirt.

I felt my stomach get thick with nausea. I smiled anyway, like the guy to my right. If I missed with either blade strike, Enrique would shoot me.

But it would be better than being dragged to a secondary crime scene. That was where Hell meets Earth.

The tension of this situation gripped me, and I fought not to freeze. Fear grew in me with each second. It tempted me to do nothing but just stand there motionless until they walked over, grabbed each one of my arms and would lead me to the car. Fear is what makes people get led to slaughter like a sheep. At all cost, that could not happen.

The line between imagination and reality thinned a bit more. I wondered who I was to do something like that. Who would I have to become?

The driver took his hand off the pistol and took two steps toward the camper, then reached out and put his hand on the doorknob. I moved fast, picking up the leaking carton of orange drink and whipping it hard at him.

It was a practice move for what I was thinking, but I wondered if it tipped my hand.

The plastic jug contacted the small sliding glass part of the door that moved over the screen. It exploded in an orange burst of fluid that sprayed in his face, over his cotton shirt and all over the camper door. As the jug hit the ground, he spun reaching for the firearm he had shown me a moment ago. Smiley, to my right, reached in his pocket and came out with his knife. It snapped open with a distinctive click.

Years later in life, when I was a police officer, I attended the Iowa Law Enforcement Academy. I saw a video in a training class entitled, Surviving the Edged Weapon. It was a documentary highlighting what a terrible thing it was to face a knife in combat and included interviews of survivors of such incidents. As I watched that film with forty other cops in a classroom setting, I relived that incident in the campground in great detail while trying to concentrate on the message of the film.

In the next moment, no one seemed to know what to do. I slowly picked up the big, black-handled survival knife. The element of surprise was gone now. If Enrique pulled the gun, I could throw the knife and try to move out of the line of fire, but I was trapped between the bench and the table.

My fucking imagination worked against me in attempting to play the outcome. It showed me throwing the knife, missing, and then toppling backward as I was shot. I had to believe something else for this to work. I got scared shitless then.

Enrique glanced over to the left, kept the gun in his little shoe leather holster, and looked back at me. I glanced to my right to see what he saw. One of the guys eating at the picnic table two campsites down was looking at us. His attention had been drawn by the exploding orange drink gallon jug on the camper door and the big Mexican pulling a switchblade on me.

Enrique moved in my direction with his eyes locked on me. Taller man with the dirty-teeth smile folded up his knife, moved toward him, and stopped him before he got to me.

They spoke Spanish to each other softly and looked around, then moved to get back into the Lincoln. Smiley looked at me with his piss-colored smile and shook his head.

"Mi Madre," he said and imitated the hip gesture I had made earlier when I told him his mother was in the camper. I laughed too now. I put the knife down and did the hip gesture again and moved my hands like I was pulling a woman into my groin.

"Your mother," I said and worked the image hard, throwing my hips into it and slapping at an imaginary ass in front of me. I kept it up until the smile finally slid off his face like a dog turd from a dustpan.

Once inside the car, he rolled down the window and as the Lincoln backed up, he said, "Tell your Dad we'll be back. You can bet on it, Gringo." He made a gun gesture with his hand and shot me with it.

I made a gesture with my right hand, catching the imaginary bullet and flipping it into a middle-finger bird at him. As a kid, Tim had taught me how to do that: you bend the wrist back and hold the thumb out to the side, so the middle finger is served-up like on a platter. I wished I knew how to call out "Fuck you, douche bag" in Spanish, but Professor Berlitz hadn't covered that in his course.

I waited a few minutes and cooled off. Then I went over, picked up the jug of orange drink, dumped out what little was left in the jug, and tossed it into the garbage can. I got some paper towels out and soaked them in soapy water, then started cleaning up the door of the camper.

Laughter came from a few campsites away. People were enjoying each other's company, having fun, and eating a shared meal. To me, those were sounds from another planet.

As I wiped up the sticky orange drink from the vinyl cover of the two-part door, my heart was fluttering, and my hand was shaking.

CHAPTER 15

Truly my soul waiteth upon God: from him cometh my salvation.
Psalm 62:1

November, 2019 Marinette, Wisconsin

I pulled into the parking lot of the Marinette County Sheriff's Office. As I walked in the door, I said a prayer for God to help me find the answers I was seeking.

At the glass window, a lady listened to me through a small, circular opening with a grill over it. I explained my mission: that I had asked for and gratefully received a report regarding my brother's death in January of 1985. I indicated I was grateful for the report being mailed but there was an indication of photographs having been taken and I was wondering if I could see them, and perhaps take them with me today.

I pointed to the words in Deputy Jerue's report that I had highlighted: "photographs of the scene and the autopsy. See photo file 85-11." Then I pushed it through the slot at the bottom of the window.

The kind lady looked at the paperwork and recognized the case number. "I was here when Jerue was working. He retired not long after I started."

I felt a glimmer of hope.

"Is he still around? I would love to get a chance to speak with him."

"I don't know. I don't know where he would be or if he is even alive." She flipped through the pages. Another lady stepped up behind her, looking over her shoulder.

"I think I looked for this before…I was the one who took your call."

My eyes widened. "I understand the incident was a long time ago, but my mother is growing older, and this is an unanswered question in our lives. I would like to reassure her it was an accident and not something else. I hope you can understand." I spoke the truth knowing that it always carries a powerful ring to it.

She did understand and stated she would help me. She asked me to sit down and wait for a while. I sat down on a wooden bench in the tiled-floored lobby where law-enforcement pennants, awards and slogans hung on the brick walls. I sat with my back to a floor-to-ceiling window and prayed.

A blonde woman with a little girl of about six years old came in through the front door. They walked across the floor to a steel jail-cell door across the lobby. The blonde woman spoke to someone through a small slot in the big door and was told to wait. They stood a few yards away from me, the young girl looking at me. She hid behind her mom's legs. "Am I going to see Daddy now?" she asked her mom.

"In a few minutes, Honey." The woman's voice had a wet nasal texture to reveal she had been crying.

After a half-hour, the kind woman called me to the window. "I looked in that file and found some pictures of an automobile accident, so something got misfiled. I kept looking and I found the photos from the incident that you are looking for." She showed me a stack of photos in her hand. "If you want to leave me your address, I can put them on a disc and mail them to you."

"Well, if it isn't a problem, I can wait in town. Is there a chance this could be done today?"

"I guess it depends on how busy we get, but I could try." I took out my business card, circled my cell number, and handed it to her.

"Wonderful. I am going to stay right here in town, and when the photos are ready, I would love to come back and pick them up. You are very kind, thank you."

I walked out of the office with the sun rising higher in the morning sky and the promise of answers to questions that had been on my mind for most of my life. Perhaps this will be an avenue to peace.

13 July – 29 August, 1984
Ministry in Europe
A Sojourn for Christ
Shawn P. Finucan

A situation in Greece that touched me was seeing a man with no hands, sitting cross-legged begging. He played the harmonica with his feet when money was tossed in front of him. As we walked by the other Christians I was with, I dropped a tract in front of him. Later we walked by him and turned around; he had the tract held in the stumps of his arms and was looking at it. It was so pitiful.

I prayed to our heavenly Father if I could see him again before I left Greece. The Lord answered my prayer. I saw him again and sat down next to the man. A number of people stopped and watched us. I could not communicate with him, nor he with me. God allowed me to help him another way. In that moment I hoped he felt less alone in his struggle.

Perhaps someday I would see him again and ***communicate*** *with him in his own language.*

1984 Long Beach, California

The Jeep was overheating, the temperature needle staying just below the red line. I softly blew air at the gauge in the flat dashboard like that was going to cool it off a bit. My heart rate increased. The new purchaser of the Jeep and camper was sitting next to me and showing the signs of being in the throes of buyer's remorse. Since arriving at the campsite, he noticed the new tear Dad had put on the camper, and now the Jeep was overheating, too.

Dad was driving a rental car, a Chevy Caprice, behind me while I drove the Jeep pulling the camper to the buyer's house in Long Beach. The new owner was in the shotgun seat beside me looking doubtfully at the camper behind us in the side rearview mirror.

Before the purchaser had arrived at the campsite, Dad had wandered over to this hippie bus that was parked a few campsites down from us. It was a refurbished school bus with a cosmic planet scene painted on the side. The guy who lived in it was Surge. He had long hair and wore an eternal pair of cut offs and a tie-dyed shirt. The smell of pot wafted out of the windows on a permanent basis.

When Dad reappeared at our site, I was cleaning up the camper and getting it ready for final sale. I asked him where he had been, though I had seen him go into Surge's bus. He said he went for a walk. His eyes were red and he was floating around in a daze. As I looked at him, he lit the wrong end of a cigarette and dragged hard on the tobacco end. When the butt flamed, he threw it in the fire and reached for another.

Dad decided that the support posts on the front end of the camper were not fully extended, so he pulled out the handles and started cranking on them to extend them more. I was cleaning the Jeep while listening to the ratcheting of the support post, wondering what he was doing, when I heard the tarp rip.

He stopped and looked up at the top end of the camper. The tear was significant. I went over and tried to back down the other support, but Dad had hyperextended them and now they were broken. We tried to close the camper, but now it didn't quite close right. A big flap of the canvas bulged out giving it a junky look. Also, we didn't know what to do with the broken supports.

We stuffed it all together, but it looked like crap.

The buyer was committed, however, and after walking around the camper shaking his head, he gave me the cash and we started on our way. As we drove through Long Beach, I kept up the comments about "what a great time it was to camp in it." I kept glancing at the circular temperature gauge mounted in the flat dashboard. I had been watching it climb to just below the red line as we powered up the freeway, then into a residential district where this guy lived.

The wafting odor of burning rubber and hot copper gave me the impression there was an electrical fire taking place somewhere behind the vertical dashboard. I laid on the verbal sauce of "Jeep off-road capability."

"Tell you what…you get bored with a road, you just head this rascal off-road and tear it across a desert dune like you belong there. That's what I like about a Jeep," I said enthusiastically.

He smelled it too and leaned over to look at the gauges. "Does it run that hot all the time?"

"Shouldn't be a problem. We've been in traffic for a while." I was trying to make sense of my own words as they fell out and nodding my head back and forth. All the while in my mind a voice was saying "no, no, no, no." We made it to his house and pulled into the driveway of a nice house in a luxurious neighborhood. I handed off the keys to the entire touring package and waved "goodbye" to the powder-blue Jeep. I walked away from an era of my life.

I jumped into the rental car. As Dad and I drove up the coast on Pacific Coast Highway, I took in the California beaches as they slid past the window. I saw the bikes, the skateboards, the bikinis, the surfers and the pedestrians make their way about in the sunshine. The blue Pacific Ocean broke majestically on rocky shorelines with mansions perched like lighthouses on the cliffs. The highway hugged the cliff line precariously at places as we drove north into a new part of California.

The people we passed by might have been from a different planet. They wouldn't know a hard winter and were accustomed to sunshine and ocean views. How would this difference in lifestyles affect their thinking as opposed to someone from the Midwest?

The waves broke on rocks in a crashing rollick of white spray and sea foam under a sunset of blood mixed with Mercurochrome-orange across the entire horizon sky.

As we crossed the Golden Gate Bridge, I looked out into the harbor to see Alcatraz in the bay.

In San Francisco, we got a hotel room on a steep street and checked into the room for the night. Dad fell apart. It had been a long day, a long week, and maybe a long life because he wept in internal agony like only the mentally ill can.

My attempts at consoling conversation fell outside the realm of perception. The walls of isolation that he was behind could not be broken down with any battering ram of verbal pleasantries. He didn't speak when submerged this deep in the attack. There seemed to be no words that he could use to describe what was going on inside his mind, so any communication was abandoned. He was beyond it. Anything I spoke was a foreign language.

He was afloat on a mental raft of despair that could know no consolation from anyone. He clung to his very existence with deep breaths strung together. It was terrible to witness, and I could only imagine what it was to endure.

At times, he sat up fast and clutched the bed with both hands. It appeared that he was struggling to breathe. I had watched him endure this since I was a kid and would not be able to gauge or estimate the amount of trauma it had done to me until later.

I was exhausted. After a while, I felt myself crashing into despair along with him. I held the remote and wondered if I should turn up the television loud and drown out Dad's breakdown with *Knots Landing* dialogue.

Perhaps his response was *appropriate*. The decisions I had made were certainly leading to a life that could mirror his, and wasn't I right alongside him in this? Internally I touched a dark knowledge that there may be something in me that was just as dysfunctional. The knowledge of my own alcoholism brushed against a wall of splinters in my self-evaluation. I wondered if it was my own fate to deal with society on the outer fringes—as an outlaw like my dad.

The future appeared to me like an oncoming hurricane. In some of this time, Dad and I had each other for support but, now, his raft and mine were separated in the torrent of madness and severe depression.

The sounds of a grown man crying in despair were too much for me to endure, so I took my key card and left the hotel room. The heavy door closed behind me like a vault, sealing in Dad with his pathology in solitude.

There was nothing I could do for him.

Though I was thoroughly exhausted, I strolled out onto the streets for a walk in the cool of the northern California evening. The steep streets of San Francisco were remarkable; they dropped away toward the bay like a child's slide on a playground. I could see the track in the street for the trolley cars.

Down by the ocean the night was splashed in a tepid fog, bringing a humidity that Southern California didn't have. The air was sweeter in the northern part of the state. I played a tune by Jackson Browne in my head, "The Pretender," and opened up my writer's eyes. I recalled *The Streets of San Francisco*, a television show with Carl Malden that was popular when I was a kid. I envisioned all the cars that passed me speeding around and launching into the air and then crashing down. I pictured Steve McQueen ripping by in his Mustang from the movie *Bullet* and remembered the *Dirty Harry* movies.

I tried to tease out the chemical dump that used to occur in my brain—that feeling of déjà vu that brought the taste of vanilla and pushed something in my mind to trip me off into a world of fantasy. But it had stopped occurring in my early teens, perhaps from too many concussions.

After a few blocks in the fantastic night air, I noticed a couple walking up the steep sidewalk toward me. Both about thirty, the man wore a suit, the woman in a black dress. Her long, thick, black-raven hair fell around her shoulders. They were in playful conversation; she was touching his arm as she walked beside him.

Her big dark European eyes noticed me. She pulled out a cigarette and held it in front of her mouth. She spoke something to the man. He patted his pockets.

"Do you have a light?" she asked me with an accent. I remembered the Mexican Disaster commemorative lighter in my pocket and pulled it out. The firelight flickered on her face in a magic moment of enticement and mystery.

I held it in front of her face and her big brown eyes held mine. Her hand touched mine as she held the flame still. She lit the cigarette and smiled at me.

I turned to watch her swish away in her dress and high heels. It was the first time a woman had touched me in months.

I envied the guy she was with for everything I wasn't in that moment. I became aware of, and regretted, every stupid decision I had made in the last three years of my short life. I felt like I had set fire to my destiny and walked away from my future without turning back. That is what the brunette did to me right then.

She was a symbol of my life, walking away from me without a kiss goodbye.

Some sort of nighthawk bird soared over the dark street and made a cry.

I enjoyed a fantasy about the woman asking me for a light:

"What must a traveler do on a misty night?" she asked me.

"Don't meet yourself coming back on the road in life," I reply, completing the spy identification code.

"Do you have the package?" she asked me.

"Do I ever," I say and pull her in for a kiss…

As it started raining, I hit the rude re-entry of reality. I looked around and found I was lost. With the bay for reference and another fifty minutes of walking in a steady sprinkle that pressed my clothes to my skin and made my shoes heavy, I found the hotel.

Inside the room, Dad was sleeping, collapsed on the bedspread with his clothes on. I took a burnt down cigarette butt from his fingers and tossed it into the ashtray with a dozen others. His snoring sounded like someone keying the ignition on a 1968 Rambler that just wouldn't turn over.

I felt better. It was important to get some distance from Dad so that I could remember I was young.

My imagination needed to be let out of its cage and walk around without a leash on. Maybe now, with God's help, I could sleep.

After a few days, Dad was on his feet again. The depression attack had passed. I was quiet in the room and spoke softly, in soothing tones. If the television was on, I tried to find something that would be appealing, like old reruns of *The Rockford Files* or Chuck Connors in *The Rifleman.*

It took time for him to recover. He slept a great deal, then would be on his feet to smoke cigarettes on the balcony of the room. He would eat some of the food I brought in from a small corner store. His expression went from despondently staring at the wall to blinking and focusing on the room, then asking me a few questions as he worked toward having a conversation with me.

He found a payphone in the lobby and, for privacy, used it to call the team when he could communicate. A few days later the phone rang in our room. It was the front desk manager telling Dad there was a letter for him there. He left to go get it and came back with an airline ticket to Singapore for some work he was going to do.

It was tax shelter or investment work, I suspected with ill-gotten gain, but I didn't know. Dad seemed to think that not telling me anything was a way of keeping me innocent of any charges if something should go wrong. Looking back from here, this assumption was erroneous.

It was time to mobilize again, and I was glad. Hanging out in the hotel room was driving me bat shit. Hanging with someone who had severe depression was taking its toll on me.

We drove the rental car by the Zen Center building at 300 Page Street.

"It's right here in the Haight-Ashbury area. This is the origin of the big hippie movement in the sixties," Dad said as we took a cruise by the building where I would be dropped-off and abandoned for the next six weeks.

"Great." I pictured a group of sweaty acidheads, half-naked walking around the streets with starry eyes and baked brains. "Every city ought to be famous for something." The streets were clean, and the community of people on the sidewalk was vibrant and eclectic. Some could be hippies, some were bikers in leather, others were dancers sashaying around like they were trying out for the play *Fame*, and maybe they were.

I watched a big, mean-looking biker dressed in leather walking down the street, drunk and swinging his thick sleeveless arms around and arguing with someone who wasn't there. He looked at the car and then at me. He gave me the finger and started swearing obscenities at me, then broke into a run after the car like a dog. There was no chance he would catch us. I watched him chase us as he frothed at the mouth. Dad drove on oblivious.

"This is the district that Dirty Harry patrolled in his movies," Dad reports.

"No kidding?" I puzzled why Harry Callahan would be whipping out his six-inch barreled .44 Magnum here in forgotten hippie land. I pictured in my mind the movie scene where Tyne Daly is running around with a briefcase in one hand and a pistol in the other, chasing after a bad guy. She gets mad when the bad guy gets away and slams the briefcase against a wall. Later she learns the briefcase contains a bomb and she throws up. Was that scene shot right there? I turn my head to look at a building.

Then there was the one with David Soul who plays a rogue cop, killing bad guys, *Magnum Force*, I think. David Soul made a hit single. I give my mind a moment then start playing it in my head. "Don't give up on us, Baby, we're still worth one more try." The tune made me think of Jamie and I wondered what she was doing right now. I missed her like my wallet in a subway station. Sometimes it was frantically like hands patting pockets and looking around for recovery of the item to make me whole again. Sometimes subtly with an aching sense of loss, but always in the undercurrent of moments, or in the background like a radio softly playing classical music in the corner of a woodshop. There was no salve for this infection of sorrow, and I hated how it unified me with Dad in brokenness.

"Hey, Kid, did you hear me?" Dad asked, glancing at me as he rolled the rental Chevy Caprice into a right turn, cutting off a flamboyant gay-looking guy who was the spitting image of Freddie Mercury from the rock band Queen.

"I said we'll need to stash the guns in a bank safety deposit box and then we'll get some lunch down at the wharf. I have to get to L.A. to catch my flight. I'll send for you in six weeks, and you join me in Singapore. Sound good?"

"Sure." Six weeks in a Zen Monastery. What the hell had I gotten myself into?

"Now, they will interview you, this director of the Center. They'll want to know why you're here. If you tell them it's just to lay low for a while, that might not go over so well. So, let's go over some Zen Philosophy. You've seen those books I have, the ones on Zen?"

"Yeah, sure."

"Tell me what you've learned from them when you picked them up. I know you have because you read everything."

"It's stuff that's incongruent—like 'the best way to control your cows is to give them plenty of room.' That book you had was something like *Zen and The Way*, but basically it said that there was no way."

"Right and who was it by?" Dad quizzed.

"Alan Watts. It was full of stuff like, 'The practice of Zen is to abandon the extra and meditate,' and meditating is just sitting still in the lotus position and focusing on your breathing with your posture straight, and that's so you can sit still for a long time. They talk about kindness and patience, and encourage you to ask yourself questions like 'What will all this extra effort in life do for me?' So, you sit there breathing. Honestly, I don't get it," I said. "It's like, 'Why be ambitious and do anything when you can do nothing and breath' kind of crap."

Dad was smiling. "It appears that you do get it." We stashed the pistols and knives into the biggest safety deposit box we could rent at the Bank of America and leased the box for a full year because we didn't know when we would be back. I remember being affected by that commitment--Would I really be here, in California, a year from now? We parked the Chevy by the wharf and walked around in the bay air and gentle sunshine.

A departure loomed before us, and we moved around keeping our nervous minds off it. We were great friends who understood each other and enjoyed each other's company. Now we would be alone.

The day was sunny and bright. The wharf was full of business, fishing boats, people shopping in the outdoor centers, stands of food, a few jugglers, some mimes.

"Did I ever tell you about my Uncle Joe who's having a hard time getting a job?" I asked Dad. He looked over at me in befuddlement.

"I'm pretty sure you don't have an Uncle Joe."

"He's a mime with Tourette Syndrome." I stopped walking, made sure he noticed and was looking at me. Then I did my bit where I started feeling an invisible wall, then started shouting swear words uncontrollably. I shook it off, then tried to pull on an imaginary rope, leaning away from some unseen object. Then I stomped my foot and yelled out a bunch of expletives that got some passersby to stop and look at me with concern. Dad gave it a genuine laugh. We would maintain the humor throughout our goodbye lunch at a restaurant that looked over the ocean. I would remember that same courage of goodbye humor at his deathbed one day.

It was tough to think of this as goodbye. We had been close to each other as best friends for the winter, spring and well into the summer on a traveling adventure. But now, we laughed with each other in the ultimate show of strength.

On Dad's deathbed, I will always remember that he did the same with me in those moments, displaying a courage that I hope to have when my time for exit from this life is near.

I was enjoying the fresh fish, a cup of coffee and my Dad's company in the sunlight of a window as we looked at Alcatraz Island. I didn't know where I was going in life, or sometimes where I had been, but I knew that right here it was good place to be. I soaked it in.

"Do you need anything, before I go?" Dad asked.

"A weapon—this is the land of the freak."

The waiter was an old guy who knew his business. He was charming and efficient, and we never knew he was there until we needed something, so we tipped him big.

We went into a sporting goods store, and it didn't take me long to see what I wanted. An original Balisong butterfly knife with the metal skeleton frame lay under glass in the manned display case. The price was hefty—a hundred and forty bucks, but the craftsmanship instilled in the weapon revealed it to be worth it.

"Can I see that?" I asked the man tending the counter. He unlocked the case, slid back the panel and laid it out in front of me, like it was a jewel. I wiped off my hands and picked it up. The weight was right. It was balanced to perfection, the corners smoothed, and the blade was sharp.

"Are you a student of the martial arts?" he asked me. I said I was. I opened the knife using the latch-drop opening, then flipped it shut. I opened it again with a horizontal double-flip opening, then a horizontal double-flip closing. I brought my other hand into it and did a double-hand exchange. The steel blade swiveled in my hands like it belonged there, opening and closing fast with the clacking sound of the steel handle slapping on itself. I worked a few more opening techniques and closes before I laid it down on the counter.

A few people at the counter were staring at me. The salesman laid out the Kevlar case it came with to fix to the belt. He waited for me to say what we both knew I would: "I'll take it." As we walked out, I felt better about my situation. I still have that knife today as one of my prized possessions. It is soaked in memory. Dad and I had understood that sometimes giving someone a knife is a great way to make them feel better about life. We called it "knife therapy."

CHAPTER 16

And call upon me in the day of trouble: I will deliver thee, and thou shalt glorify me.

Psalm 50:15

I believe that it is better to tell the truth than a lie. I believe it is better to be free than to be a slave. And I believe it is better to know than be ignorant.

H.L. Mencken

Jesus took a blind man and led him out of the town and used saliva from his mouth on the blind man's eyes, he put his hands on him.
Jesus takes me to lonely places to perform a work on me.
God will lead me, for He will take my hand.
From the notebook of Shawn Finucan dated March 9, 1984

"If anything should go wrong, and something should happen to me, I want you to know that I was doing this for my family."

Dad On the way to the airport.

October 2019 Merrill, Wisconsin

I got home from my trip to the Marinette County Sheriff's' office with the disc containing the photographs of the scene of the incident and the autopsy of Shawn in my leather attaché case. I basked in the love of my wife and enjoyed a quiet evening. I left the disc upstairs in my study and put it aside for a while. I felt tender, like the skin beneath a scab that has been pulled off prematurely.

I focused on the business of my search firm. But I knew I would have to face the images.

I thought of what the dispatcher had said to me when she handed me the disc. "I put them in separate files so you could look at them in stages when you are ready. I put the scene in one file, and then the autopsy is the last file you will open. Good luck and I hope you find peace."

When I picked up the disc from the sheriff's office, I had dropped off a small bouquet of flowers I had purchased at the local Aldi's store. The lady was grateful. I felt a great deal of gratitude to her for all her help.

13 July – 29 August, 1984
Ministry in Europe
A Sojourn for Christ
Shawn P. Finucan

God also gave me boldness to witness in Thessaloniki, Greece, and He has given me a desire to return to Europe—if He allows Greece to be used to win souls to Christ. It is a privilege for a Christian to be a tool in the Master's hands to help harvest souls of men, "You have not chosen me but I have chosen you and ordained you that you should go and bring forth fruit and that your fruit should remain…" (John 15:16)

"Deliver those who are being taken away to death, and those who are staggering to slaughter, oh hold them back." (Prov. 24:11)

1984 San Francisco, California

At the Zen Center, I sat on a wooden bench waiting for my interview with the director. The stone floor was clean and polished and smelled of fresh wax. The longer I waited, the more nervous I became. What would I do if they rejected my request to stay here? I had a few hundred bucks in my wallet and a small shoulder bag containing some toiletries and a few other items, but not much else.

I imagined myself walking out of the door with my little bag on my shoulder, like David Banner in the television series *The Incredible Hulk*, a lonely man on the road searching for answers. I let the piano music from the show plink along in my mind—slow, sad and forlorn. I would be like David Banner, just me against the world, only I wouldn't be able to turn big and green and kick the crap out of anyone who messed with me. That was a serious disadvantage.

It did give me comfort to know that if I was attacked, I had my Balisong Butterfly knife, and having a force multiplier in a desperate situation could mean the difference between walking away or getting zipped up in a body bag and hauled off on a cart.

"Was the world really this dangerous, or did I have some issues?" I wondered. Well, it is great to be a man of peace, but those men of peace are protected by men with weapons when the enemy is at the gate.

I was flexing out, seeing if I could rip the shirt open on my back and biceps like the Hulk did, when I was summoned. The director was ready to see me. She had a small office. We sat in the lotus position on little pillows with plants all over the windows. I could hear the traffic on Page Street going by, and I smelled incense and tea brewing.

Her name was Cathy, I believe, a woman with prematurely white hair and a pleasant expression of peace. That conflicted with any reason why her hair would have turned white at an early age. She asked me, in essence, what I was doing here and what I wanted.

I explained that I was on a voyage of self-discovery that would take me to a foreign country in six weeks from now and I wished to study Zen here at the monastery, as I had heard a great deal about how good speakers came to lecture here from all over the world. I felt that to study here could assist me in my education of forgetting the self.

She inquired, at one point, as to how I saw my future. The question perplexed me because I had read enough of the books to think that this was something a Zen master didn't worry about. I recalled a story and thought about relating it, wondering if it might be too much, then thought "When had that ever stopped me?"

I sat up straight and tried to look solemn. "There was once a wise monk who was walking down a jungle trail…" I began. Cathy's eyes opened slightly wider. I had the impression she was thinking something like '*Oh, I gotta hear this…*' "…when he was confronted by a ferocious tiger. The monk backed up only to find that he was on the edge of a steep cliff with jagged rocks hundreds of feet below. As the tiger advanced, and with no apparent escape and no other option, the monk jumped from the cliff's edge." I paused to give effect, hoping she had not read the same dusty book from Dad's collection.

"As the monk fell, he was able to grab hold of a vine growing out of the cliff's wall and it stopped his fall. As the vine began to pull out of the wall by its roots, the monk happened to notice a big strawberry in full season, perfectly ripened at the end of that very vine. Just before the vine pulled free, sending the monk to his gruesome death, he plucked the berry and popped it into his mouth, then commented, 'My, but how delicious this succulent berry is, in its perfect season.' And then fell to the jagged rocks below." I let the story sink in, glancing thoughtfully away. I held a pensive look for a count of nine slow seconds, then tossed a glance at her. She was smiling. I hoped that was a good sign.

"With regards to the future, I think that story illustrates how each moment of life is precious and if I could just live in each moment, without worrying about tomorrow or even the next minute, I could achieve a type of enlightenment. So, when you ask me about the future, I am not quite sure how to respond. Perhaps my studies here will give me more vision. But right now, I am only concerned for the day."

"You have answered well," she said with a smile. I thought she might be playing her part, like I was.

I was invited to stay. She summoned a tall guy wearing a long, brown robe with a rope sash and a bald head. "Issan, would you show Jamie to the men's dormitory? He's going to be staying with us for a while."

I was in.

It took me only a few minutes to figure out that Issan wasn't his real name. He was about fifty-something and had a nervous hack in his lungs.

"We get up at five-thirty a.m. and meditate for two hours each day before sunrise. We do that in this room." He showed me a room full of pillows against a wall. "The evening meditation time is an hour. You are required to make mediation times at the beginning and the end of each day, unless you have an authorized commitment." We moved down the wide stone halls and he gestured to show me rooms. We walked into a large, brightly lit kitchen with stainless steel fixtures and a huge, butcher block preparation table. On it was a big, steel bowl of pitted cherries that I would learn was always filled from the farm on the edge of the city.

"Mealtimes are scheduled. The kitchen closes in the evening at eight, no snacks after that. Breakfast is in silence here. We don't speak until 10:30 in the morning. Breakfast is usually cereal and yogurt, something light."

He showed me a big room with Tatami mats for people to kneel and sit on and room at the front for a speaker. At the Center of it all was a big statue of Buddha. "This is the lecture hall. We have lectures each week on Wednesday; this week is Akihiro Sakki from Japan. It should be excellent."

"How long have you been here?" I asked, my head swiveling around at the artwork, the stone floors and the courtyard with open roof that allowed California air and sunshine in through the halls.

"Years. I've lived in San Francisco all my life. Lenny Bruce gave me my first fix," he replied as he threw open the double doors to the dormitory. About twenty thin mats lay on the floor and big windows flanked the room that swung inside to open. They looked right out onto the street, protected by bars that kept people out and, perhaps, me in.

"Lenny Bruce, the comedian?"

"Sure."

"First…fix, right?" I had to think. It took this small-town Midwesterner a moment to figure out he was talking about heroin being injected into his arm. He was an old hippie; this is what they did when they aged. This was his claim to fame.

"This dorm is empty right now, but it won't be for long. People will be coming to stay from all over the world. We work in the morning. Sadie will meet with you tomorrow with your weekly work detail. The workdays are long and there is plenty to do. You will work here or at the farm at the edge of the city. I'll see you around." He pranced away like an ancient, forgotten Brothers Grimm fairy.

I went over to the window and set my bag down on the mat closest to the light from the afternoon sun.

I was undercover, as a Zen monk. The James Bond music didn't seem to fit with this situation. It would be more like a flute and zither or something.

I learned to sit still in meditation for hours at a time without moving. I silenced the "monkey brain" of chattering thoughts flowing through my mind by focusing on my breathing—deep and calm. I released my anxieties about the future, my angst about the past and the restless writhing that tortured the addicted mind.

I learned to listen to myself, and I developed an appreciation for silence as a young man being weaned off loud rock music. This would be integral to writing. I let go of thoughts instead of chasing them down rabbit trails that led to distraction and self-absorption. I straightened my back when I sat and positioned the weight of my body on my spine, keeping in mind the curve in the lower lumbar so I could sit for long periods of time without suffering pinched nerves between the discs.

I worked hard and enjoyed doing so. It was a great gift to be able to do this, for not everyone can. My assigned duties kept my mind from depression and anxiety, while releasing endorphins that gave me a sense of reward and fended off my restlessness and haunting concern that my potential was being wasted.

I kept in mind that it didn't matter what the task was. If I did the task well, I was worthy of it and the task worthy of me. I scrubbed floors with a big mop and wooden wash bucket, washed windows and cleaned bathrooms, and polished stone floors with a big disk polisher that, when no one was looking, I tried to ride. It spun me around as I clutched the long handle, and then slammed into the wall, putting a big mark next to a painting of a woman washing her hair in a mountain stream.

I washed pots and pans in the kitchen. The cook took his job as seriously as a meditation and didn't want help in food preparation. I learned to respect people's boundaries—how to be helpful without interfering.

Visitors came and stayed in the dorms, then shipped out to other parts of the world or to another city in the United States. A small team of French Canadians came to stay. On that day, two men and a woman fell in beside me during the labors of the day. That was when I met Sara.

In the evenings, in the courtyard, after the light, vegetarian meal that always left me hungry, I would meet up with this pretty girl who had such sunshine in her disposition that I found myself looking forward to sitting with her for hours, just talking. She would get excited when she told me about Quebec. When she wanted to emphasize a point, she would lean over to touch me on the knee or shoulder, and her voice would raise an octave as her speech quickened.

She spoke many languages. When her mouth enunciated English, the words formed so exquisitely that she could have been singing.

She had such passion. She explored her life like it was a process to be studied, rather than a series of planned or happenstance events. She fascinated me with her natural femininity.

I would find myself waiting in anticipation for the ending of a story she was telling, only to learn that the dramatic conclusion was that her father rescued her on a lonely, desolate road when her vehicle broke down. But as anti-climactic as the ending was, I felt gratified to hear it because I cared so much for the main character in the tale: her. This would tell me something vital to storytelling in my writing. The reader won't care what happens if the reader doesn't care for the character.

She asked me questions of specific details in my life, listening while never interrupting. She gave me the impression that she hung on my every word and asked me thought-provoking questions that gave me new perspective on situations and people. She listened skillfully; I felt she understood me. I heard the most incredible descriptions of experiences I had had in life come out of my own mouth and found that in hours of conversation, this woman could bring out a side of me that I didn't know existed.

In the whirlwind of this developing friendship, I was unaware that it was the little gestures she made, like pushing her long, brown hair over her head away from her face, and the way her eyes squinted when she laughed, that told me that there was something in this connection that was unique and powerful, and that I would never forget her.

Thirteen days she was there. During the evenings we spoke in the courtyard or on the roof overlooking the city of San Francisco as the sun set. We discussed philosophy, books, ideas, writing and travel as a broadening experience in life. She had been everywhere and gave detailed descriptions of places that I hadn't even dreamed of going.

Her father was American and her mother French-Canadian. She would have bilingual conversations with her family at the supper table. On the roof, we talked next to

Mira's plants, where she had a few chairs out for the rooftop smokers.

"What do you do in the Midwest?" Sara asked, leaning forward with her elbows on her skirt-covered knees.

"We hunt, fish in streams and lakes, and swim. We ski, we walk in the woods and on forest trails and we…love."

"I like that last one." Her smile was sly, maybe not so innocent. The big sunflower next to her was in an explosive display that matched the yellow stripe on her blouse.

"We read books, write and tell stories. We dream of achievement and hope to master understanding as well as to be understood." Did I say that? I wondered what had gotten into me.

"Do 'we' pursue achievement?" She studied me now, qualifying me perhaps.

"We haven't figured out how to pursue things like that…yet," realizing it was true as I spoke it. She laughed. I was going to tell her who I was and not try to be something I wasn't, just because I…really liked her. And if she was going to like me back, she was going to like me for who I was, or not at all. I had made this covenant with myself in relation to her.

She paused a moment, then answered, "That's a frontal-lobe development—that's the part of the brain that is responsible for planning and executing maneuvers that come to fruition in the future. It prepares us for growth. When we are young, it isn't fully developed yet."

"Really?" I asked. It made sense to me and explained some things.

"Sure," she smiled a million miles deep. The sunset appeared as a beautiful, smashed rose, along with yellow dandelion tops dropped behind her on the horizon. The sun was going down too fast.

A pigeon that looked like it was wearing a blue business suit dropped down onto the roof and walked around on the black tar. It regarded us with one eye.

"How do you develop the frontal lobe? By reading?"

"No, it happens with age, unless you have hindered it." She looked at the bird, then at the big orange sunset, then gently at me. "Have you?" She was no fool and had an idea of who I was.

"Yes. I've been…drinking for the past two years." Her smile faltered, her brown eyes darkened. In that moment, I regretted confiding this to her.

"I see. I'm sorry. I have some knowledge of this affliction. I mean, I've seen what it can do."

"It's okay. I quit." I wanted to reel her back in. My chemically-damaged self-esteem inflamed.

"Is that something you can do?"

"Ask me in a year." I wanted to change the river-like flow of the conversation. "How does that work, to have bilingual conversations at your dinner table at home?" I asked.

"My father would ask me in English if I would like to ride with him on his motorcycle to get something he needed. My mother would ask me in French how my studies were going in calculus. I would answer my father in English that I would love to ride on the motorcycle, and I would go put my boots on. Then I would turn to my mother and answer her in French, telling her it was a struggle, but I was meeting with Mr. Stradler, my tutor, on Thursday night, and that she should not worry."

I drank that in, playing out the scene in my screenwriter's mind. She must have seen my eyes moving in my vision and then she leaned forward so that I could smell her perfume and spoke a sentence in French. It sounded erotic and beautiful. "What was that? What did you just say?" I asked as soon as she stopped speaking the French words.

"I can't tell you." The mischievous smile touched her pouty lips again and she held my gaze.

"How come is that?" I asked, moving to the edge of my wooden lawn chair.

"It wouldn't be appropriate." Some silence unwound like yarn from a ball of string with a cat playing with it.

"Well, what's the point in saying it to me if you didn't want me to understand it?"

"Because the thought of talking dirty to you, if only for my comprehension, was irresistible to me," Sara responded. With a thump, a flame of desire lit within me.

"Yeah? Well, I speak some French myself. Don't you think I might know what you said?"

"What can you say in French?" Her brilliant eyes lit up. Her pouty bee-stung lips looked soft and delicious.

"Voulez –vous coucher avec moi, cesoir," I said, the only thing I knew in French. It was from the song "Lady Marmalade," a song I had heard back in the seventies by Patti LaBelle. I can remember lyrics to songs really well, so I was able to grab it. She tried to hide her laughter at first, but then started cracking up.

"Ok…what did I say?" I had to ask. She laughed so hard and looked so cute doing so that I started laughing too.

We continued laughing together until our shoulders touched. We were both enjoying the moment, but she was the only one who knew what we were laughing at. When we both finally stopped, we were sitting forward in our chairs. I leaned in for the kiss on those soft rounded lips, but a woman named Mira came out with a damn watering can and started pouring from it onto the damn plants—like they needed it. It had rained for the past two nights in a row.

Sara kissed me on the cheek and then got up from her chair, moving slowly, shifting her curvy weight to the front of the chair, and poured herself into her shoes. She started to walk away, her backside swinging in her skirt.

"Hey, what did you say? In French, I mean." She looked back at me over her shoulder as her hair fell around her face. She pushed it back with an open hand on the top of her head.

"That's for me to know."

"Ok, so what did I say?"

"You asked me if I wanted to sleep with you."

Mira stopped pouring water onto the sunflowers and looked over at us.

Sara winked at me as she walked out of the door leading downstairs, leaving me in a tizzy of a boy's dream.

"Sleeping isn't what I had in mind, if you know what I mean, Mira." She didn't even glance at me, just kept to her task. I had never heard her speak a word in all the time I was there.

Sara was the first friend I had made in eight months. With friends like her, I could use more friends, I decided. I thought about taking her to the movies the next night. In my mind, I went over the entire layout of Zen Center to consider a place where Sara and I could be alone. That would be tough to achieve.

That night I lay on the straw mat in the dormitory with seven male guests, all snoring and farting in the open room. Moonlight was shining in through the window while the sounds of light traffic filtered in from Page Street below. I lay there humming that stupid racy song by Patti Labelle until I outlined a story in my head. It was about a private detective who is hired by a woman who then seduces him as part of her plan to kill her husband. I would call it "Trouble has Legs." I could see it as part of a series—dime-novel type of stuff.

The next morning at five-thirty a.m. meditation, Sara wasn't there. At breakfast, in silence, I saw her leaving with her two male companions. She was holding her bags and stepping outside the doors of the Center. She had no intention of saying goodbye and would have slipped out without so much as a glance but, in the second before she was gone, she looked back, and our eyes met for a moment. In her expression, I saw what I hoped for. In that half-second of eye contact, she told me, or maybe I wanted to read into it, "that she was sorry to be going, and that she would remember me."

The heavy, wooden door closed behind them, and my heart broke in the early morning silence. I was abandoned once again.

I worked that day in a collapsed loneliness. I sought comfort in memories of my friends. John Purcell, Kyle Kolka, Dave Hoffman, Erik Lange, and Jim Grund would all be in boot camp by now, just a few hundred miles down the Pacific coastline in San Diego. They were members of an elite brotherhood that I would never share in. They would receive training, have their future laid out for them and have a job to do. They would have a "purpose," while I was flopping around the state like a smelly hippie in a Volkswagen bus.

I used the evening meditation time to quiet my thoughts. This settled the muck in the river of my mind and released the tension from my disappointments. I focused on my breathing and learned that, thankfully, my mind could only focus on one thing at a time.

CHAPTER 17

As the hart panteth after the water brooks, so panteth my soul after thee, O God.

Psalm 42:1-2

Statement given to the Marinette County Sheriff's Department on January 31, 1985

By Leslie Ollila

We returned to the college property and pursued the footprints that we had observed earlier. We had also received information from Mr. Dubrow that he had observed fresh footprints in the snow on the road and also into a field next to his property. We then went to the area indicated by Mr. Dubrow and followed the footprints. We then shined our flashlights and observed a body lying face down in the snow and a gun case by a tree. We discovered the body between 8:00 PM and 8:30 PM. We then returned to the college and contacted the Marinette County Sheriff's Department.

1984 San Francisco California Zen Center

After the Wednesday lecture, the students prostrated and bowed to the statue of Buddha. They knelt and put their heads on the floor. They lifted them up, then did it again, three times. Everyone, that is, but me. I sat there waiting for them to finish.

Eventually, as I knew it would come, Issan found me in kitchen duties, washing the big pots and pans.

"Cathy would like to see you, Jamie," he said in his tone of authority. I found her waiting for me on her lotus mat. I took my spot on the mat opposite hers, straightened my back and took a deep cleansing breath.

"How are you feeling about being here with us? Are you enjoying your stay?"

"I am, also I am learning a great deal."

"You are a very good guest, Jamie. You work hard. Everyone enjoys your company, and you have a great disposition here. You attend all the meditation services except on Sunday, and I understand you go to Mass on Sunday morning."

"There is a church just up the street."

"I understand that at the conclusion of temple, you are not participating in the bowing to Buddha."

"Yes, Ma'am, that's correct."

She focused on my eyes and asked, "Can you explain to me why that is?"

"I'm not bowing to that statue."

"Why not?"

I shifted my weight on the mat, trying to feel more comfortable in what I perceived as an evolving confrontation. "I don't bow to statues. It's a religious thing. My God is a jealous God, and He doesn't like that."

"You see, Jamie, you're not really bowing to the statue. You are bowing to yourself. The statue of Buddha represents what's inside of you."

"I have heard that perspective and disagree. It is what we do that defines us. I see a room full of people bowing to a statue. I don't mind if I don't bow to myself, as you say. Mankind has many ways of perceiving himself to be a god." I was not moving on this point. I felt frustration from her for the first time.

"You are making others uncomfortable during the service by not bowing."

"I can't be responsible for their feelings, only my own, Cathy," I replied, while wondering where I would go if she kicked me out of the center, then wondering why I didn't have a plan B for the occasion.

"Well, then, you can excuse yourself from the service and leave before we perform that part of the ceremony."

"I will do that. Thank you, Cathy." That night, at the end of the lecture, before the conclusion, I got up as gracefully as I could and went to the back of the room. Then, as the roomful of people leaned down and bowed to a ridiculous statue of a smiling man with a pot bell, I slipped out the double doors into the courtyard.

The Zen Center had a phone on the wall by the offices with a chair next to it. We were allowed certain phone privileges but had to write down the number on a pad of paper if it was long distance, and then put our name next to it. I called home and spoke to my Mom and my stepdad, Bob. They were kind and genuinely glad to hear from me. I missed home in their familiar loving voices.

"We took a trip and someone that you know robbed the house in our absence," Mom told me. "Hanz Gruber broke in, drove your brother Tim's Corvair around town and damaged it, stole your bicycle and we think some other items from your room. He was seen by the police on your bike wearing a big trench coat and they questioned him. He told the police you had given the bike to him. He stole some money from the drawers as well."

The trench coat was an off-white one with a big wide collar. It was a London Fog and fit me great. Dad had given it to me. "Jeez, what else did he take?"

"Oh, I don't know. I guess he sort of moved in while we were all away. We aren't really sure. He stopped by before we left looking for you. Bob mentioned to Hanz that we were all going to be out of town and he thinks that is what gave Hanz the idea to rob the place."

"Yeah, he's a career criminal, a thief by profession. He has an extensive criminal history. What was he stopping by for?"

"He just said he wanted to talk to you. He acted like you guys were friends. He asked me for your address, and I gave it to him," Mom reported.

"You gave him my address out here, at Zen Center?"

"Yes."

"Why would you do that?"

"He said he wanted to write you. As I already told you, he acted like you guys were friends."

"Well, I think we can figure out now, that after robbing the house, he is anything but a friend. He's a psychopath with some serious issues. If anyone else comes around asking where I am with that qualification, do me a favor and don't tell them."

"Ok," Mom agreed, my sarcasm going right over her head. I hung up the phone after signing off and wondered if Hanz would trek the two thousand miles from Wisconsin to find me out in California. I doubted it; later I would realize I had underestimated him.

A man who was tall, thin, about thirty-five and wore a scraggly beard came to stay at the Center when I was there. His name was Damon. He had a gentle spirit and good nature. Most important of all, he was funny. Damon was a world traveler looking for a place of rest or, perhaps like me, to lay low until the next adventure.

At night, in the big dorm room, Damon chose a mat way on the other end, away from everyone else. After I fell asleep on his first night at the Center, I learned why. I awoke sitting up to a miserable cry of horror. It took me a few moments to figure out it was not coming from outside the window but right in the dorm. Just about the time I was ready to lay back down and go back to sleep, it erupted again. A guy from Malaysia, who didn't speak a word of English, woke up and spewed out a stream of what I thought were curse words.

Damon was sleeping with his right arm folded over his face and was screaming in his sleep—the most inhuman, horrific, guttural wails a man could make. He would belt out a shriek, be silent for a while so that the rest of us would start to lie back down, then let out another that was even more unnerving.

Someone turned on the light and as Damon wailed in fear and anguish, we glanced at each other wondering what to do about this phenomenon. He was dreaming, that was certain, but no one seemed to know if we should interrupt him. It became clear that unless we did, there would be no sleep in the dorm that evening. After we awakened him, he looked around as though trying to figure out where he was. I asked him what he was dreaming about and he made a reply of words that were so jumbled that I couldn't make out anything in his response.

In a few hours, we were up for five a.m. meditation. Ironically, Damon was the only one who looked refreshed in the pre-sun light.

At the end of the day, I was heading out in the early evening for one of my restless walks and I invited him along. We walked down Market Street, past the bums and drunks asking for change, and made our way to the wharf. I gave the bums on the street some money, knowing that "But for the grace of God, there go I."

On different nights after work detail, we went through the park in the Haight-Ashbury area that was so famous in the sixties for the hippies tripping on acid, having sex in public, and wearing tie-dyed tee shirts and sandals, and not bathing. Later in life, some of those hippies would get into powerful government offices and make laws.

Damon told me of his travels and about his ex-wife, who wanted him killed and had actually hired someone to do it. She had started having sex with an insurance agent. The two of them had conspired to hire a college kid who was studying police science to shoot Damon when he was coming home from his factory job one night. He had escaped his front yard, running away through the neighbors' yards under gunfire.

His wife and her lover were both in jail but were only sentenced to a few years. Damon then set off on a journey of the spirit to find his mission in life but was lost. This we had in common.

He talked about the variety of jobs he had, from working a ranch in Texas, to selling cars in Kansas City, to working at a fishing resort in Canada. He had just returned from India where he traveled around with a small missionary group. I asked him some spiritual and religious questions but found no real foundation in his reply.

The walk was important to me at least three times a week. Even with all the physical labor in the building or at the farm, without pushing myself to the limit, I would not sleep. One evening, with chores done, I was getting ready for a walk. Damon saw me putting on the horizontal sheath of my Balisong Butterfly knife and pulling my shirt over it.

"What's that?" he asked. I lifted the edge of my shirt with my thumb, opened the Velcro sheath, pulled out the shiny steel knife in one smooth motion, did a latch-drop opening and showed him the blade.

"It's my knife," I revealed, thinking it obvious. He looked at me in astonishment and held out his hand. I presented it handle first. He marveled at it, then returned it to me, pointing the blade at me as he handed it back.

"Why do you carry that thing?" He said "that thing" like he was referring to a dead rabbit.

"You have to ask?" When I saw that he did indeed have to ask, I continued. "For protection."

"This is a Zen monastery, man."

"It is in *here*. But it isn't *out there*. It's a big city with its own game going on, and anybody you can imagine is walking around out there. And its nightfall, the cockroaches come out." Damon looked disappointed in me. I put the knife back in its sheath.

"You really believe that?"

"I do. You've been all over the world, Damon. I'm surprised that you don't. Wasn't an attempt made on your life"

"The world is a giant mirror. If a man smiles at it, it smiles back at him. If he looks at it in anger, it will look back at him in anger."

I smiled. Those trite sayings were no consolation during a physical attack.

"Okay, sometimes the world is a mirror and it's full of smiles and giggles if you have the right attitude. But sometimes the world is a parade with all sorts of floats and characters passing by that run out and interact with the spectators. They dress like clowns and throw candy to the children. Fun and delightful characters inhabit some of the floats. But some of the floats are full of pathology and sickness and are driven by characters that are wretched and evil.

"These people are monsters disguised as smiling clowns and they feed on the flesh of the spectators, slipping out from the floats and mingling with the crowd, creating victims. Some of those spectators become victims, while others are defiant warriors who stand up to the darkness that invades the land and sends the evil back to where it came from and, in doing so, they protect the lives of the innocent."

Damon appeared confused. "I have been all over the world, several times," he answered, "and I have not had a problem. The problem, Jamie, is always of our creation."

"Most of the victims would disagree, yet that is what you believe, Damon. But know this, if we are walking these streets and we encounter one or more of these evil assholes, you will have to be defended by me and my knife, because your belief system will have you woefully unprepared. So, you put a heavier burden on me, because you won't be able to defend your pleasant self behind your smiling mirror."

"I'd rather take that chance than live in the darkness of your world," he said in justification of his position.

"So you say *now*, here in the safety of these walls, today. But those feelings are fickle. If I had to save your life by acting violently, from that point on, your perspective would change, and me and my knife, we would be like your Daddy."

"My Daddy was an asshole." Damon turned and walked away.

I headed out into the street to stretch my legs and take in the night air. I thought of all the conflict I had endured in my short life so far and wondered if Damon was right. I considered a vital question that I would ask whenever I had a problem: "What in me is causing this problem?"

I heard a voice yell at me from my right, "Hey, you think I'm supposed to be afraid of you?" I turned my head and saw it was the big angry biker I had seen weeks ago when Dad and I had driven past the Center. He wore a leather vest and jeans, his long beard trailing down his wide chest. He was looking right at me and walking toward me, closing the distance.

I couldn't imagine what would have made him select me from the crowd of people in this night, but there he was, without a doubt, moving toward me. I didn't break stride.

"Not as far as you know," I called back. He swung his bare arms around as he walked faster to intercept me. I kept walking, widening my stride. I picked up the pace but didn't run. I kept my eyes on his advance and knew I could outrun him if I had to, and if I couldn't, well…God forbid it to be, please, I had my knife.

We moved on, the distance staying between us. He fell behind me in the pedestrian traffic. He was just another phantom of the street that existed in a hazy line between a real threat and a harmless sociopath who was only a danger to himself. I was grateful that I didn't have to risk my life in making that determination.

The lecture in the hall was from another guest speaker from Japan. Uzaki Ummamoto was a man who spoke broken

English but I could understand him. His message was about finding peace within yourself and others.

I tried to focus on the lecture but my mind strayed.

My time at the Center was growing short. I had received a letter from Dad from Singapore. Having taken a week-and-a-half to get here, it informed me that I would be receiving a letter from a travel agent that would have my ticket in it. I was to find transportation to LAX, be it cab, bus, or pay someone at the Center to give me a ride, and I was off. The voice of his letter was strained, tight with tension and exhaustion. Dad was under tremendous pressure. In circumstances less than this, I had witnessed him collapse mentally and render all his brilliance disabled. I hoped he could keep himself together on his mission until my arrival, and then I could help.

Some of the language Dad used had me wondering if he was concerned that the letter might be read by a government official before it left the country. I was getting restless here in this hiding place and adventure called to me.

I was recognizing that these Zen studies had no external source of power, grace or support. They seemed to think that any answer could be found within, but within was where my problems were.

Damon leaned over from his sitting lotus position next to me. "Jamie, ask Uzaki about knives. When he's done with his speech, he'll take some questions. Ask him about carrying a knife and how peaceful that is."

I smiled. I recalled how many times in my life, through school, I had sat next to some screw-off who made monkeyshines during a lecture.

Damon raised his hand and interrupted the speech. The Japanese guru stopped and looked at him in surprised astonishment. "Student Jamie has something to show you. He has a question." The thirty people in the room looked at me—the guy who left before they all bowed down to the statue. "Show him your knife," Damon whispered with urgency to me.

"Ask him about your knife while doing your Clint Eastwood impersonation."

I shook my head, waved-off the attention and waited for the speaker to continue. We all sat in the silent room for an agonizing series of moments. I kept a placid expression on my face to show that I was peaceful within, and he ought to just get on with the lecture.

Why would anyone have a moral objection to someone being able to defend themselves? In those moments I wondered who these people would pray to when attacked by a savage. With eternity hanging in the balance, would their pleas be directed to a brown statue of a smiling pot-bellied man sitting in the lotus position in some Buddhist chapel, or would they suddenly pray to the God of the Universe?

And, if it was my God, would he hear and answer them? Why should He, when they had turned from Him to pacify their soft existence with idolatry and self-worship?

The next day I received a letter from Hanz Gruber, the career criminal who had broken into my house in Merrill, stole things and damaged Tim's Corvair car. He was in California working for a company installing security systems, of all things. The letter was written like we were old friends, which added to the creepy nature of the fact that he had traveled across the country to confront me about something.

The only thing I could think about was the money he had brought to Harry's Drive-In restaurant and laundered while I was working there. His letter indicated that he would be at Zen Center in a few days to visit me. I felt certain Hanz had been charged with other cases of theft, assault and potentially drug charges, so he had violated parole to come out here.

I threw away the letter wondering if he had graduated high school this year, and if he did, though he was a sociopath and casebook study of criminal behavior, he had a higher level of education than me.

The night he was to visit, thinking nothing of it, I walked out that evening and went to a movie, *Ghostbusters,* at a theater a few miles from the Center. Knowing my days were numbered here in the city, I took special interest in the surroundings and culture around me.

When I returned from my movie night to Zen Center, the inside guard of the Center handed me a letter in an envelope. I had forgotten about the visit. I saw that it was a letter from Hanz Gruber. He had been here, traveled two thousand miles, had visited the Center and had left an ominous letter.

He wrote that he had some business to discuss with me and the fact that I was not here tonight would not deter him from eventually catching up with me.

CHAPTER 18

Jesus answered, "Verily, verily, I say unto thee, Except a man be born of water and of the Spirit, he cannot enter into the kingdom of God."

John 3:3

If you stand right fronting and face to face with a fact, you will see the sun glimmer on both its surfaces, as if it were a scimitar, and feel it's sweet edge dividing you through the heart and marrow.

Henry Thoreau

21 September. 81
Very busy.
A lousy day really, except tonight I sat across from Cory in the library.
I gave him Proverbs 18:24
(Authors note: Proverbs. 18:24: "A man that hath friends must shew himself friendly: and there is a friend that sticketh closer than a brother.")
He coolly gave me Proverbs 27:17
(Authors note: Proverbs 27:17: "Iron sharpeneth iron; so a man sharpeneth the countenance of his friend.")
The artist series sounds great.

The Next to Nothing Book (notebook of Shawn Finucan)

1984 San Francisco, California

That night I had a dream that I was in the woods of Wisconsin and my foot was caught in a big bear trap. It had steel jaws with metal teeth like a saw blade that had slapped down over my ankle. I was on the ground trying to pry it open.

Approaching me were the two assholes from Mexico. The smiley one with the pockmarked face held his knife out in front of him and he was happy to see me. The other one with the dented head held his little pistol at his side, looking inconvenienced, and said something to me in Spanish. As they closed the distance to me, I saw The Snake, my 357, lying on the forest floor, in its glory, out in front of me. I stretched out and writhed around to reach for it, but it was just out of reach. The more I struggled to get it, the more my leg hurt and pulled against a chain tethering it to the ground. I yelled in agony and stretched my fingers just short of the rubber grip.

They were just a few yards from me when I saw a stick next to my hand. I knew that if I grabbed the stick, I could move The Snake into the reach of my hand. I stretched to reach the stick, and I yelled.

My yell turned into another that seemed to come from somewhere else in the woods. It yanked me from my nightmare, and I crashed into reality sitting upright on my mat.

The dorm was quiet, moonlit, and still. I breathed deep and sat in my night sweat feeling slimy and shaken. Another yell had the other students getting up. One turned on a flashlight and shined it on Damon. He lay with his right arm folded over his eyes, trembling, yelling and sleeping.

I looked out the window to my left. The full moon in the sky was bathing me in its blue light. I lay back down and focused on relaxing my neck, then my shoulders, then my chest, stomach, and legs. I breathed deep and let the tension out. Damon yelled again. I let it go and kept working at dropping off to precious sleep.

Damon woke up and took some guff from everyone. They expressed great displeasure with his sleep disorder. He looked around like he didn't understand what the problem was and looked hurt. I got up, left the warm cover of my blanket, and pulled some clothes onto my slick cooling skin. "Come on, let's go get some coffee," I said to Damon as I walked past him.

"But the kitchen's closed," he answered over a hoarse voice from yelling.

"It's three a.m. There's no one awake to kick us out," I said. We found some instant coffee and sat at the counter in the dead of the early morning. The endless, stainless-steel bowl of pitted cherries was there, and I grabbed a handful.

"Tell me about these dreams you have, Damon."

"I got into some bad demons in India," he confided.

"I heard you say that before. What do you mean?" He ran a trembling hand over his long hair, then over his oily beard and looked at me for a moment. I waited and sipped the coffee. It was time to be silent and listen.

"Well, you know some cultures believe that if you tell someone a story of a curse, you infect that person with it."

I wanted to ask him if this would be a long story but instead, I said, "I believe a problem shared is a problem half-solved."

"I've been traveling around. I was in Nepal a year ago, traveling with this group of mountain climbers attempting to summit Everest. I'm not a climber, so when they went to Katmandu, I broke off and went to India. It was cheaper to travel there than other places.

"I fell in with this cult, though I didn't know that's what they were. I was drinking with them, and the night was very hot, I remember. They drugged me at a ceremony by the Ganges River and threw me in the water. I recall falling, hitting the water, then flailing around in the river. I'm not really a swimmer. I would get to the surface but sink. I kicked and struggled just to make it to the surface, breathe and then sink again. With the drug they had given me and my wet clothes, I knew I was going down for the last time when something bumped into me and then grabbed me.

"I was sure someone was helping me. I clung to this person, kicked, around and kept my head out of the water enough to see in the dark night the lights on the shoreline and I kicked us both in that direction. The man who was rescuing me asked me a question on the water's surface. He said, 'For saving your life, what will you give me that you posess?' I am certain he spoke those words to me in the darkness. I only struggled to breathe and he asked it of me again before we moved further toward the bank of the river.

"When we got to the shore…"

"Wait," I interrupted, "please tell me before you go on, what did you then say?"

"I told him whatever the hell he wanted. I thought what an odd question and what the hell good was anything I had if I was dead? Anyway on the shore…"

Again, I interrupted against all manners I had been taught. "Sorry, wait, after you said that to him, what did he then say to you?" Damon was disturbed by my interruption. He opened his mouth to answer the question and formed words that didn't come out at first. I waited in the sterile silence of the stainless-steel kitchen sinks and stove tops that seemed to gleam in the overhead white light.

"He said, 'Your soul'…" Damon looked down without finishing the sentence. I felt a cherry pit between my teeth crush and a bitter taste touched my tongue. "…I helped my new friend, as he had helped me, and pulled him up onto the soil…" He continued but I reached across the table and touched his forearm with my fingertips to stop him.

"And, Damon, what did you say in response?" I asked, looking him in the eye.

"I said, 'of course', what was I going to say? What would anyone say?" He shrugged and looked down again. "Anyway, on the riverbank, when I crawled out of this disgusting water, I pulled him up after me. He just lay on top of my legs, not moving. After I caught my breath and thanked him, I moved him off my legs, wondering if he was all right. That's when I realized it was a corpse. This dead guy was wearing a suit, and most of his flesh had been burned off. His face was twisted in horror. His eyes stared at me, and I tell you, they focused on me. I swear these things."

The big refrigerator motor kicked on and started humming.

"I tell you these things, Jamie. That his eyes were open and looking at me, and he had been clinging to me with closed hands and arms in the water, like he was alive, and he spoke to me."

"What the hell?" was all I could say.

"I mean, there is an explanation for some of this. The Ganges River is sacred, so these people have funeral pyres when someone dies. They put the body on a plank and cover it with wood, set it on fire and push it out into the river to burn. Only there's not much wood around and it's expensive, so the body doesn't really get burned and the bodies just sort of sink or float around."

"Isn't there a health code violation here?"

"Yeah, well, not so much. They drink from this river, float dead bodies in it, and it's also loaded with human feces. We're talking third-world stuff here. Everywhere you go, you won't find regulation streets and clean bathrooms in this world. The people of India think the river is sacred and that it will heal them, and if they die in it or next to it, they will go to heaven.

"Anyway, the body was alive, moving when I bumped into it. I know it. It grabbed me around the neck with both hands. It saved my life. It…rescued me from drowning. I'm telling you, it was stiff and rotting when we…it got to the river bank, but in the river, it was alive. Yes, I was drugged, but I know what I saw and felt."

I spit a pit from the cherry into my hand and lobbed it at the wastebasket. This one made it; the other three on the floor I would need to pick up later. I looked at my watch, no time left to get any sleep before morning meditation. This would be a long day of chores.

"Now, sometimes when I sleep, I feel this dead, burned body wrapping its arms around me and he's telling me he's going to drag me to Hell. He's clutching me, pulling me down into this cesspool of water and filth."

"Damn," I replied in sympathetic astonishment. I thought of what my brother, Shawn, might say right now. I felt a little shock and embarrassment, but one thing I always had was plenty of nerve.

"Damon, have you ever considered accepting the Lord Jesus Christ as your personal savior?" He looked across the table at me in amusement. "That's the only way I know to prevent being dragged to Hell. You see, Damon, Jesus saves."

"So, the guy who carries a switchblade knife is going to preach to me?"

"It's not a switchblade—it's a butterfly. A butterfly is a very beautiful thing. You see, you sold your soul to the Devil, but the truth is, it was already paid for by the blood of the Lamb, Jesus Christ. You just need to claim your right. That's the only way I know for you to be saved from Hell."

"Give me a break," he snapped back.

I failed in my first evangelical attempt. I was beginning to understand what Shawn felt when we gave him a hard time about this born-again business.

Damon got up from the table and took a few paces away, then turned back to me. "Do your Clint Eastwood impression for me," he said with a smile.

I was tired and not feeling it, so I just looked at him.

"You can tell a lot about someone by who their heroes are," Damon offered.

"And you can tell even more about a man who has no hero," I said in my uneven "Clint" rasp. He turned the corner and vanished. I was alone in the creepy silent kitchen.

"Hey, Damon, don't meet yourself on the road coming back in life," I called out to him, still wondering what that even meant. I looked at his half-full coffee cup on the table and thought, 'Some people go their whole lives without learning how to pick up after themselves.'

Sundays were a day off and I found myself getting anxious about the end of the week. With no work, I was restless. I wrote in my notebook and read, but without a work schedule, I grew lonely, reflective, and depressed.

I went to Mass at the Catholic Church just a few blocks away. The religious ritual was soothing to me and offered me time to pray and ask God for help and protection. I drew strength knowing that God was watching over me.

After the service, I stayed in the pew and let the congregation leave, while taking in the growing silence. The church was huge, with high ceilings, stone pillars, statues of saints and Christian imagery painted on the walls, like Michaelangelo, himself, had been at work here.

The parish priest, Father Fleckinger, came out to the altar, his robe off, now dressed in black trousers and shirt with the white collar. He glanced at me as he snuffed out the candles. I looked down, wanting to be left alone and to isolate in silence. I was a transient and had been living that way for a while. I stayed in a place then I left. Sometimes transactional conversation seemed burdensome to me.

He sat down in the pew next to me. I turned and he introduced himself. He asked me some questions about who I was and where I was from. He wanted to know what I was doing here, and who I was with, where was my family. He didn't divert from the issues. He wanted to see where I was, spiritually. He was doing his job.

He reminded me of the priest that Carl Malden played in *On the Waterfront*, a tough Irishman with a direct approach to helping people, whether they liked it or not.

It wasn't long before he knew that my dad was an attorney, involved in some shady dealings and I was going to Singapore to be a part of it. We were not in the protection of the confessional, but I felt I could trust him with this information.

"Why are you allowing yourself to be drawn into this criminal enterprise by your father?"

"I'm not allowing myself to be drawn into anything. This is my decision to go along. And I don't know for certain that it's criminal. It's tax shelter work, and it could be legit."

Father Fleckinger looked me right in the eye. "Is that what you're going to tell the authorities if something should go wrong?"

"I'm not really a part of anything. I'm just along for the ride."

"It doesn't really work like that, Jamie. If you're in a car and someone stops to rob a bank and jumps back into the car, are you a part of the bank robbery?"

"What? No, we're not robbing any bank, Father."

"Is this the mafia that your dad is involved with?"

"No, well, it's not *the* mafia. It might be considered *a* mafia. No, these are just some guys who…well, look, I think you're making more of this than it's worth."

"Am I? What kind of father takes his son on a drug-running, money-laundering mission?" He waited for an answer, and I let him wait. "If your dad were here right now, I would tell him just what I think about this. You say he's a lawyer? Well, he knows the legal implications of what he's doing and he has you involved in it. This pisses me off." His tone was quiet, even and controlled, one of those tempers that yields a slow burn.

"What do you think can happen in this situation if something goes wrong?" He stared at me. I looked up at the giant crucifix hanging on the high wall behind the altar. The artist had painted a realistic spear wound to the side where the Roman soldier had satisfied himself that the work of the day was done, making sure Jesus was dead and my sin debt paid in full.

When I looked back at Father Fleckinger, he was still staring at me.

"I suppose Dad could go to jail."

"How about you?"

"I haven't done anything."

He raised his eyebrows and waited for me to explain myself. I didn't speak, so he went on.

"I know people who are in the drug trade, Jamie. From my position I can tell you stories of horrific acts."

"Yeah, well that isn't me."

"I can tell you that going to jail isn't the worst thing that could happen to you, when you are involved in an international drug smuggling ring."

"Look, Dad's been homeless and broke. He's disabled and has a hard go of it. *We're poor in spirit…*"

"You're what? Is that an expression your dad used, 'poor in spirit'?"

"As a matter of fact, it is. When a man's back is against the wall, he finds himself doing what he has to. Ordinary circumstances don't always apply."

"Being poor in spirit doesn't mean being broke, or in a tight spot. When Jesus said, 'Blessed are the poor in spirit,' He was referring to people who were humble—who realized their sinfulness and their dependence on Him, and therefore devoted themselves to God. They weren't using their poverty as an excuse to smuggle drugs.

"Poverty is not just a financial or physical condition, but a spiritual one. To be spiritually poor means to recognize that you need God. Being homeless doesn't make someone holy or sanctimonious. It just makes them homeless. Being poor doesn't, by default, bring you closer to God. It just means you're poor. Someone who is poor in spirit is not self-satisfied, proud, and damn-sure not engaged in the underworld of crime."

A grey-haired old lady, wearing a dress and a big shawl, moved up the aisle, stepping on unsteady legs. She knelt in the front pew and put her head down. Her stooped shoulders inferred that gravity seemed to be pulling her down to the ground as I looked at her.

"Do you have enough money to get on a bus and go back to Wisconsin to your mother's house?"

"Look, Father…"

"I asked you a question."

"Yes."

"Then do it. Get out of the situation and run from this influence. Start over with a new approach to your future before you find yourself in a situation that you wish you could go back in time to fix. You can put yourself in places in life very quickly that offer no escapes, and you are heading into one."

"You mean like, 'Meeting yourself coming back on the road in life'?" I questioned. He looked at me like I was speaking my broken Spanish.

"I will be praying for you. It was nice to meet you, Jamie. There is a lot of good in you—preserve it and don't let the world extinguish it from you." He shook my hand and walked up the aisle.

Father Fleckinger slid into the pew next to the old lady. When she noticed him, she leaned over and said something to him. He put his arm around her and she started weeping, leaning on him.

I got up and headed back to Zen Center. I was hungry and the only thing that had any protein in the diet at the Center was peanut butter, so I was looking to put together a fat peanut butter and homemade orange-marmalade sandwich with a huge handful of those Bing cherries that were always on the counter.

Maybe Issan would have left some of the goats' milk in the fridge and he wouldn't miss a cup of it.

The letter came from a travel agent out of Los Angeles the next week. The envelope contained a hand-written letter from my Dad that had been relayed by the travel agent, along with my ticket from LAX to Singapore, and instructions on where to go once I arrived in that country. The condominium complex had an English address, Upper Thompson Road. When the immigration officer asked me if I was arriving for business or pleasure, I was to say "pleasure" and be prepared to show the address I was issued as my destination.

I was to be careful of what I brought—only a small bag of necessities. Chewing gum was illegal. I was also to leave behind my journals and remember that all my items could be laid out in front of me, read and rummaged through. This country had a strict rule-of-law that caned people and hung criminals without hesitation.

Also, he hoped I had remained drug free. If I failed a drug test, I could be imprisoned or executed. Possession was a crime, and they didn't mess around.

My return flight was five weeks after my arrival. Dad wrote about how proud he was of me and how much he was looking forward to my help, as he had been working very hard and was exhausted. I was relieved to learn that at the time of writing the letter, he had been able to keep it together and had not been incarcerated.

I was nervous about what I was getting into and excited at the prospect of traveling to the other side of the world. My date of departure was only a few days away. My stay at Zen Center was ending.

I sensed an "end of an era" again, so I savored the remaining hours, taking special note of the people I worked beside throughout the day. I asked more questions of the inhabitants of this strange and peaceful world in the middle of a bustling city.

At Zen Center, I had learned how to sit still and listen in silence to what was going on in my mind without fidgeting. Without moving or being distracted, I could allow my thoughts to return to my breathing and let my mind flow without seizing on a thought and obsessing on something inconsequential.

I had learned that adapting to an environment was important, but I didn't have to sell out my beliefs to do so. I could assert myself when I needed to. I had worked hard and felt the camaraderie of doing so next to people of all ages, creeds, religions, backgrounds, and ideology, and had done so in peace.

I had met some interesting people and made friends.

I jumped onto a moving trolley heading downtown. I went into the bank where the safety deposit box was. I opened the box and deposited my journals and the Balisong Butterfly, laying it on top of the shiny, scoped Ruger revolver I named "The Snake" and Dad's Browning Hi-Power 9mm. It was the same pistol he had scooped up from in his backpack when a psychopath unloaded a magazine full of bullets from a rifle at him through a window when I was eleven. I would later write a book about that incident entitled *Wild Counselor-1977: The Summer of the Hunt.*

The items lay there, like solutions to desperate problems, awaiting deployment. I closed it up, imagining, with my screenwriter's mind, a camera angle from inside the box, looking up at me as I did so—fade to black, and made my way back to the Center.

CHAPTER 19

For scarcely for a righteous man will one die: yet peradventure for a good man some would even dare to die. But God commendeth his love toward us, in that, while we were yet sinners, Christ died for us. (Romans 5:7)

Singapore says drug smuggling worsens even as hangings rise.
Reuters

Greetings
Desire to be a missionary in Greece
Desire to learn the language
Who I am – born again
When I plan to go
When I was there
I would like to be a Christian missionary in your country. I have known some people who are doing this now over there. Are there any laws or regulations in your country concerning the practice of spreading the Gospel? What paperwork is involved? Currently I am a mission major and have a desire to serve my Savior, Jesus Christ, in that country. Please write me information concerning your country, paperwork regulations, etc.
From a notebook of Shawn Patrick Finucan

1984 San Francisco, California

I paid a staff member of the Center to drive me down the coast to LAX airport and I got there early for my international flight. I felt like Ethan Hunt in *Mission Impossible* as I browsed around the airport bookstore looking for a novel to read. By chance, I excellently picked up a copy of *Empire of the Sun* by J.G. Ballard.

I lost myself in the flight seat with the story of a boy who was separated from his parents as they fled the Japanese invasion of Shanghai.

I read the pages shaking my head in exhilaration at the writer's description of war, and what the boy had seen. Reading the pages, I reveled in the sensation of intake, as I do when I eat sushi. How wonderful it was to be alone, yet surrounded by my fellow world travelers, bearing down on an adventure, traveling the world in my nifty little compartment with my sense of adventure and exploration enhanced in pages laid out before me on the seatback tray.

I quelled apprehension with the fact that God was with me and would let no harm befall me. The window offered the planet laid out below me; the life I knew now so distant. It gave me the thrilling impression that I was disconnected, free of the force of gravity and wrapped in possibility.

I was on the biggest jet I had ever seen, flying Singapore Airlines. The flight attendants were beautiful Asian women in long skirts with the finest of service skills. They were wonderful at casting a spell with a smile on a young man who thought of sex every ten seconds. They moved up and down the aisles of the jet like gentle, pleasing, stimulating dreams of comfort and excitement at ten-thousand feet of altitude.

The eighteen-hour flight seemed surreal. The plane became my new temporary habitat. Each hour took me further from America and deeper out over three oceans, the continent of Africa and India. I considered dual theories: how huge was the globe—and yet how small. I could get on a plane and be anywhere on the earth in a matter of hours.

The flight attendants kept serving me water and I drank it. The air was stale by the time we zeroed in on the runway of the island country. By then, I was both exhausted and thrilled.

When the doors opened after the landing, I remember the heat descending on me like a blanket of wet fire. The airport was as spotless as a science lab. I made my way to baggage claim, picked up my small duffel bag and got in line for immigration.

The immigration officers were all business. If they ever smiled, it was only on the inside. I thought of Dad doing this and wondered if he had carried into the country anything he shouldn't have. A thought went through my mind that something had gone wrong, and they had him under arrest, or in a prison, when learning of my pending arrival, and they were lying in wait for me in an ambush.

I pushed the thought out of my mind. My heart beat faster as I approached the inspector who looked me over and asked me for my passport and visa. I handed it to him and smiled. He held up the passport and looked at the picture of my face, then held it up to my head. His two-tone pupils moved back and forth from me to the photograph slowly.

He lowered the document and looked through my bag. When he got to the book I was almost through, *Empire of the Sun,* he stopped; all his movements froze. He looked slowly back at my face, then flipped through the pages of the paperback as though something might be inside it. When he got to the Bazooka Joe gum wrapper comic I was using for a bookmark, he took it out, held it in his fingertips and read it. I remembered what it said.

Bazooka Joe says to the doctor, "Doc, I can't sleep."

The doctor wearing a white shirt and glasses says, "Did you try counting, Joe?"

Joe says, "I counted to 467,465."

Doc says, "Then you fell asleep?"

Joe answers, "No, it was time to get up!" Doc is slapping his head.

I didn't expect him to laugh at it, but the look he gave me had me remembering that chewing gum in Singapore was a cane-able offense. Damn, I remembered, 'Didn't I have a handful of that bubble gum in my side pocket?'

I was smuggling, I remember thinking with a spike of fear stabbing through my heart and gut.

He asked me something in a language that sounded like Mandarin Chinese. I recalled the only phrase I knew in that language. "Ming How Ma," which meant something like, "Hello, how are you?" I thought of saying it but decided against it. I've found that knowing a phrase of a language and nothing else can get you in deep water when they assume you know how to speak it.

I didn't know what he had said to me.

Slowly he looked up from my book and his two-toned eyes settled on mine. He waited. An immigration officer checking someone else a few yards away stopped and looked over at me. I looked around, saw a big mirror on the wall and remembered what Dad had told me. "They have people watching you from all angles. They have a squad behind a big installation of one-way glass evaluating your every move."

A sweat broke out on me; okay, it was hot and muggy. But my heart rate had dramatically increased and I felt nervous. I didn't know why. I had nothing to hide and was only just arriving to see my Dad. He spoke to me again in Chinese and this time I said in English, "I speak only English." He leaned forward, trim and taunt in his polyester uniform with ironed razor-sharp creases.

"I asked you if your trip to our country is for business or vacation?" He enunciated his words clearly and slowly. Damned if I didn't forget what Dad had told me to say. I opened my mouth to speak, and the lips moved like a silent movie. Halfway through my third sentence, words stumbled out of my mouth.

"It's vacation, kind of business, but vacation." Oh, shit. A slight smile touched his lips, like on the Mona Lisa. His eyes stayed on mine, and he waited. "I'm a writer, so I'm here to write. I'm on vacation, too."

"What paper do you write for?" he asked slowly, over emphasizing his words.

"Oh, I don't write for a paper. I'm a freelance writer."

"What books have you written?"

"Well, ah, nothing, so far. I'm just getting started." I was feeling like I was going to turn to liquid in my clothing, starting with my bladder releasing. I could almost feel the body temperature liquid soaking my underwear around the groin, around the back, down the legs and then sticking my warm clothes to me. He would smell it, no doubt. I tried to devise a strategy for what to do next after I pissed my pants in the customs line but my mind could only stay there on that image. If it focused on that image too long, I knew it was fully capable of producing the result. That was the way the subconscious mind worked.

"So, you are a writer who does not write?" he said without a smile. I would remember those words and his expression for the rest of my life when I stared at a blank page waiting for my fingers to move over the keyboard.

"Well, no… I haven't written anything famous…yet." My face flushed like I had just swallowed a suppository.

"Where are you staying?" I tried to remember the address but drew a fucking blank. It was in Dad's letter, in the side pocket of my bag, but if I fished the letter out now he would certainly read it. What had Dad written in there? I tried to think if there was anything incriminating. I couldn't remember. My brain was dinging like I was walking through a casino.

Then it came to me—the name of the street where I had received the letter from, in the corner of the envelope. "Upper Thompson Road," I said. I hoped he wouldn't ask for the house number. He put the book back in my bag and handed back my passport.

"Have an enjoyable stay, Mr. Finucan." He said my last name perfectly. I was sure there was a hint of suspicion in his tone. I picked up my passport and bag with the contraband bubble gum in it and moved on, feeling like I had just pulled off something. The *Mission Impossible* music played in my head. My screenwriting perspective followed me in wide-angle through the airport.

From Changi Airport, I took a cab to Upper Thompson Road. The journey was only about a half hour. I rode past skyscrapers, business districts, reservoirs, and parks in a tropical setting. Even the industrial part of the city was impeccably clean and highly functional. It looked futuristic in some way; I pictured a George Jetson stepping off his plane car onto a moon deck.

Dad opened the door of the condominium and was delighted to see me. He was clean-shaven and dressed in jeans and a sweatshirt, and I noticed business attire hanging on the back of a tall stool with polished shoes beneath. His eyes were tired, and he had lost weight. The condominium was without a fleck of dust, and nothing was out of place. Dad's items, a pen, glasses, and drinking water, were lined up as though measured with a protractor. His exactness in handling and placing the items told me the level of pressure he was operating under. As we made greeting conversation, he moved over to a legal tablet, tossed it into his hard-side briefcase and snapped it shut. Decades later I would find that briefcase in my basement and open it. All the items from that trip were in it, preserved like a time capsule.

I ate some fruit from a bowl on an immense countertop and told him about my flight. His face was gaunt, his eyes had a haunted look to them and there was a sense of exhaustion in his movements that unsettled me. I carefully composed my questions to him about what he was working on, and I found him evasive. After a few attempts, he ended the evening. "It's so good to see you. I've been counting the days until you got here. I have been staying up late and it's been a long day. Now that you're here I'm going to bed." He smiled his goofy grin, went to his room, and shut the heavy, solid door.

Outside the window, a tropical night spread itself in a humid blanket over a lush landscape of huge, green trees. A reservoir wall jutted up in the distance. The sound of traffic from a freeway near by drifted through the glass of the closed window. A ceiling fan made from big parchment paddles spun high up above the loft and blended with the other gentle sounds. I made my way up the big, open, wooden timber stairs to my room. There was a bathroom attached to my bedroom, which seemed huge and palatial to me after living in a tent, then a camper, then sleeping on the floor at Zen Center.

I looked in the mirror and saw a tired young man looking back at me. There was a concern in my eyes, like I had seen in Dad's at the door. I took out my shampoo and soap from my dopp kit. Each sound I made reverberated off the tiles. I had the sensation that I was watching myself move from outside of my body.

The showerhead threw a gentle stream of water like a woman's caress. It washed away eighteen hours of plane funk and regurgitated air. A handful of coconut-scented shampoo encased me in lather, and I rinsed away the remnants of America, land of the free with constitutional rights to protect its citizens.

I'm here now.

I pulled back the incredibly tight, crisp, starched bed sheets and wondered if they used an air compressor to get them so tight. I stopped. I considered going downstairs and opening Dad's briefcase to see what he was working on. I tried to dismiss it. Then, knowing I would, in my underwear I made my way down the open stairs and tried the latches on the briefcase. They were locked.

I hadn't seen him lock the latches when he tossed the legal tablet in and shut it. He had gone to bed, got up when I was in the shower and locked the latches. Now, the rhythmic sound of his snoring was purring from behind his bedroom door.

My bed was firm and luxurious. I was glad because I had been sleeping on a floor with just a thin mat. The stiff sheet was just enough cover in the air-conditioned room to reflect my body heat. I saw myself for a moment as a Zen monk unfamiliar with such decadence.

I wondered if ignorance was a defense in my position of being involved in something in a foreign country where they dispensed the death penalty like traffic tickets. I was eighteen years old and responsible for my actions. The sensation swept over me that I had made the biggest mistake of my life in coming here. I was in a place I had no business being in and now was left with no way out.

Back in the states, Lynn Seidlitz, my childhood friend from Lake Pesobic, was beginning her studies at UW Eau Claire. John Purcell, Jim Grund, Erik Lange, Kyle Kolka and Dave Hoffman were all in Marine Corp boot camp in San Diego. I was on the other side of the world, hip deep in some international shit storm I wasn't even fully aware of, and in a country where I didn't speak the language.

My mind, usually infected with insomnia, spiraled into a dive as I felt my bodyweight melt into the cool, firm mattress. In exhaustion, I crashed like a low-flying Japanese Zero over Shanghai, under heavy anti-aircraft fire. I ejected and felt the snap of my parachute open, then the punch of it deploying when it filled with air. I floated down toward the lush, green, island country with the sound of wind in the canopy above me while bullets from shoulder-fired rifles whizzed past.

It took a few days for me to recuperate from the jet lag. Dad and I caught up on stories and ate meals prepared in the kitchen, or we dined at a restaurant that Dad had trekked to over the past weeks. Dad went to meetings with an investment firm, dressed up like a lawyer, which triggered vague memories from my childhood of him leaving the house to go to work as an attorney, years before he became homeless.

As I watched him leave the condo, I was filled with astonishment and a too-good-to-be-true sensation. In this past year, he went from a vagabond sleeping in the parks in Merrill, to a professional again, having meetings with other professionals. The transformation had happened before my eyes. I found myself recalling the dreams we had sketched out in the dirt in parks, like the law office he would open and with me as an investigator. I was thrilled that it might happen.

Then I remembered that he was also smuggling cocaine from Columbia in hollowed-out golf bags, passing through major ports of entry, and the dream crashed. God does not bless criminal behavior. Nothing good would come of this, I knew.

In the evenings, fatigued, Dad drifted off into despair. "I'm hollow inside. None of this could mean anything without your mother with me," he would say in a flat monotone voice that to me sounded like a rock rolling down a hill that nothing would stop.

It was unnerving enough when he mentally crashed on American soil, but here in this draconian world where we had no constitutional rights and caning and hanging were carried out monthly, it caused a grinding in my guts that was bringing on acid reflux syndrome.

Dad would seem operational for a while, but more frequently he would sit in a chair or on the couch with his head in his hands, tremble, and sometimes weep. He smoked cigarettes and spoke to me with an effort to try to get out of his own head. He asked about Mom, the other kids, and about my last communication from home.

He was posing in this role, playing a part that wasn't him.

The team had provided him with money for his mission, but it wasn't making him happy or at ease. Dad mentioned that he would need my help with a presentation to a company called Nakamura Financial in a few days. He would do the talking and I was to hand him files from his briefcase when needed. He showed me how it was organized and what file to grab when he asked.

When the walls of the condo seemed to close in, I broke out and took a cab to Lucky Plaza, a shopping district a short distance away. It was easy to get in the cab and say "Lucky Plaza." And away I would go. After a few days of rides, I started walking the distance, strolling beside the busy highway on the sidewalk.

There were notifications on signs, some in English, that informed me that spitting was a disgusting habit and punishable by a fine or caning. That information, along with the fact that chewing gum was illegal here, had me astonished at the level of oppression.

A motorcycle ripped past me on the freeway more than once in a week. It was very distinctive, a Suzuki 500, painted up in red, white, and blue, with words on the back fender—USA #1. Two guys were on it and one day when I got to Lucky Plaza, I saw it parked in the lot.

The bike was like one that I had owned a few years back. I had purchased it from my brother, Tim. I had destroyed it by the end of the summer by forgetting to pour oil into it. Heath, a mechanic in town, gave me thirty bucks for it, fixed it up and made himself a nice profit at my expense. I was recalling this and looking at the bike when a voice called out to me in Chinese in an uncomplimentary tone.

Two guys were walking toward me. The taller one was half smiling. The other had an angry look on his mug. He said something else to me in Chinese, so I tried my line, "Ming How Ma." I earned more staccato verbiage, with attitude, from the brown-haired man of about twenty years old.

"I was just looking at the bike," I said.

"I see what you doing. If you touch that bike, I kick your ass," he threatened.

"You couldn't kick your own ass," I called to him. They were closing the distance fast. I slid my right foot back and raised my elbows to "fighting stance," as I heard my instructor say in my mind.

"I kick your ass." Rather than attack, he walked around me, looking me over. The taller man went to the bike and put a key into it.

"You got a bike?" he asked.

"I used to have one like this," I answered, dividing my attention between the two of them. I didn't like the way the shorter one in polyester pants and a floral animal print on his button-up shirt was circling around behind me.

"Your bike has training wheels on it," he jeered, leering at me from over my left shoulder. The taller one had on a Members Only jacket. He pulled a cigarette pack out of the pocket and offered me one. I refused it.

"You are an American?" he asked as he lit up.

"Yes."

"You not an American, you fucking Canadian. I can smell dem. Canadians haven't done shit," shorter guy said and finished his sizing me up, then moved up close, looking me hard in the eyes. A physical confrontation was the last thing I needed. This would draw attention to us. I had to remember I wasn't in Kansas anymore.

"Who the president of the United States?"

"Ronald Regan," I answered.

"That was easy, anyone know dat. Who playing the World Series?"

Damn, baseball was a weakness of mine. But I had viewed part of a game in the airport in L.A. before getting on the plane. "Padres and the…Mets."

He threw his head back and raised his arms in exasperation. "Wrong, dumb ass. It Detroit Tigers. He don't know shit, Jun Long. He no American. There someding fishy bout heem."

"I'm Jun Long and this is Chong Yeow," the taller one said.

"Jamie," I offered. Chong Yeow looked away and made a tsk sound. I gave his contemptuous look right back, but I liked a few things about them. They liked my country and I appreciated the way Chong Yeow put his disdain for me out front with no passive aggression. I understood and respected his communication style. And, if an opponent like this could be won over, they might make good men to have on my side.

"Did you paint the bike up like this in red, white and blue?"

"No, but I had it done by someone who knows how to paint." Jun Long stepped back, admiring it alongside me. "America is a great country. You lucky. You can be free there. Can own a business, get rich, have what you want. Ideas are grown and developed there. Some of the best inventions in the world come from there—electricity, car, the phone. Know why? Because people are free. No government stepping on your neck."

He drew on his smoke. "In your country, men and women can do anything, have anything, if they work."

"Right on, brother," I smiled. I felt a deep connection to this man from the other side of the world that I hardly knew. He knew more about freedom and appreciated liberty more than some Americans I knew.

"Yeah? Then how come so many people who live there hate their own country?" Chong Yeow piped up. "I study to be an electrical engineer, went to Canada, and took a semester in Montreal. Fucking Canadians don't like you Americans much." He looked at me, waiting for my response, then went on. "Some American students there, too, talk shit about their own country: how everyone oppressed, and racist, greedy. Like these little punks would know oppression."

"Why is that?" Jun Long asked me.

"Critical theory," I replied. I reached out to touch the bike. Chong Yeow slapped my hand. The strike was fast, like the hands of a gunfighter.

"What's that?"

"What's what?" I said.

"Critical Theory," Jun Long replied.

"In the early thirties, Carl Marx had a plan to destroy America from the inside. He sent a team of idealists to penetrate the educational structure of America and install themselves into our highest learning institutions, like Columbia and Princeton. Their job was to spread a critical theory of the United States by promoting a subtle form of communism, known as socialism, and spread the idea that capitalism was wrong. Their goal was to connect capitalism to greed and make the claim that America was oppressive and racist and that the only good things in any country are handed out by a government. It was very successful."

"So much for the last beacon of hope," Jun Long said sarcastically.

The three of us stood there for a moment in the tropical heat of the city with cars passing on the freeway and shoppers making their way to cars.

"Hope is for losers," Chong Yeow said in disgust. "If you want anything, you fight for it."

"We go get some food. Want to come?" I said I did and we walked into Lucky Plaza. They knew of a restaurant. I walked with them in the wet heat that they didn't notice and lived in every day. In the restaurant, I took the menu from a pretty, oriental waitress and I looked at it in confusion. "You like Bak Kut Teh? It's good here," Jun Long said pointing at the menu.

"Yeah, that sounds good. Haven't had that in a while." I ordered it, though I had no idea what it was.

"How you like Singapore?" Jun Long asked. I said that I did and he asked me questions about America. Jun Long did an impersonation of Sylvester Stallone, so I did my Clint Eastwood, but they both just stared at me, not knowing who he was.

When my dish came, it turned out that Bak Kut Teh was pork ribs with spicy herbs. It was delicious.

"So what you doing here, Jamie?" Chong Yeow asked. He said my name like mockery. My plans to befriend him were going up in smoke like a Chinese sky lantern.

"Having dinner with some new friends," I said in a hopeful dodge. His eyes stayed locked on mine between bites of his stringy noodles. He didn't let it go.

"Not what I mean. What you doing in Singapore?" He said it like "Sing- a Poe." "You a long way from home." I devoured the meat from a rib with my nervous energy. They watched me.

"My Dad has business here."

"What he do for a living?" Jun Long asked. I got uncomfortable deep inside, and this produced the kind of tension that people can feel, even if you don't show it. In Zen Center, I learned that thoughts radiate out from within.

"He's a lawyer."

"You in some trouble? That why he here, to bail you out?" Chong Yeow asked. His eyes still hadn't left mine. I smiled. I remembered a Samurai quote: "Welcome your opponent and send him on his way."

"Naa, he's a business attorney. But I got a feeling if I hang around you much longer, I'm going to be in trouble," I said to his cocky face.

"What kind of business does he have in Singapore that he bring you?"

"He's meeting with Nakamura Financial about investments." After I said it, I had a feeling I shouldn't have.

"I know someone who works there."

"You do?"

"Yeah, so why you try to hide that?" Chong Yeow said. He smelled my evasiveness.

"I didn't try to hide anything."

"You got pretty cagey when I asked you what you doing." He had the gaze of a cop who suspected furtive behavior. I ate now with the feeling that I had damn well said too much. I felt self-loathing for letting myself get trapped in this conversation with this asshole.

The waitress came to the table and interrupted the challenge. She spoke to Chong Yeow in Chinese and he answered her. Then she spoke to Jun Long and he smiled, then said something. The two of them laughed. Jun Long gestured toward me.

"This is Jamie. He's an American, and he's my new friend." Jun Long was proud to know me and was showing me off. "Jamie, this is my sister, Kuan." She smiled at me in the gentlest manner, like a garden breeze in the tropical heat. I stood up and wiped my hands on my napkin. She offered no handshake, so I just said, "Hi." Her eyes shone with the sparkling refreshment of a drink of water with mint leaf in it.

The tension left the table for me. I had that stupid smile that I get and can't help when I meet a girl I instantly like. I didn't know when I should sit down and wondered if I should have stood up. When I did, I noticed an increase in hatred for me from Chong Yeow. In my glance at him, I became aware of four axioms immediately: he hated me, he liked Kuan, she liked me, and he was aware of the last axiom—that this made him hate me more.

"Jamie, maybe you would like to take Jun Long's motorcycle for a ride after dinner," Chong Yeow offered. The idea appealed to me.

"Sure," I responded. I envisioned careening around, beating the heat on the red, white, and blue cycle, while flying around the island. I would take the afternoon, check out the coast, burn up a tank of gas and feel the tropical wind in my face. "Maybe Kuan could come with me," I chanced.

Kuan spoke to Chong Yeow harshly in Chinese and left the table.

"What did she say?" I asked Jun Long, making myself not glance at his sister in her skirt as she walked away. Jun Long finished a bite of some kind of stew before answering my question.

"She say, 'Chong Yeow should stop it.'"

"Stop what?" I asked.

"Trying to get you in trouble. You don't have a license to ride a bike."

"I have a driver's license, and it's endorsed to ride a bike in America."

"Maybe, but you don't have one here. If you got stopped, you would be in trouble. You would need your Dad to get you out of it."

"What's the fine for riding a bike here without a license?"

"Three years in jail and one-thousand-dollar fine."

I picked up a rib and shook my head. "You people don't mess around."

"Mess around, what they do in America," Chong Yeow said, making a jerk-off sign with his hand, and finally looked away from me in disgust.

CHAPTER 20

If we confess our sins, he is faithful and just to forgive us our sins, and to cleanse us from all unrighteousness. (1 John 1:19)

June 12, 1983
To: Shawn Finucan
From: George Schefdore
International School Bangkok
Bangkok 10110, Thailand

Dear Shawn,

I was surprised and pleased to receive your letter. You requested my phone number so we could get some offences verbally cleared. This would be very difficult. My working hours are irregular. Also, the cost would be very high (maybe $50). If you would like to continue to write to me, I will be happy to answer your letters. Perhaps, we could talk together when I get back to Merrill around the middle of June.

I am not aware of any offences between us, Shawn. In fact, I cannot remember the last time we spoke to each other. If you absolutely must speak to me before June, you can try to call me at 252-7200 (Bangkok) any day, reach me between 6:00 a.m. and 8:00 a.m. (Merrill time). The call will reach me between 6:00 p.m. and 8:00 p.m. at my house. However, I cannot promise I will be home and this could be an expensive gesture. Also, since my maid is Thai, she might not understand you when you call and simply hang up the phone. I recommend that you wait until June to talk with me.

Sincerely,
George Schefdore

When I found this letter in Shawn's notebook, I recall how, after his spiritual awakening, he had reached out to many people with an extension of an apology for almost any infraction, often things none of us were aware of or could remember. I recall his apology to me was vague and left me confused.

1984 Singapore

The office of the Nakamura investment firm had a stunning view of Marina Bay. I entered the room with Dad and looked out the floor-to-ceiling windows at the blue ocean bay with about twenty ships of all sizes moored in the harbor. Some freighter ships were arriving with steel, multimillion-dollar yachts were tied to docks and cruise ships were coming into port. A panoramic spectrum of color from the ocean, the ship and the sky spread out before me. The sunlight sparkled off this dazzling, iconic view of the island. It brought to life this fantastic place where I found myself—on the other side of the world from where I grew up. To the right were high-rise business towers made of steel and glass done in amazing architectural design. Mixed in with it all were the tropical trees and vegetation amidst a bustling city.

The windows were slightly tinted to soften the light coming into the room. The office was immense, plush, and, like everything in Singapore, spotless. Two Japanese businessmen greeted us formally. One gestured toward a conversation table and chairs to sit at, rather than the long, dark wood conference-room table.

I was dressed in a suit, black shoes, and a red tie I had purchased in Lucky Plaza. Dad was wearing his suit and had had his hair cut and combed. No one would have guessed he had been sleeping under a picnic table to keep out of the rain at Riverside Park in Merrill a year ago.

"I'm Pat Finucan, Chief Legal Counsel for The Wellington Research Institute and this is my son, Jamie. I believe I have met with a few of your associates." I smiled and nodded; they did the same.

My job was to hand Dad things that he needed. The briefcase was in my charge and, when Dad needed a file, I knew which one he wanted, and I grabbed it. When he needed a pen, I had it ready. He had only to hold out his hand without breaking conversation and I would load it. We had rehearsed it with key words and the Japanese people we were meeting with liked it. Family in business was something they seemed to appreciate.

Dad shared with the Japanese businessmen his investment strategy regarding the stocks he had researched. He told them about Cooper Industries and how the stock had gone up significantly after he had purchased the shares and he relayed other successful strategies. I had watched him research this information in the park, at the picnic table, with the resources he had snuck out of the San Clemente library and now they were being laid out to these men on the other side of the world as we all wore suits. I marveled at this moment.

One of the men asked Dad whom he represented and how they had earned their money. Dad evaded the issue. Mr. Yamamoto handed Dad back a letter of introduction Dad had sent ahead. It had the familiar letterhead on it that I had seen before—the Wellington Research Institute address of 2 Boulevard Royal, Luxembourg, as the main office.

"We attempted to photocopy your letter of introduction and it only printed off as a black paper. Used up a lot of ink," he said and laughed.

"Yes, that letterhead doesn't copy, Mr. Yamamoto. It's designed that way." Dad continued with his presentation. At the conclusion of it, I recall the Japanese wanting to schedule another meeting to further the conversation before accepting the investment money. Dad gently pushed them to approve the acceptance of the funds he had available for transfer to their care, today. He stated that their record was impeccable, and Dad was certain they were the right firm to handle the currency.

The Japanese were kind and professional, but cautious. We left the meeting and stepped into the elevator. Once the doors closed, there was a silence and Dad seemed to deflate. His posture drooped and his face fell, signaling a disassociation that I had often seen in his depression.

I hailed a cab and when Dad got in, he collapsed. My paranoia wondered if the cab that pulled up was a plant from the government to gather information on us after the meeting. I looked out the back window to see if we were being followed but I wouldn't know what kind of car to look for.

In the condominium, Dad sat on the sofa and stared at the floor. I went into the kitchen and made Kaya toast. I toasted four pieces of bread and opened the jar of Kaya Jam. I had found this treat in a store when I went for milk. It was a paste of Malaysian coconut-egg spread, a departure from fruity jams and peanut butter.

I thought I had discovered my next comfort food the second I tasted it. So, I spread it out on the toast and covered the Kaya with a thin slice of butter. When done right, the butter melted from the heated toast over the Kaya as you ate it. I didn't think he would come to the kitchen counter, so I carried out the two plates and set one down in front of him with some milk.

I hoped that if he tasted it, it would bring him around and we could talk about the meeting.

"I'm not really hungry right now, Jamie," he said despondently. I ate mine and drank both of our milks. I put Dad's sandwich in the refrigerator, (which Dad still always called an ice box).

I sat next to him on the couch in the silence of the condo until a tropical bird chattered outside the patio window.

"I have screwed up everything in life. I'm not sure why this should work any better. I keep thinking that if this works well, I could have something. Maybe I could get you kids back. If I could undo my mistakes in life, I could correct some things, but as I'm here, now, I just don't see that happening. I'll always have to walk through life alone."

"*I'm* here, Dad."

"I'm coming apart, Jamie. I don't' know how much longer I can keep this up." I had heard him talk like this for years. It took on a special significance with relation to where we were. Just forty minutes ago he was verbally dueling with two, brilliant, international financial experts; now he was shattered.

The condominium was spotless, the cleaning lady had been in. Up in my room the bed was remade with fresh sheets. My dopp kit had been cleaned and even my toothpaste cap was wiped free of debris. My razor handle looked like new. I turned it over in the light and inspected it. What kind of maid cleans out your toiletry kit? I looked up into the bathroom mirror and saw a young man with concern and fatigue in his eyes, wondering what he had gotten himself into.

I went down the wide, cut-timber stairwell to find Dad on his feet now.

"What time does the cleaning lady come in?" I asked.

"I used to see her around ten-thirty in the morning, but lately it seems to be when I leave for cigarettes or to go have coffee at the corner diner."

"When you leave the flat, what do you do with your legal papers?" He dragged on his cigarette hard, looking at me thoughtfully, getting my drift.

"I keep all the work locked in my briefcase." I looked at the Samsonite hard-side case. A professional could pick that without any trouble. What would they learn about our mission if they did? I had no idea. I didn't know what was in the briefcase, I didn't know what he had brought into this country, and I didn't know enough about what he was doing to get a grip on my anxiety. He transferred wealth to this tax-haven nation and set up financial shelters here.

Part of me wanted to know what was going and another part didn't. If I was interrogated by authorities, what could I say and what were my rights? Did I have any here? I was having glimpses of this situation being critical and then I would second-guess it to calm myself down.

I took a cab to the restaurant where I had the Bak Kut Teh with Jun Long and Chong Yeow. I asked the driver to wait, and paid him his fee in case he didn't. I went inside and scanned the wait staff until I saw Kuan. I walked over to an empty table and sat down. I glanced at the waiting cab. In a few moments Kuan came to my table with that gentle smile and handed me a menu. "Today special is Laska noodle soup. Would you like to try?" she asked in a sweet accent and a smile in her Asian eyes.

"Yes, that sounds great. What time do you get off work?" I handed her back the menu.

"Three in the afternoon. Why?"

I looked at my watch. Two hours to kill. No problem.

"Will you go for a walk with me after work, show me around?"

"Show you around?"

"Yes, give me a tour of the area." She nodded in understanding.

"Yes," she replied and retrieved the menu. Her hand brushed against mine as she took it. I went outside and gave the driver ten dollars American money; it was stronger here than their yen.

"What's your name?" I asked the cabbie.

"Swami," he said with a crooked tooth smile.

"Can you come back here at three p.m.? Give me a ride, Swami?"

"Sure, where you go?"

"Where is there to go to take a date?" I asked. He smiled and winked at me.

"Botanic Gardens, somewhere…fresh, smell nice, pretty," he replied.

I went back inside and sat down just as Kuan, with a smile, was setting my soup in front of me. She used both of her hands to handle the bowl, like she was serving a king. I noticed everything about her, and she blushed.

The Laska noodle soup was fragrant and rich. It had a buttery taste to it and Malaysian spices that stimulated my palate. In this dish, I tasted the East and embraced this place, this culture. Laska noodle soup would be the next food I would look for in the stores. Maybe if I made it for Dad, it would cheer him up.

Swami was there waiting, like a pro. Kuan suggested we go to the Chinatown area of the city of Singapore. I agreed and abandoned my plan to go to the fancy park. We walked around Chinatown, she shopped, and we made small talk. On the sidewalk, we approached two, erected stone slabs with etching on them.

The writing on the top stated "Sook Ching Massacre." I stopped and started reading it. "What's this monument about?"

"Not a monument, a memorial. Big difference." Her face took on a dark and tender expression I had not yet seen.

"What massacre happened?"

"The British occupied Singapore in World War II, but the Japanese invaded and defeated the British on February fifteen, 1942. After the British were defeated, the Japanese massacred seventy thousand people in Singapore." I imagined the number that was seven times the population of people in my hometown. I was astounded.

"But…why?"

"We don't really know, but it was all planned. They went door-to-door and took the men from their homes. My Grandma saw her sisters and brother bayoneted along with three children, so they wouldn't have to waste ammunition. They issued a general order that had everyone report to an interrogation screening, and if you didn't pass, you were sent to an execution point. Changi Beach Park was one of the biggest slaughter areas. They killed hundreds of men there and then threw them into the sea. The tide washed them up for days. They kept transporting more out to sea, shooting them and feeding them to the sharks, but the bodies just kept washing ashore for days."

I read the memorial, placed there on the street so that people would always remember what happens when they submit to other people.

"The British that surrendered to the Japanese were made to bury the bodies. The Japanese call it Operation Sook Ching. It means purge by cleansing."

We stood there in silence for a while. She sniffed, found a tissue in her purse and wiped her eyes.

"Chia Chew Soo had to watch her father, uncles, aunts, brothers and sisters be bayoneted one-by-one in front of her by a Japanese soldier in Simpang Bedok Village, not far from where we are standing right now."

I waited in the silence for the story to be over, not knowing what to say to honor her dead ancestors but she, like the massacre, went on.

"I study this in school. There are eleven major sights of execution in Singapore, including what is now the airport runway. Did you fly in to Changi Airport?"

"Yes."

"That runway is where many Singaporeans killed."

I imagined my plane arriving over the bones of so many innocent people slaughtered like cattle. I thought of the book I had read on the plane, *Empire of the Sun*, about a boy, Jim or Jamie Graham, who incredibly to me, uses either name interchangeably, as I do. He gets separated from his parents during the Japanese invasion of Shanghai. As I walked the streets of Singapore, I recalled his vivid descriptions of a war-torn city with the beggars stopping people in the streets, the affluent people running for their lives, possessions of luxury being stolen or whisked-off down streets, and people scurrying in horror as the Japanese took the streets and instituted their own law.

I looked around me and unleashed my imagination to flash back in time. The cars in the streets became old Packard's,

Mercedes and Jeeps, weaving through groups of fleeing citizens. In the air, the skies full of Japanese Zero's and a British Tornado plane doing a dogfight over the city. I could smell the acrid fumes from exploding bombs, burning gas, charred buildings, death and fear in the rancid waste around me.

Kuan was looking at me. "In America, I mean," she said, staring at me as we walked together. She was waiting for an answer to a question she had posed. I tried to think of what she might have said.

"What? I mean…yes." I tried hard and came back to reality. It was as if the past wanted to claim me there.

"I have to study for an exam. I have to go home. I'm done at work tomorrow at three. Can you come see me then?" Her invitation tasted like honey in the mouth of my soul. The gentle positive aura of a woman could leave me tranquil, thrilled, and intoxicated in bliss, even on the other side of the world.

"Of course, I will." I wanted to lean in and kiss her, but she was moving away already. I watched her walk away and wondered if the authorities caned you for kissing in public. I made my way home on the bus and felt an inner trembling—the contrast of learning of the Sook Ching Massacre from a gentle, beautiful Asian woman.

The next meeting with Nakamura Financial Corporation was in the same office. Dad was silent on the way there. After the fifteenth floor, we were alone in the elevator.

"If they offer anything to drink, take it and drink it all. Sit up straight and smile. Hold just enough eye contact to show confidence. Say nothing. I'll do all the talking. If you are asked questions, answer them in two or three words, no more."

In the mirror of the elevator door, just before it opened, Dad straightened up and put on a look of confidence and ease. Before my eyes, he transformed. We walked out like the Mod Squad, or part of the Mission Impossible team, or Felix and

Oscar in *The Odd Couple*, or maybe Abbot and Costello. I wasn't sure of the duo we were closest to representing.

The conversation was financial and business like. I was bored for the most part and tried not to look it. Behind me was a stunning view and I wanted to keep turning my head to look out at the bay. I had to keep remembering to correct my posture.

One businessman was new to the conversation, the other one was gone. The new guy looked at Dad's business card.

"We called to check on your credentials and we were unable to find The Wellington Research Institute as a company," he said. The statement hung in the air for a moment, and I stopped breathing but tried to move my chest to look like I was. They seemed to be watching me closely.

I wondered if these men were the descendants of the Japanese who rounded up seventy thousand people and slaughtered them like poultry in a processing plant. Was there steel behind the eyes that were upon me? Perhaps a razor wire where blood veins could have been?

Dad smiled slightly. "That is exactly what I would hope that you would find, Mr. Oshida. Our society is a Societe Anonyme. Our shareholders are unregistered and collect dividends by surrendering coupons attached to their share certificates. The company does not advertise or wish to be known. We make our investments in secret and hope for that advantage to be returned by the people that we work with. Confidentiality is key in doing business with my clients, as I was expecting it would be with you. I would think you could appreciate confidentiality, gentlemen. Am I asking too much?"

The two Japanese men looked at me, Dad, each other and agreed with him.

"What I am doing here is enjoying and taking advantage of the fact that Singapore is a tax haven. My clients feel that they have paid enough in taxes and hope to find some relief and feel confident that you are just the organization to be able to help them achieve this while maximizing an investment strategy. I have filled out the proper paperwork with your government. I assume that makes this legitimate. The history of success of Nakamura Financial is evident in the corporate earnings report. We feel your philosophy and that of the Wellington Research Institute is a match made for success."

I exhaled through my nose, corrected my posture, and let my breathing come from the pit of my stomach. In a moment of silence, I inhaled a visual image of healing menthol herbs that would relax and bring me a peaceful sensation in the luxurious office while my stomach flipped over.

They asked to schedule another meeting a few days out. Dad's expression was that of resigned disappointment. His pitch to close this deal today had failed. Dad extended his hand to me, and I snapped open the briefcase and took out his planner. I opened it and saw that we flew out a day before the date they wished to schedule. I thought of saying this, but Dad snapped his finger and instead of saying anything, I handed him the planner.

I waited for Dad to see the flight date and ask to reschedule the meeting.

"It looks like that day works well for me. I will see you at two p.m.," Dad said. The Japanese men nodded and smiled in calm agreement. I wondered what Dad was thinking. I didn't like this delay. There seemed to be no apparent justification.

We stood up and ended the meeting. I took the briefcase to the door. Outside the incredible window, the ships moved in and out of the harbor in a living picture of history and achievement.

Before we left the room, I resisted the urge to ask the two men if they knew about the Sook Ching Massacre. That would be disastrous to the mission.

That would piss off Dad and throw a wrench into this underworld bullshit. I was glad when the elevator door closed and sealed us off from them. For some reason unknown to me, my destructive impulses were writhing within me.

Chapter 21

Ye are of your father the devil, and the lusts of your father ye will do. He was a murderer from the beginning, and abode not in the truth, because there is no truth in him. When he speaketh a lie, he speaketh of his own: for he is a liar, and the father of it.

John 8:44

"But they also showed a meanness and viciousness toward their enemies equal to the Huns. Genghis Khan and his hoards could not have been more merciless. I have no doubts about whether the atomic bombs dropped on Hiroshima and Nagasaki were necessary. Without them, hundreds of thousands of civilians in Malaysia and Singapore, and millions in Japan itself would have perished.

Lee Kuan Yew, Singapore's Prime Minister

People hate the truth for the sake of whatever it is they love more than the truth. They love the truth when it shines warmly on them and hate it when it rebukes them.

St Augustine of Hippo

October 2019 Merrill, Wisconsin

I need to write about what happened to Shawn so that I can process it. For my entire life, I have never had an answer to this mysterious question of what happened to him. Now, at age fifty-three, I face everything. Especially the past; there has been too much hiding, ducking, running.

I want to embrace the truth. I am committed to receive it and deliver it, and do it with honesty and uprightness, because not doing so would be evil. I have to practice honesty in all of my affairs. or I will be back in the slum of wasteland again.

I pushed the disc into the side of my laptop, and it was accepted. The silver plastic disappeared, and a buzzing noise came to my ears as it was identified, manipulated, and finally opened. On the screen before me were four files, just as the information clerk had said.

I double-clicked on the first one. A series of boxes opened in the file. The fan kicked on in the hard drive and the Howard Miller clock on my desk ticked. I took a deep breath and double-tapped the mouse curser on the file furthest to the left. The image opened and I saw my brother, Shawn, dead, looking up with lifeless eyes. I was shocked to see his face again, so white, and lifeless. I didn't want to remember him like this, but I knew I would never be able to forget this image as long as I lived.

His right hand was raised in rigor mortis just above his head. It took me a second to realize that this was his crawling position. Someone has turned over the body to examine and photograph him. Shawn had been knocked down by the velocity of the bullet and was crawling to get himself help.

He was wearing the big, rabbit-fur jacket that was open slightly at the top. His face had an expression of opposites—acceptance and surprise. His slightly parted lips revealed his teeth. His head and neck looked so young and slight. I remember now that he was a smaller man, like me, maybe 150 pounds, not thin but trim, muscled and fit. He looked like what he was, a disciplined young man recently out of the Marine Corps.

I will never forget the eyes. His pupils were clouded with the blue film of death. He stared into eternity and another dimension.

Was he looking at Jesus in this moment? I heard once that the first person you see when you die is you, or the person you should have been as God intended you to be. That's who takes you to Jesus.

If that were true, it would be the same guy I was looking at. Shawn was spiritual, kind and strong. He would be looking at himself, as I was looking at him. There are more pictures in this file. But that's all I could look at for tonight. I turned off the laptop and sat back in the chair. Once again, I felt the loss that all of us in the family have had to carry since that day.

1984 Singapore

Kuan took me by the hand and led me through the crowded streets to a depot where we got on a train. The air-powered doors hissed behind us like a dragon operating a time machine. The floor was clean, the seats shined in the sunlight and a slight waft of cool air poured out from a vent overhead. The people on the train looked tired. Most of them were sleeping, exhausted from work. Kuan's gentle, smooth, almost oily, soft hand found mine again when it was time to get off. We had gotten on the East West Line and now stepped out of the train into a beautiful tropical park called The Chinese Garden.

As we walked through a lush preserve of flowers and plants, reeds, ferns and trees, it reminded me of a scene in *Willie Wonka and the Chocolate Factory*; it could all be made of candy. A tall Chinese pagoda stood like an ancient palace before us. The walking path was bathed in an intoxicating fragrance from the flowers that hung in the humid island air.

Kuan told me about her family. Her brother, Jun Long, was her protector since her father had died of a brain aneurysm.

"Jun Long looks after me and Mother. He would like to go to America but doesn't want to leave us behind. He likes you and wonders if one day you will sponsor him in America," she said, her head framed by Birds of Prey flowers. She cast a glance at me looking for my reaction. I gave none.

I wondered how that would play out, Jun Long figuring out that my dad was really a street lawyer who slept in the parks in my small town. The thought brought me back to my situation; I was knee-deep in international dealings that may not be ethical or legal. We had another meeting with Nakamura Financial scheduled a day after we were supposed to leave and I had not resolved that yet.

"Are you listening to me?" Kuan asked.

"Yes, of course." I hit re-entry hard and skidded across the stratosphere.

"Chong Yeow's father is a policeman with special intelligence division. He wants to be a policeman like his father. He wants Jun Long to go into school for law enforcement."

I broke stride next to her on the path and let go of her hand. I thought of Chong Yeow's sneering questions about my Dad and his look of contempt. He had a cop's nose and smelled something amiss with my presence in Singapore.

"Well, that's a good field," I replied. We started walking again. A barrel of concern spilled over in my mind and ran down to my heart and into the pit of my belly, turning everything inside me to acid. I thought of exactly what I had told Chong Yeow about who Dad was meeting with. Like an idiot I had mentioned the name of the damn company.

"For some reason Chong Yeow doesn't like you."

"What's not to like?"

"I don't understand why. He doesn't even know you."

"It's because he likes you." I turned toward her. "After all, here we are, you and I." She faced me. I felt a compulsion to shake off the tension of my situation and lose myself in this woman. I swelled with a yearning to escape into her gentle nature and enclose myself in her femininity and tenderness.

I wanted to touch my forehead to hers and find a mutual longing in her exotic eyes. I wanted to brush my nose and mouth against her cheek and kiss her ear and breathe in her pheromonal scent at her neckline. I could escape into her sensuality and feel her straight hair press against my face and her trim figure in my arms. In her cool, soft oriental skin texture I could find a reprieve from being hunted.

Maybe I could feel, if only for a moment, a measure of solace and reprieve from the tension of constant crisis and she could touch me with her gentle lips and fingers. She could remind me I was man, made to connect to life through the love a of woman. She could have me remember that there was more to life than pressure and pain, there was joy and fulfillment and it could be found here with this sensual, beautiful woman from the other side of the planet.

I leaned forward, kissed her lips and tasted exotic beauty. Her eyes closed for a moment. She didn't lean into me, but didn't reject my advancement. I pulled back and looked into her eyes. The polar opposite of our ancestry was stimulating. I imagined our offspring virally strong—her Chinese heritage mixing with my Irish would make for a wide gene pool of ancestral strength and health. I felt like a raider on a voyage finding a bride.

Kuan's beauty among the colorful flowers and lush vegetation framed her like a portrait of an exquisite model from a sixteenth-century artist. I leaned toward her again, closing the distance gently with hopeful expectation.

This time Kuan put both of her hands on my chest. She gently applied enough pressure to stop my advance. Her eyes looked down at the path, then around, in…shame? Her rejection brought a cascade of anxiety and despair I had hoped to evade. I suddenly perceived what I was doing as foolish. What was I thinking? Here I was in a strange land with draconian laws with my disabled Dad who was involved in some shady business behavior, and while his mental composure was coming apart at the seams, I was in the park playing patty-cake with a girl.

I felt like Jim in Empire of the Sun, abandoned behind enemy lines, not knowing the lay of the terrain, surrounded by a changing set of circumstances that offered no solace but only consternation. We walked past two giant marble lions that were beautiful, but all I could think of as I looked at them were that marble lions don't have any heart. For all their apparent strength, something made of marble might be hard but didn't really have any courage.

Dad and I had gone out to dinner with the owner of the condo, Victor Chue. He was a big man who liked us, and took us out to an expensive restaurant that offered another incredible window view of the Indian Ocean.

Victor snapped his fingers when he wanted wait staff to move faster and, in Mandarin, spoke tersely to let them know his displeasure at their service. He ran into Mr. Chang, another businessman, and introduced Dad and me. Victor emphasized proudly that we were Americans.

Mr. Chang stood beside our table and regarded both Dad and me with an intense eye before speaking.

"What a wonderful industrious nation you represent. It's no wonder many of the world's marvelous inventions and leaders have come from the United States. It is the stronghold of freedom in the world. But can the utopia of entrepreneurial design survive?" he asked me with a smile and savage bright Asian eyes.

I considered his question and, as I did, he continued. "The tyrants will attack your nation. Its beacon light could inspire slaves to think they, too, could be free. America is a threat to oppression everywhere."

"I agree with you in part, Mr. Chang. But this attack will not be outright from another country. They will invade and usurp us from within our own walls, using our own rights." Victor stopped eating and both men waited for me to continue. "Very much like a business that is built on ambition and determination, but can't really be passed on to the next generation in the family because there is no appreciation of ambition or determination. My nation will face the same challenge.

"Highly-educated knuckleheads will give away the freedom that others have given their life to achieve and defend for us." I took a bite of my chili crab. It was an incredible dish of chili added to stir-fried crab in sombal sauce, a shrimp paste-like mixture with tomato soup, as far as I could tell. Dad shot a glance at me. He didn't want me to engage in this type of conversation.

Mr. Chang nodded upward. Perhaps he hoped for a controversial topic, and I had provided it. "What university are you attending, young American man?"

"The University of the World, Mr. Chang. Instead of a classroom, you find me here." I gestured around me. "Isn't a university's method of instruction to assign reading, then issue a test on it?"

"With a lecture by a trained professor…" Mr. Chang countered.

I had not thought to ask him his profession and I wondered if he was employed in education.

"That's the part I can do without. What can I learn from a lecture from a trained Marxist who has spent his or her entire life in academia?" Chang's eyes widened a bit. A beautiful woman approached our table, put her hand on Mr. Chang's arm and whispered into his ear.

"You are very young, Jamie. I hope your position will change, as there is much to learn in a fine institution. I suspect that you have had some bad experiences in school and perhaps you have built up some resentment toward formal education." I let his admonition stand, thinking of my suspension for mooning and getting kicked off the swim team for drinking.

"Perhaps I have, Mr. Chang.

"I am so pleased to have made your acquaintance, Finucan and son. You are excellent emissaries of your country."

"The pleasure was mine. You are a truth speaker, Mr. Chang," I replied. He gave a nod and moved away swiftly across the bustling floor with what I believed to be his wife beside him. I envied him. Seeing a man with a woman by his side in a well-balanced relationship, it seemed to me that with the right partner anything could be conquered.

It took me a while to put my finger on what I was also feeling. I was astonished to get a lecture on my attitude toward education from a man I didn't know and learn something from him.

I thought of the book *The Catcher in the Rye*; I felt like Holden Caulfield—lost, rejected and inwardly in turmoil from the mixing forces of youth, life, expectation and anxiety. I wished I had taken along my copy of that book when I left Merrill.

Dad spoke with Victor, but I could tell he had crashed during the dinner.

When we got back to the condo, I paused before opening the front door. I looked for a small blue thread that I had pulled off my trousers and had closed into the bottom of the doorjamb before we had left.

It was gone.

Inside, I examined the floor carefully and swept my eyes over the white tile. The housekeeper came yesterday and was due in tomorrow. The thread was gone, so I knew someone had been in the condo and that it was not the cleaning staff.

So if the thread fell out of the doorjamb, where would it have gone? I was vexed and unsettled as I searched. I glanced up at Dad. He was watching me. He put his cigarettes and Zippo lighter, along with his wallet, down onto the table and loosened his tie, like it was a noose. The analogy surfaced in my brain, and I felt my stomach drop. "What are you looking for?"

"Just wait," I said and kept my eyes down. I would find no peace with it missing. Minutes went by with me moving slowly and rolling my vision over every inch of the floor. I used the same skills I had developed from finding and following the blood trail of a wounded deer from a bow kill. I found the inch-long piece of blue thread from one of the culturally forbidden blue jeans on the stairwell going up to my room.

The intruder had stepped on it coming into the condo and tracked it up the stairs where it had fallen off. He or she had not noticed it when he went down to leave, if in fact he had left. I went upstairs and checked my room. It appeared as I had left it. No one was there. My gut told me a listening device had been installed.

Someone had come into the condo and gone up to my room. Why? Several scenarios went through my mind. None helped alleviate my perception of doom.

"We may have to delay our leaving and keep this meeting with the Japanese," Dad spoke up. "I hate to do that but I feel like we're close. I really don't want to go back and meet the team without having this done. We don't want to meet ourselves coming back on the road in life."

He sat down on the couch, put his head in his hands and breathed deeply. I knew he was keeping his composure together by the minute. Gone was his sense of humor, his appetite, and his questions to me about how I was doing and any plans of the future.

The silence seemed to overtake the condo. The room felt airtight.

"I just don't know if I can do this," Dad whined while lighting a cigarette. "Here I am investing someone else's money, drug money, ill-gotten gain and taking tremendous risk, and for what? Hardly anything. This should be *my* money I'm investing. Money I should have been earning instead of living like a bum because I can't function.

"What a joke I am. What a failure. This is what I got? This is how it worked out? What a putz I am."

I took a few steps down the stairs, sat down opposite of him in front of the polished mahogany table and put down the small piece of thread.

"I put this in the bottom of the doorway to our condo, about three inches from the end of the bottom of the door when we left for dinner with Victor."

"Is that what you were doing?" Dad's eyes were tired and narrowed just a bit in confusion and displeasure.

"I looked for it when we came in and couldn't find it. I just found it on the fourth stair going up to the loft. So the door was opened, it fell to the ground and someone stepped on it. The thread stuck to his shoe and came off on the stairs." We both looked at this tiny thread. Dad exhaled smoke for three breaths.

"The cleaning lady comes in all the time. Obviously, it was her," Dad explained. His eyes drifted off past mine to the wall, then up to the ceiling. He put his head back against the sofa. The silence of despair hung in the air again, like the smell of death. "If your mother would have given me another chance, we could have made it work. When we were at the courthouse for the divorce, I begged her not to go through with it."

I took a deep breath of the air in the room, now contaminated by the disgusting smoke. 'Keep it clear, simple, calm,' I told myself, thinking of the Zen training.

"The cleaning lady comes in every other day. She came in yesterday. I just checked my sink where I left a gob of toothpaste. It's still there. She would have cleaned it up. She cleans the hair out of my comb for fuck sakes. I'm telling you it wasn't the cleaning lady that was in here while we were out to dinner. Someone paid us an evening visit. They probably watched us leave."

Dad's stare moved to the big, overhead ceiling fan, back to me, and then drifted past me. He drew on his cigarette as a quarter-of-an-inch of paper turned into ash. His eyes were far away. I was losing him.

"Listen, Dad, I need you to promise me you won't cancel our flight on Tuesday. You still have your ticket right, and your passport?"

"Sure, it's in my briefcase," he said softly from the dark corner of his tortured, depression-flooded mind.

"Ok, we're out of here in two days, Dad. To hell with this meeting with Nakamura Financial Corporation. Let them be waiting for us and we don't show." I stood up to show some finality to the situation.

"I didn't come all this way, put all this work into this project to go home before it's done, just because of your schizoid paranoia. You watched too many movies or something. You know, sometimes, Jamie, you slip away into another world, and I wonder if you're ever going to come back. This isn't one of your screenplays or some fantasy that you trip off to. This is reality and the stakes are high.

"These people I'm working with, they're dicey enough. These are tough guys; they're not bullshit. You just don't back out on a job. There are consequences for such actions, and they make that clear," Dad said as he jabbed his cigarette in my direction.

"Yeah, well this country is onto us. They're closing in and we need to get out while we can. I'll help you with those jerks back in the states; we're in some international shit right here and now."

"No, you stay out of this," Dad said, pulling rank.

"It's too late for that. I'm in this now. And I have a say. We leave on Tuesday, or I do. And you're in no shape to be here alone." His vision drifted off again and he stared at the wall.

"Dad, I got a feeling the authorities are going to be there in that meeting on Thursday."

"I'm tired and going to bed. Leave me alone now, Kid." I had lost him for the night.

I went upstairs, lay on the stiff mattress, and stared at the ceiling and the paddle fan that gently rotated. I breathed deeply, letting the air billow around in my lungs and then gently expelled it. I imagined it feeling like a healing, menthol vapor that moved a relaxing tonic through my body, relaxing my muscles and clearing my mind. I worked at it for hours with my gut turning. The early morning hours and first light were threatening to appear before I was able to drift off under a thin sheet and sleep for a few hours.

I dreamt of Japanese soldiers shooting Chinese people lined up by the ocean. I was standing there trying to talk to one of the Chinese victims, telling him to run for it. When the ocean came up to my feet, it turned from salty sea foam to blood. Off to my right, Kuan was crying in the background, telling me all this was my fault for some reason and I seemed to understand this to be true.

I looked past her down the bloody beach of washed-up bodies and saw Chong Yeow walking toward me with his chin down and arms swinging with each step. There was a squad of men following him wearing police uniforms. They fanned out behind him on both sides, quickly closing the distance between us.

I woke up in the morning light, yanked the sweat-soaked sheet off me and breathed hard. The sound of systematic gunfire was ringing in my ears, following me from the other world, violating the thinning boundaries established between the two dimensions.

I went out onto the patio and listened to the brilliant-colored exotic birds talk to the growing light until the air-conditioning unit kicked on and drowned out the chattering mating calls. I went in to get a second cup of coffee and saw Dad walking out of his room slowly, looking at the floor with wide eyes. I greeted him and got no response. He wasn't mad at me, just didn't have it in him to look at anyone or speak.

It had taken me a while to learn that.

After urinating in the bright, white, antiseptic water closet, he shuffled back to his room, leaning heavily on each foot fall, swathed in depression. He closed the door softly, a symbolic apology.

I let a few hours pass, then went into the kitchen and prepared a breakfast of Kaya toast. I knocked on his door and took it into his room. Dad poked at it, took a few bites but had no appetite. "It's good, Jamie, I'm…just not hungry right now."

"You're losing weight. This being-attorney stuff is trimming you down." It was the first time I had seen Dad function in the business world since I was seven and it was wasting him. He chewed a small bite slowly and looked wide-eyed down at the plate, then handed it back to me. He was lost in his broken heart and mind.

"There is a park not far from here, Dad, with a great view of the ocean, beautiful flowers planted along the pathway and a Chinese pagoda standing high up, like in the movies. I thought we could go for a walk, get some air." Rather than answering, he lit a cigarette with unsteady hands. After a few drags he put his hand over his face and sobbed. The noise seemed to squish out between his fingers in soul-tearing agony. There was no remaining dignity, no remnants of honor to be found in his pathological situation.

I stood there, shattered.

CHAPTER 22

I am willing. Be healed.
Luke 5:13

I prayed to the Lord and He answered me, freeing me from all of my fears.
Psalm 34:4

The goal of any writer is not profit but truth.
Simon Van Roy

Worldliness is a tyranny of the present over the eternal.
A note Shawn Finucan wrote in the back of his Bible.

There is no escaping this simple truth:
I failed to keep my boy alive because I failed to give love when it was most needed.
All the other failures of my life are small compared to that.
From a notebook of Patrick Finucan

October, 2019 Merrill, Wisconsin
I closed the door to my study and booted up the laptop. Up came photographs of the scene where Shawn died. I begin to click on them to gain understanding. Shawn was lying in the white snow in the blood trail, lit up by the camera's flashbulb in the subzero winter night.

He had been out there since five a.m. in the morning, so it was at least fourteen hours before anyone thought to search for him.

The 30.06 bolt-action rifle lay in the snow where he had dropped it after it fired. He had been leaning over it in the pathway of the bullet. The rifle barrel was down in the snow with the stock lying atop the white crust as though he had dropped it spinning or pushing it away after the impact of the bullet. Debris of the forest lay around, including sticks on the snow. Nearby there were leaves blown off an oak tree, a pinecone or two, things one would see in the woods. A blanket lay spread out next to his body.

The deputy had taken a picture of a trail of footprints that went to the target. I couldn't tell if he had made one or two trips to the target from his shooting blanket to check how accurate the weapon was firing and determine if it needed sight adjustment. Another photograph showed the target with three holes stitched tightly in the bull's eye. I remembered that Shawn shot Marksman in the Marine Corps. It was difficult to estimate the distance from the photo, but I guessed maybe sixty yards from the target to his shooting platform.

A heart-breaking photograph showed the bloody trail in the snow that he had made as he crawled, sixteen feet perhaps. I couldn't tell the direction from the image carved out by the flash but guessed it was toward the road. He had understood that his situation was critical and was trying to get help. It would make sense that he would try to get to the road, perhaps thinking he could make it back to the school.

The severity of the situation would have struck him. Maybe he knew that he was badly hurt, and he would not make it. What goes through a man's mind at twenty-four when he knows he is breathing his last? Perhaps it was images of his family, loved ones, people he is leaving behind, words left unsaid, opportunities missed, chances not taken.

Shawn loved winter. He found peace in the still, tranquil, cold temperatures. I know he was confident in his salvation. I had hoped in his last moments before he met Jesus that, in this location, he found peace in the winter beauty around him.

1984 Singapore

I hung around a while, not wanting to leave him alone in the dangerous terrain of his own mind. But too much exposure to his energy pulled me down, so I left the condo and headed out on my own.

I looked over at the cab stand by the condo and saw a yellow taxi with Chinese writing on it. The same cabbie who had driven me before was in the driver's seat reading a magazine. I approached his window. "Swami, can you give me a ride to Lucky Plaza?" It felt great to know a driver in Singapore and call him by name, like a local.

"Sure thing, Joe, hop in." He smiled his crooked-teeth smile at me like an old friend and I let it fill me with joy. When I got in the back, I leaned back and said "Lucky Plaza" again, because I wanted to be the guy who jumps in the cab and shouts out where he wants to go, like in the movies.

"Right away, Joe," Swami called out enthusiastically, playing his part in my screenplay. We accelerated into busy traffic and I left the gloomy world behind me. I wasn't sure why he was calling me "Joe", but if that's what he wanted to call me, I was Joe.

"Swami, a cab driver is waiting for a fare when a totally naked woman gets into his car. The cab driver turns around and stares at her. She says, 'What's the matter, haven't you ever seen a naked woman before?' Cabdriver says, 'Sure, I'm just wondering where you have my money." Swami looked at me for a moment too long in the rearview mirror, then seemed to figure out it was a joke. He laughed a braying, mulish spray of chuckle that almost made me jump.

"Hey, we Singapore cab drivers are paid for driving clients away!" Because it was a one-liner, I waited for more as he looked at me in the rearview mirror, then I got it. I gave him some laughter back. I didn't want it to sound fake but it came out like his braying. I felt my face turn red.

In the mirror, his eyes left mine and looked higher in the mirror. Instantly his face hardened. His eyes went to the road in front of him, then back to the rearview mirror, not looking at me anymore. Joke time was over. I stopped all movement and resisted the urge to turn around and look out the rear window. Swami put both hands on the wheel and straightened his back. I waited.

"Hey, what's he want? My license is up to date, I wasn't speeding…what this cop following me for?" he said more to himself than to me.

"What's back there, Swami?"

"Police…not traffic enforcement, the special intelligence cops. I can tell by the plate number and the inside track lights. They drive through the city like they own it. When the sirens are turned on you better move." In the mirror, Swami's eyelids narrowed and the skin around them turned pale. He slowed down and moved behind a car in the right lane. "He's staying with us."

I sat up straight, breathed from the pit of my stomach and let the air out slowly, imagining a rush of menthol filling my lungs on the next breath. My hands were sweating. I wanted to look at the car but to crank my head around would tip the tail that we burned him.

We arrived at Lucky Plaza, and I handed Swami his fare with a tip. "I'm going to look around here. Can you be back at four o'clock?"

"Yeah, sure, if I don't have a fare." I closed the door and he rolled away. I turned slowly but didn't see a car that stood out more than any others. The traffic flew past me in a steady stream. A light drizzle rolled in off the ocean. I walked over to the restaurant where Kwan worked and felt a spike of elation when I saw her in her uniform taking an order from a customer. Her hair was pulled back and she was nodding in agreement with a smile as she made notations on her pad of paper.

I waited until she lifted her eyes and saw me at the entrance, then I smiled and waved. She froze and her smile dropped when she saw me. She turned away and walked back to the kitchen with her order pad clutched to her chest, leaving me hanging with my arm waving in the air. My gut dropped three inches more since the cab ride. I willed myself to breathe. I turned to walk back through the plaza and mingle with the pedestrians walking through the shops and across the big open hall. I felt a sickening surge of adrenalin dump.

I walked past a shop that sold Rolex watches and jewelry and stopped to peer down into a glass case. A British guy was talking to the clerk asking if he could verify that the watches were authentic.

"I'm not paying these bloody prices for a knock-off. I want you to guarantee me that it's a real TAG Heuer. I want to know it's genuine, and I'm not getting that from you." The clerk was speaking in a low tone, nervous, assuring the Brit that it was, but this guarantee didn't come in writing, and could he please keep his voice down, as there was no need to speak so loudly.

I looked in the mirror behind the counter and saw a man in a business suit standing in the open area of the plaza. He didn't seem to be walking anywhere, so he stood out. I kept watching him, waited, and there it was—he glanced over at me. I looked back down for thirty seconds, looked up again in the mirror, and saw he was still watching me. He was five-foot-nine, a hundred-and-sixty pounds with short black hair and a tight, trim jawline.

I stepped out of the store into the shopping center. I walked past the shops of clothing, trinkets, home furnishings, and a few more food stands, then turned a corner and found a stand with a guy selling ties. I paused, took one off the rack, and held it up to my chest. I looked in the small, square mirror to capture the view behind me. I saw the man in the business clothes and short hair was walking in my direction. He saw that I was looking in a mirror and changed his direction. His suit coat printed a bulge above the right hip.

My shadow was packing a firearm.

I didn't want him to know I suspected he was tailing me, thinking that it would trigger the final outcome, so I tried to act causal as I shopped around. My breathing kept wanting to run shallow, my heart felt like it was fluttering in my chest, and a strong sensation of nausea stayed with me as the water in my belly churned.

Time crawled by. I had a moment of hope that it was all my imagination when I went into a money-changing store, came back out and didn't see the shadow. I did a double-take, then looked around slowly to make sure, but then I saw him sitting on a bench, trying to look bored, sixty yards down the open market area.

I sweated in the constant humidity and purchased more water for my dry mouth. As I drank it, I noticed a slight tremble in my hand and almost had to run to a restroom to throw it back up. At four o'clock I was not surprised to find Swami absent. It seemed that he and Kuan had deemed me a marked man. Or was it my imagination that was so often overactive? I considered hailing another cab, but since it was only a few miles to the condo on Upper Thompson Road, I chose to walk.

I stretched out my legs in stride and moved along the sidewalk while the traffic blasted past me like a continuous train. In the humid air, a light drizzle gathered weight on my damp shirt and pants and settled moisture on my face and brow. I glanced over my shoulder and saw a figure following behind me at an estimated seventy yards.

I couldn't see the face but the clothing color was correct for the guy shadowing me in the plaza. The feeling I had, got me thinking of the creepy painting by Edvard Munch called *The Scream*: an image of a person walking with a mouth-open scream of horror stretched over his face, hands raised to each side of his head with two shadowy figures walking behind him.

I felt like sprinting in the drizzle, as though I could run away from this situation on this island, and sail home like Max in *Where the Wild Things Are,* then find my dinner on the table still warm. My imagination triggered to lift me away, as it has since my earliest childhood.

The landscape around me changed to reflect 1945, as I imagined a war-torn city with roads bombed and people moving around me wearing anything from rags to silk dresses and suits. I saw rickshaws powered by skinny men moving around abandoned vehicles, like Packard's, Rolls Royce's, and a Chrysler. I stepped aside as a Jeep moved past me with Japanese soldiers on it. One noticed me and yelled something rude at me. Another soldier rode along, clinging to the running board with a rifle with a fixed bayonet slung over his shoulder. The distinctive sound of a Japanese Type 92 light machine gun rattled off in the distance. With its stuttering-like cadence and slow rate of fire, I understood why it was nicknamed the woodpecker. I wondered if it was massacring a bunch of lined-up civilians.

I heard babies crying and beggars asking for food. Car horns were beeping and a Japanese Zero was flying low over the city. Plumes of smoke extended up from bombed buildings, like black fingers on the horizon. A woman wearing an evening gown moved past me, clutching a small handbag. Her tear-streaked makeup run down her face. She made a whimpering sound as she hobbled by with the high heel of one of her shoes broken off.

I smelled diesel burning. The dust of demolition, mixed with fear and urine, descended on me as I walked through time. Knowing that my ability to stay here in this realm was limited, I returned and felt refreshed. I straightened my gait, threw my shoulders back, and extended my stride, which provided relief from the anxiety. My mental trip into the past reminded me that there was only the "here and now"—this moment to be lived. And, right now, I was free and alive. Trouble might be sixty yards behind me and gaining, but it was still behind me.

"When a woman is done with you," Dad opined, "she kicks you to the curb and wants nothing to do with you."

"We have to be ready to get on the plane tomorrow, Dad. Are you packed?"

"It's incredible how quickly it turns on, and you stand there wondering what the hell happened to the love you shared. You are already gone in her eyes when she looks at you. You're a ghost."

"Let me see the tickets. Why don't I hang on to them?" I suggested and moved over to the couch where his briefcase was.

"The love of your life looks through you, like you are dead already, or not even there." Dad was focusing past the wall somewhere. "And that is, in effect, because you are already gone and just haven't figured it out yet."

"Dad…listen to me a minute." I paused while going through the briefcase that I knew so well.

"I begged her not to do it on the courthouse steps," Dad continued. "I said, 'Judy, don't. I'll do whatever it takes.' She didn't want to hear it. She had already made up her mind. I was already… done." Dad was speaking to me or some unseen audience.

His cigarette ash was two inches long, pinched between his left index and middle fingers. The red ember seemed to be just moments from burning his hand.

I swooped up the ashtray and moved it under the spent cigarette just as the ash dropped off. He threw the butt in the ashtray without a glance. "If only she would have given me a chance. Look, I quit drinking. I've been sober for all these years now."

When I went into his room, I found half of the clothes in his grip folded tightly with creases and a few other items strewn on the floor. I started picking up things and stuffing them into his grip.

"Hey, Kid, get out of there. When it's time to go, I'll pack. I don't need you shoving me out the door. I'm thinking we need to extend our stay through Thursday and catch a flight out after the meeting with the Japanese."

"We went through this already, Dad." He was still transfixed in the past. I realized there may be a connection to the way he shifted "out" and the way I drifted "into" fantasy. I would escape to live in another life. He would go to his own torture chamber of the past in what could have been.

The realization hit me like a spit wad between the eyes. I soaked in horror. "Oh, my God," I thought.

I sat down in the chair opposite of him so he could see me.

"Someone is searching our apartment. Did you lock your briefcase when we went out to dinner with Victor the other night?"

"You think this because you found a thread on the stairs?"

"I was followed through Lucky Plaza yesterday, tailed all the way there in a cab and on the way home on foot when I decided to walk."

"Listen to me, Jamie. I'm your father and I know you well. You have this imagination and when it becomes active, you drift off. When you were a kid, I worried about you. Your mother and I talked about getting you some help…"

"I met two guys and a lady in Lucky Plaza two weeks ago. I got to talking to them about America. One of them didn't like me, the lady did, and this pissed the guy off. Anyway, his dad is a cop of some kind. So, I think he put his dad onto us. This is not my imagination. I'm not making this up. We need to be on that plane tomorrow at five-thirty a.m., so we need to get some rest tonight."

"Give me that again, about the guy's dad being a cop." Finally, Dad was in his analytical state. I went over the events again in detail.

"Did you tell these kids what we were doing?"

"I just said you were a lawyer."

"You didn't tell them who I was meeting with or what we were up to, did you?"

I imploded at the question.

"I just said you were meeting with Nakamura Financial." The room got silent like outer space.

"You didn't. Tell me you didn't."

"Yeah, I did."

"You revealed our mission to some strangers you just happened to meet at the mall, and one of them is directly related to law enforcement?" He looked at me for an answer. I could only stare back at him.

"You jeopardized this mission with your fraternizing. I come over here under false pretenses with a fictitious identity that, if we get caught, hangs us. I file paperwork with international agencies, maneuver through a land of spies and security, and you hand us over by shooting your mouth off to a bunch of kids at the mall?" He looked at me with stabbing incrimination. I had nothing to say to his summary.

My heart was doing that fluttering thing and my mouth was dry. I reached into the "jar of something to say" but my hand was caught.

"It was a mistake to bring you here." His tone sounded like a sentence issued by a judge. He went into his room and closed the door. I weighed his words in my mind, in silent agony, and found them to be true.

The crushing Singapore silence had dismantled my own mentality until I resembled Dad just a few minutes ago. His psychotic condition had transferred to me, from one man to another, like a vampire bat that crawled off the shoulder of one onto another, and then feeds.

I sat there staring at the wall for a while, then went upstairs. I set my travel alarm clock for four a.m. That would give me four hours of sleep and an hour-and-a-half to get to the airport. I sat on the edge of the bed and wondered if Dad would be coming with me tomorrow and if he did, would there be police to arrest us when we tried to board the plane? I felt a huge wave of anxiety overtake me.

I felt like there wasn't enough air in the room. I needed the hot tropical breeze out on the patio. I thought about going outside but knew I wanted to go to bed. I lay down and pulled the thin sheet over me. I had the sensation that it was a heavy blanket and that it made it hard to breathe, so I sat up fast and threw it off. I drew in the air and felt my heart race. The walls seemed to close in.

I felt I was suffocating and that if I lay down my chest would collapse. I suspected that this anxiety originated from a strong feeling of isolation at a maximum level. There was no way I would sleep now; I might as well stay up.

I remembered the meditation lesson from Zen Center, straightened my back, and breathed in slowly and deeply. I imagined I was breathing in thumbtacks and exhaling small marshmallows, pink and blue ones. I imagined my heartbeat slowing down. I drew in a breath from the pit of my stomach of cleansing cotton balls. I let them scrub the inside of my lungs and gently, slowly exhaled soapy bubbles that drifted up to the ceiling. I imagined I heard them popping and releasing a eucalyptus fragrance that filled my senses with a calming aroma that removed the tension from my body.

I laid down on the bed. When the panic wanted me to shoot back up, I resisted it gently and prayed that God would grant me a good night's sleep. I breathed and repeated the Psalm that gave me courage so often. *You are my hiding place; You protect me from trouble. You always fill my heart with songs of deliverance.*

Away from the horror of letting Dad down, away from the fear of reprisal for our actions, and away from my torturous anxiety, at last, I drifted off to sleep.

CHAPTER 23

And He began to say to them, "Today this Scripture is fulfilled in your hearing."
Luke 4:21

Truth is by its very nature intolerant and exclusive, for every truth is the denial of its opposing error.
Luthardt

Jim knew that he was awake and asleep at the same time, dreaming of the war and yet dreamed of by the war.
J.G. Ballard *Empire of the Sun*

October, 2019 Merrill, Wisconsin

I braced with a deep breath, then opened the file of autopsy pictures of my brother, Shawn Patrick Finucan. I am again struck by his slight frame, his youth, at twenty-four. He never had a chance to age past this. Maybe one hundred forty-eight pounds of lean muscle lay out on the table in the harsh light. I had always thought of him as being a giant by the way I looked up to him.

I look at the hole made in his body from the 30.06 rifle at close range. Clearly, the image of the wound in the back, by the scapula, was small and tightly constructed, but the hole in his chest was blown out. My eye told me the front was an exit wound. I have hunted and killed dozens of North American White-tailed deer in my life. I had seen what a bullet can do on big game and I translated that to what I thought it can do to a man. I fought the feelings, but tears come out of my eyes as the wound inside my heart broke open again. I clicked from one photo to the next until I can look at it no more and shut down my laptop.

After reading Jerue's report, I was furious at Dad and others for perpetrating this story that Shawn had been shot in the back, and that the bullet had exited the front. I considered that Dad had formed this theory in his mind so that he could deal with the death of his first-born son better. It was an explanation that prevented us from thinking that Shawn might have done this to himself.

After reading Jerue's report, I loathed the whole family legend of explanation, but I had taken the word of Jerue and assumed that his examination was accurate.

Now, as I considered the evidence, I wondered what Jerue could have possibly been thinking. It was clear as day. The wound to the chest was a huge blown-out mass that was as big around as my fist. The grossness of the miscalculation had me examining conspiracy theories in my mind again; the emotional turbulence had thrown me in one direction and now I swung to the other in counter-discovery.

I was sorry for having felt that silent rage toward Dad. In that moment I missed him terribly, like I had so many times, especially in trouble or facing anxiety.

I looked over the reports again, rereading witness statements, and considered anyone who was questioned in the investigation as a suspect. My stomach soured at the injustice that was done. I was feeling that this was exactly what I was concerned that I would find. When I calmed down, I tried to re-examine the potential outcomes that would have led to the bullet wound being fired into his back in a level trajectory.

I then doubted my own findings and resolved to wait a few days and reexamine the photograph evidence again with a new and calmer perspective. I thought about calling my brother Tim or my sister Deirdre to discuss my findings with them. "You go asking these questions, you're going to find answers you don't want to know," Tim had said.

His warning was to me that there would be no peace if I investigated it. There had not been yet, but I intended to seek the truth so that there would be. I would no longer run from anything in life. I would turn over every stone to determine what happened on January 31, 1985, at five-thirty a.m. I would do it for any of my siblings. I hoped they would do it for me.

1984 Singapore

The early morning motion was quiet but active for me. I was pumped up with adrenalin, feeling great after my four hours of sleep. I was glad to pack up the dopp kit, stuff my clothes in my grip, and be taking off for home.

Dad was moving slowly.

Time was running out for us to get to the airport. We had to keep on schedule. Part of my mind wondered if Dad was going to sabotage our escape from this island to fulfill a destiny of self-imposed failure. I stepped out of the air-conditioning and into the heat of the dark, early, muggy morning. I looked out where Swami might have had his cab, but he was not there.

I ran out to the highway and stood there as an eastern drizzle began. I watched the headlights of the cars blast past me. Minutes passed that we didn't have to spare. A few cabs went by, not seeing my waving arm. I looked at my watch. Time was ticking away. I stepped in front of a yellow cab and the driver slammed on his brakes. The car behind him did as well, turning sideways. The yellow cab slid, skidding, drifting sideways on the rubber tires to a halt, a foot from my leg.

The doors of the vehicles were opening with people screaming at me. I pulled a hundred-dollar bill out of my wallet, handed it through the opened window of the cab, and pointed to where I needed him to be, down, off the freeway by the condo's. Then to make sure he didn't drive off with my C-note I jumped in the back seat.

He drove us away from the pissed-off drivers. The cab driver was a short, stubby man, who just shook his head. "You didn't need to jump in the street. I saw you waving twenty minutes ago and had to drop off my fare. I was coming back."

"Right, sorry."

"Damn near got me killed," he murmured, but looked at the hundred-dollar bill and slipped it into his pocket with a smirk. My American money was worth six dollars to one of theirs.

Dad was leaning with his head on the door of the condo when we pulled into the parking spot. I loaded our bags into the trunk and checked my watch like it was a scoreboard. We were now behind schedule. If there was a line at security, we were going to miss the plane. I opened the door to the cab and waited for Dad to move. If I wasn't careful, I could push too hard and mentally tip him over.

With a weariness in his voice, Dad softly said, "Just like everything, it's been a failure. Like me, like everything I touch. It turns to ashes."

Gently now, I said, "God gives beauty for ashes. Come on…get in, Dad. Our work here is done. Our plane leaves in forty minutes, and we have to go through customs and security. If we miss this flight, I've got a feeling we are going to be in trouble." He looked around, then at me, and got into the car.

On the highway, the traffic to the airport was thick. I wondered if these people ever took a day off from work. Did any of them sleep? I recalled on the trains and busses that they appeared beaten by fatigue. The commuters, in droves, were on their way to work at six-fifteen. I admired them—their work ethic of the island state. But now I loathed them and wanted them all to get out of the way.

The windshield wipers squeaked on the glass and the engine droned as the cab cut through the early morning darkness. I thought Dad might have fallen asleep, but he was resting his head back on the seat, staring at the ceiling of the car. The intermittent windshield wiper moved every four seconds.

When we finally got to the airport, I looked at the runway and watched a jet take off into the early-morning, tropical light. I hoped it wasn't our plane.

The taillights gradually lifted and banked right over the ocean to another part of the world. My imagination flickered, skidded, then jumped. I saw the plane flying over the bones of the civilians buried beneath the runway from the massacre of Operation Sook Ching. I pictured the event: the Japanese soldiers in their distinctive uniforms shooting or bayoneting hundreds of men, women, and children, and then making the conquered British soldiers bury them in the ground, barking orders at them while families screamed in the background, the area turning into Hell.

The disturbing historic visualization assaulted me in a chaotic murder play that unfolded as the ghost who wanted to be remembered called out to me.

A rickshaw passed me as I got the bags out of the trunk, and I breathed deeply to pull myself back to reality. We skirted through security, reaching the jetway just as the last of the passengers were loading. We fell right into step without a moment to spare.

We took our seats on the Boeing 747, the biggest jet available, with four isles of spacious seats stretched across the cabin. A gorgeous Singapore Airlines stewardess smiled and walked around shutting overhead bins and making the final preflight preparations. I prayed the police wouldn't come onboard to arrest us before we could get off the ground, like in some World War II movie.

As the angular cabin door was at last shut and sealed, I thanked God for His mercy.

The plane was half-full. Dad had the window seat. The work he had been doing had taken its toll on him. He was trembling and silently crying in an emotional and mental breakdown as the plane took off. He sniffed hard, wiped his eyes, and kept his face turned to the window. A concerned flight attendant asked if we wanted coffee; I said we did. After it arrived and sat on the tray in front of us, I was already wishing I was sitting anywhere other than next to Dad. He shifted in his seat, bumped the tray, and spilled the hot coffee onto the crotch of his pants.

He yelped in pain and lifted off the seat. Steam came up in front of him. I leaned away and asked him something like, "Are you alright?" He groaned in agony. I jumped up to let him out so he could make his way to the restroom. I stood up and waited. When he returned he sat down without looking at me. He was imploding into a helpless puddle of emotional quicksand and defeat.

I know of, and have experienced, three types of pain: physical, mental, and emotional. The last two seem to be closely related and I am uncertain as to which is worse. Dad appeared to be at the maximum threshold of what he could handle.

I knew there was nothing I could do for him at this point, so I got up and moved away down the aisle. There were plenty of open seats on the plane. I found one in the back, with my own window seat, and settled in. I felt drained in every way. I looked out the window at the Indian Ocean, knowing there would be nothing but blue waves and water beneath us until we flew over Sri Lanka. Then we would fly over Africa, the Atlantic Ocean and then over the entire United States before we would land in Los Angeles.

The flight would take eighteen hours of confinement at twelve-thousand feet in this metal tube with ridiculous wings affixed with jets. I prayed thanks to God for delivering me safely, and then asked Him to heal my dad and relieve him of his horrible internal agony.

At last, we were safe, heading home. I closed my eyes and thought of Jamie, as I would so often in life when I needed to lower my blood pressure and think of the only sweet thing in my life.

We landed in Los Angeles, exhausted and stiff from sitting so long. We staggered through baggage claim and dragged on to a car rental kiosk. We booked a white Pontiac 6000 STE four-door sedan with a 2.5-liter engine. The instrument panel looked cool, like a plane. The gear stick between the fabric seats had a thumb button release on the top at the side.

We drove up to San Francisco where we had stored our armaments in the safe deposit box. The Bank of America was closed, so we got a hotel room close to Fisherman's Warf. We were exhausted from the eighteen-hour flight. Hungry, we ordered a pizza and ate it on the circular writing table that looked out on the lights of the harbor. The fog had lifted off the ground in the cool fall air and I could see Alcatraz lit up like a castle surrounded by a moat.

I thought of the men who had escaped swimming across the current in the shark-infested waters through the night and marveled at what people will do for their freedom. My freedom was on my mind; I was gaining some clarity about my own future for the first time.

We had just finished, leaving two slices of hand-tossed pepperoni and sausage on the cardboard, when I decided this was the time to break the news to Dad that I was going back home. It had been on my mind in Singapore and especially the last few days. Thoughts of taking charge of my own life had been haunting me.

My friends in the Marine Corps were long out of boot camp and in various fields of service. Purcell was on an aircraft carrier in Aircraft Recovery, Erik Lange was learning skills to be an electronic technician, and Kyle Kolka was learning to be a cook. I was studying a criminal trade and living on the edge of existence with no perceived future to offer anyone.

I was Dad's friend and travel companion. We had grown co-dependent on each other. I thought of Dad's argument for not completing high school a year earlier: "Do you think anyone is going to doubt if you graduated high school?" It might have sounded plausible in the winter flophouse with a blizzard outside, but sitting twelve years in school and not to finish, would mean that it had beat me, and I couldn't let that stand. Besides, Dad had three college degrees. Such flippant comments were easy for him to say.

I was lost, for sure, but I knew which direction was home. My mom and stepdad were there with a house of love, stability, and support. They both worked hard and were rooted in reasonable thought. I hoped it wasn't too late to stake a claim to a regular life. I watched Dad push back from the table and light up a Marlboro 100 with his Zippo that read "*The Mexican Disaster—Lest we Forget.*"

"I'm going back home, Dad. I've had enough of the road life." He blinked a few times as the data sank in, then he looked up at me tenderly. His eyes moved over my face with understanding. Perhaps he was seeing all of this from my perspective.

"You are?" His soft words were like thin wafers that could break on his teeth when they came out.

"I want to go back and see if I can finish school. I've had a great time, and I love you. But this is no life for me. I don't think it's a life for either of us. Staying ahead of the odds is something that anyone can do only for a while. The consequence of failure in this game you are playing is loss of liberty, something vital to me. The game is too expensive to play."

"It sounds like you've thought about this."

"I have, for a while now. I have some things I have to finish, my education for one thing." There was a silence as his mind struggled to understand it all.

"You're going back to Judy and Bob, and leaving me. This tells me where your loyalties are," Dad said with his blame thrower tone.

"What do you mean?"

"You know what I mean, Kid. You've sided with them. You're on their side."

"I've always been on your side. It's always been you and I."

"Yeah, well here you are running back to them. If you choose not to decide, you still make a choice."

"Don't pull me into the middle of what you've created. Keep me out of your fight."

In nervous frustration, he started flipping the Zippo open and closed. "This is family. You're in it whether you like it or not."

"No, Dad, this is your mess. I didn't create this. You did. Don't ask me to take sides in your divorce. You are responsible for your relationships. Demanding that I take sides is unfair."

"You're speaking disrespectfully to your father," he said flatly.

"I don't mean to, but we're talking man-to-man here."

"No, we're talking son-to-father now. And that is something I'll ask you to remember, Kid." We both fell silent and let the tension in the room hover in the air like Dad's cigarette smoke. A while passed, but eventually we made gentle, tender small talk to move forward.

The rest of the night we each lay in our beds, separated by the nightstand with the phone on it, and watched a Burt Lancaster western entitled *The Law Man.* Burt Lancaster was a sheriff coming into a town called Sabbath to bring in some hooligans who had killed someone in a western town and then rode off. They thought they had gotten away with it. The bad guys worked for a rich guy who tried to buy off the problem, but the sheriff was a professional and ends up dishing out justice with his Colt .45. We enjoyed the movie. While Dad was friendly, I knew he was struggling to appear all right.

I appreciated his effort. It bonded our friendship closer, knowing that he not only understood but that he could contain his depression for a last, ceremonial night together like old friends. He drank a cup of instant coffee made with cold sink water and smoked cigarettes until I heard his distinctive snore cut through the room.

I got out of bed, took a smoldering cigarette filter from between his fingers and tossed it into the filled ashtray.

I stood at the window looking at the city lights of Frisco Bay at night. Cars passed by on roads, a boat moved out to sea, people walked down by the Warf, and someone was walking a dog on a leash. I reflected on the travels with Dad and knew I was not the same man of eighteen that I was when I left Merrill eleven months ago.

The city was like an living organ grinder with its moving parts working in unison to create this vibrant effect of a performing circus. It was a continuous show orchestrated by God for some reason and I was just a small spec in it, but I had a purpose to fulfill.

Again, the feeling of being lost settled in me even deeper. The infinite loneliness that perhaps I shared with Dad stirred inside me. I leaned on the window and felt heart-crushing sorrow rise from some dark well within me.

The television started another Western, *Ride the High Country*, a movie directed by the legendary Sam Peckinpah. The music and opening shot cemented in my mind the memory of that moment in San Francisco. Decades later, I would relive it again when the movie started in my home as I lay on the couch. Defining moments reached out to me through memories triggered by music, smell, or an atmospheric change. Life's lessons sometimes kicked in to be recalled with a final effort, like a wounded deer in the bloody leaves of the forest floor.

In such moments, I have learned to feel compassion for myself.

The next morning Dad and I were at the Bank of America and allowed back into the safety deposit room. We set the box on the little table and opened it up.

I picked up The Snake, snapped the cylinder open, and gave it a spin, making sure it was empty. Dad picked up his semi-automatic and racked back the action to look into the breach. He stuffed it in his waistband and pulled his Sperry Top-Sider sweatshirt over it. I put The Snake in my check-through bag, along with the three knives, and covered them with some socks and a T-shirt that needed washing. Then I zipped it up.

I took the wheel of the Pontiac and rolled us down Pacific Coast Highway 101. He preferred to drive, but I was leaving, and Dad was giving me leeway today. The day was sunny, warm, and windy. We cruised down through picturesque seaside towns, like Morrow Bay and Santa Maria, in a quiet, desperate sadness.

As we drove through Carmel-by-the-Sea, I looked off to the cliffs at the Pacific Ocean and admired the European-style housing. "Clint Eastwood lives here," Dad volunteered, looking out his passenger window.

"Yeah?" I looked around and slowed down. I hoped to see him crossing a street. "Seems like you're driving kinda fast through this town. I hate to think you cheddar-heads from Wisconsin are looking for trouble," I said in my best Clint Eastwood voice, complete with squint. Dad wasn't looking.

"They don't have any addresses on the houses, no sidewalks, no streetlights, and parking meters aren't allowed here," Dad continued.

"Well, that's right kind of 'em," I kept up. He hadn't acknowledged my imitation. I was going to keep it up until he did.

Dad was looking around for any women in high-heeled shoes. "Women here have to get a permit to wear high heels."

"Well that's a damn shame."

Dad gave me the laugh I was looking for, if only to have me knock it off.

I went back to being amazed at the beauty of the white-capped waves breaking on the rocks along the shoreline. The blue of the ocean was richer and darker than a watercolor painting, set off in the summer sun. The small streets of the communities had a dreamscape-like appearance next to the rocky drop-off. A single country store on the corner offered provisions for the cute stucco homes.

These towns seemed like a world protected from time—cut off from people who didn't belong in this living painting.

We stopped to eat at a little diner where the cute waitress with a tennis player's legs and a generous bottom flirted with me. It made my day. Her nametag said "Ann." When she smiled there were dimples that set her face off into a bright expression of happiness coming from her inner core. I imagined being married to her, living here as a writer of graphic novels. Somehow, we would scratch by, making a living on my royalty checks from the publisher and her tips from waiting tables.

Our house was modest, small, and had an ocean view. We were thinking of something bigger when the baby came along. I was sure we could handle anything that came our way, as long as I had her with me. My little Annie and those legs. Damn. That was all a guy needed.

She would come home and find me in my study, start massaging my shoulders and asking me how my day was. She would recount how she had stopped at the general store, picked up a steak for dinner, and suggest we walk on the beach afterward. I was feeling her oily, soft hands working into my muscles and smelling her cinnamon-like perfume when the bill hit the table, and Dad and I had to move on.

I watched her make the change from my twenty-dollar bill and thought that I could live here. I could marry her, I decided, and smiled at her. I left the diner broken-hearted and confounded at how the relationship had ended before it even began. The pain seemed as real as though the moments had all happened over years. How could I leave that life behind?

I had scooped up the car key off the table so I would be in the driver's seat of the Pontiac. Dad was funny on the drive. We cracked up in desperate, loving hilarity. This was how we showed our strength at the undercurrent of heartbreak in our pending separation. This was the result, I would learn later, of God's grace, issued in daily rations. This was why joy was so often found on the shoreline of sorrow.

Sliding into L.A. on the 405 freeway, we were hitting the city just before the traffic would start, so I mashed down the throttle. I had been to this airport before. When we hit Sepulveda Boulevard, I glanced over my shoulder at the blind spot, changed lanes fast, and hit the gas enough to stay tight to the bumper of the car in front of me. The Pontiac with the six cylinders didn't do too badly. I stayed with the traffic that clipped along at eighty-six miles per hour with Tina Turner on the radio singing "You Better Be Good to Me."

A Bonneville in the fast lane passed me on the left. I snapped the wheel left and fit the sedan into an open slot behind the Bonneville, then punched down the accelerator to move up in the chain of passing cars and blasted past the pickup truck to my right. The graph-style speedometer moved up to ninety-four miles per hour. The front end didn't shake, and the car held the road.

When the fast lane slowed for no reason, I quickly checked the mirrors, then the blind spot over my right shoulder and snapped the steering wheel right. I moved the Pontiac into an opening with six inches to spare in front and back, passing a Mercedes with an old woman tipping her head back to see over her dashboard. I fit the sedan into tight spots of traffic at high rates of speed, like Steve McQueen driving his Mustang in the movie *Bullet.*

I avoided getting boxed in by continuous positioning, just rolling with the opportunities to advance along the highway as they were presented. Driving was maneuvering, positioning, advancing, and attacking options—a metaphor for life.

Dad wanted to object but didn't. Instead, he clutched at the dashboard and the side of his vinyl passenger seat. He grimaced as though expecting impact at any moment. I loved the old man for rolling with the flow.

When Randy Newman came on the radio singing *I Love L.A.,* I wanted to sing along, but at ninety-eight miles an hour in bumper-to-bumper traffic flow, I decided against dividing my attention.

I was ready for change. I had a destination of my own for the first time in a long time. I was going home to find the threads I had dropped, and hoping it wasn't too late to pick them up and twist them together.

At the airport, I found my way to the American Airlines desk and purchased a ticket for Mosinee, Central Wisconsin Airport. I checked the bag through, hoping that if anyone opened it they would be dissuaded by the dirty underwear and socks enough to not find The Snake.

In our final time together, Dad and I had a cup of coffee. We made short-sentenced, parting conversations of carefully chosen words and bland nuances of goodbye. Our feelings were tender, like a muffler burn on a leg.

His eyes were searching around as the boarding call came. He had grown dependent upon me in his illness. In a few moments, he would face life alone again, and it would happen fast. The agony of his isolation would fix in his mind, and he would be fighting the emotional quicksand without a sidekick. I could feel his anxiety about having to face this oncoming attack alone.

I was sorry for this, but another side of me was angry for having been put in this position. Was not my life my own? How much could I be responsible for him? Wasn't he the father in this situation and I the son?

"What are you going to do when you get home?"

"I'm going to see about finishing high school, getting my diploma if I can."

"That's a great idea." He had finally accepted the value of a high school degree.

As people walked around us, the blood moved thick, like mud, through my chest. We embraced, not knowing that the next time I would see him, in just a few months, I would be picking him up at Central Wisconsin Airport. He would step off the jetway and we would embrace in the agonizing grief of Shawn's death.

The final boarding call came over the speaker.

I turned and escaped down the blue-carpeted jetway as though I was entering a portal to another dimension. I was a different person now because I was alone. I was a different young man than a year ago.

I found my seat and surrendered to being confined for the long flight. I located a pair of headphones and plugged them into a little radio slot in the armrest. I listened to music as I took off from LAX as the jet banked around, heading off to the Midwest. I listened to programmed hits of that year with bits of information on songs like U2's *Pride In The Name Of Love,* Chaka Kahn singing *I Feel For You,* and *I Can Dream About You* by Dan Hartman. I felt both relief and grief mixed at the departure. Once again, at high altitude, I looked down on God's creation, getting that perspective on the world that only this height can give.

Whatever I was flying home to, I was ready to unwrap it. I was looking forward to seeing my mom and my stepfather, Bob. A year had passed since I had been home. I was hoping to see Jamie, my girlfriend, who had occupied my heart no matter where I was in this world.

I was older, worldlier, but still so lost and in pain. If I could just shake off those feelings, maybe I could start writing. I didn't know it then, but that was the platform from which all my creativity came.

CHAPTER 24

For this cause I was born, and for this cause I have come into the world, that I should bear witness to the truth. Everyone who is of the truth hears My voice.

John 18:37

No legacy is so rich as honesty.

William Shakespeare

MARINETTE SHERIFF DEPARTMENT
SUPPLEMENTARY INVESTIGATION REPORT Case # 85-393
Conclusion: The muzzle of the weapon was in contact with the victim when the weapon was fired.

Deputy Jerue's report Marinette County Sheriff's Office.

2019, November Merrill, Wisconsin

The exit and entrance wound inconsistencies had me living in frustration for weeks. I called friends who may have any information in forensics and got vague answers about the significance of a large exit wound and a small entrance wound and how they could be confused.

The death of my brother was never far from my mind. My research only seemed to leave more questions. I wanted Mom to find solace and peace in her understanding of what had happened to Shawn.

I had a breakthrough at the gym while working out at the end of a workday. A friend of mine, Tony Schuett, was lifting big, steel-plate, free weights. He works as a sheriff's deputy for Taylor County. Tony is a former Marine (it's just "Marine," he says), who has completed three tours of duty from 2002-2006 in Iraq. As a squad leader for 3rd Battalion 5th Marines 1st Marine Division, Weapons Company, he was a machine gunner and had overseen over twenty Marines. He was involved in the invasion of Fallujah in 2004, as well as other vital maneuvers.

Tony has earned a Purple Heart for wounds received in action, and was decorated for courage in action, saving the lives of the men in his charge. As a combat veteran and a hunter, he knows a great deal about weapons and firepower.

I interrupted his squat routine and he listened to my story about my investigation into my brother's death. "The wound channel was directly through the chest. The investigation is indicating that the bullet entered the chest and exited the back, but the wound to the chest is huge, as the size of my fist, and the wound to the back is small. That doesn't make sense," I stated..

"What side of the chest was the wound on, the right or left?" he probed.

"It was on the left side."

"So he was right-handed?" Tony leaned over, placed an imaginary weapon to his chest, and demonstrated how the right hand would reach down and trigger the rifle.

"Yes…" I flinched.

"And you are saying the wound that they are calling the entrance wound is huge, right?"

"Right."

"It was a 30.06 rifle?"

"Yes."

"Well, that's a lot of velocity coming out of that barrel, Jim. That could be the blast hole. Take a 30.06 and place it tight against a watermelon and see what the hole looks like. It's…velocity. It shreds, it blows open and apart, does things to the human body."

The realization that a blast hole would be created on the body by a weapon of that caliber at such close range was an epiphany to me.

The next day I asked my daughter Leah if I could have the pumpkin on her porch. "You're not going to use it to bait in deer for hunting, are you?" asked the staunch animal lover.

"No, it's illegal to bait in this county. I would like to conduct a shooting experiment on it."

"Yeah, I guess it would be okay then." My son Kyle and I went out to the range with a 30.06 rifle that my Uncle Mike had given me. I put a glove over the pumpkin to simulate the thick, fur jacket Shawn had on. I put on my eye and ear protection and pressed the barrel against the leather glove on the pumpkin. I made sure of the target and beyond, then pulled the trigger. The blast hole was an enormous crater in the pumpkin and did resemble the damage in the picture from the autopsy.

I felt like I was back where I had been, thinking the bullet had gone into the chest. Shawn had gone out there, fired three rounds downrange into his target that he made, and then walked down to look at the holes in the target. He had walked back, picked up the rifle and something had happened that caused the barrel to be against his chest when the gun fired.

That was what I now knew.

January 3, 1985 Merrill, Wisconsin

I stood outside the high school and felt the winter wind move down the street, through my jacket, and wick away my body heat, like rubbing alcohol on metal. The sky was opaque now and the continuous Midwest cloud cover of winter made direct sunlight a rarity in this climate. I looked at the building that I had swaggered out of a year ago, almost to the date, and tasted the humble pie I was about to eat.

My appointment with the principal, Mr. Tibaldo, was in fifteen minutes. But I didn't want to go in early and sit around in the antechamber waiting. I was going to walk into Merrill High School as a guy who was supposed to have graduated last year. All the underclassmen would recognize me and wonder what I was doing there.

Eating crow, that's what I was doing there. The second semester would start next week. If I played this right, I could get into school and graduate with a diploma, a year late. But I could cover up the "dropout" thing.

The administration wouldn't have to let me do it. And really, why should they? I had been a screw-off for the years I was in this school. I had been kicked off the swim team for drinking. I was a marginal wrestler and a mediocre mile runner on the track team and had not made varsity on the cross-country team either. I had dropped out and written a "fuck you" letter to the principal from a fireside campsite in California, thinking I was funny. I had acted like an asshole. I thought I was bigger than this town, this school, and that I was never coming back here.

Yet here I was.

I saw myself walking into classes with the class of 1985 and feeling their stares. It was going to be hard to be cool. I was going to have to play the role of the flunky. I thought of sitting in classrooms with students I didn't really know, eating lunch alone and grinding out days while my friends were off on their adult lives of accepted responsibilities. My stomach churned. I thought I had left them all behind, but what happened was that they had finished this race and left me behind. And, I was standing outside, knowing I would be lucky to be allowed back in this school to endure this humiliation.

I had asked my Aunt Mary Talbot to see if the administration would let me in. She had told me, "Mr. Tibaldo wants to talk with you."

"What does that mean, Aunt Mary?"

"I think you should apologize for that nasty letter and see. You know that he was having a medical procedure and that line you wrote about him shitting his pants was particularly offensive," she scolded.

"Oh, cheeze." I ran a hand through my hair.

"Still, I think he knows you to be a charmer and wants to see that for himself. He's an administrator who wants to see you graduate. Anyway, everyone in the family knows Pat put you up to that." She flashed me her delightful smile that reminded me of Dad's.

The subzero wind knifed through my jacket and gloves making my fingertips ache before they would go numb. Four minutes before my appointment, I crossed the street and made for the door, remembering how I had sashayed out of the same door dancing to *In The Evening* by Led Zeppelin a year ago. I could have punched that kid in that memory.

At that very moment, I finally realized what the expression "Don't meet yourself coming back on the road in life" meant, because that was what I was doing right now.

At least the school was warm. I went through the dusty, scholastic-smelling halls and up the speckled hard staircase. My footfalls echoed of yesteryear.

The school secretary gave me the nod to go in, so I opened the door to Mr. Tibaldo's office and stepped inside. He was writing down something, so I went to one of the two chairs and sat down before he looked up from what he was doing. He was a portly man with a balding head and bifocals. He always wore a dark suit with a tie. "Hello, Mr. Finucan," he said respectfully without even a hint of irony.

"Hello, Mr. Tibaldo."

"It's good to see you here. What can I do for you?" He twisted off his wire-framed glasses and regarded me as though he didn't know what I was doing there. Fair enough, let's start at the beginning.

"I appreciate that you're taking the time to see me today. I'll get right to the point. Last year I dropped out of my senior year in the second semester to do some traveling with my Dad. I thought I knew quite a bit back then. My conduct has not always been a stellar example to others, but I've learned a great deal in the year that I have been away. I've learned that education is very important to the development of my future. If I am to be able to move forward in lots of areas in my life, I will need to complete my high school education, receive my diploma, and go on in life."

A character from one of my detective stories, Gross Joe, walked into the room in the world of my imagination and sat in the chair next to me. He shook his head and looked at me like I was a sellout. I wanted to give Gross Joe the finger, but Mr. Tibaldo would be confused by this behavior.

"I was hoping I would be able to re-enter school this second semester and complete the educational requirements to graduate this spring, in 1985, with a diploma. This would be a better credential than a GED."

I rested a moment. I guess I was hoping he would just agree that this was a good idea, and we could be done with it, but a part of me knew better. Gross Joe leered at me from my right side, and I ignored him. Then Gross Joe put both of his feet up on Mr. Tibaldo's desk and farted in his own rumpled up suit. I thought I could smell the foul, pungent odor of digested Chicago-style hot dogs with a side of beans.

"I see," Mr. Tibaldo said, looking down at some paperwork on his desk, then out the window at the winter light.

"What are we going to do about this curse…you put on me, Mr. Finucan? Was it one of California's more renowned practitioners of the black arts?" He looked at me and waited.

Gross Joe said, "There it is! I can't even watch this. You're on your own, Kid." And thankfully he left the room, slamming the heavy wooden door behind him.

"Yes, there is the issue of the letter that I wrote you that was quite insulting. I have no excuse. My actions were thoughtless, cruel, and self-centered. I was trying to be funny in a childish, underdeveloped way and I wasn't. I didn't really mean anything that I wrote, and I would like to say to you that I'm sorry. I meant you no harm and I hope you can forgive me."

There, I had it out there. I had prepared it the night before and memorized it. It was not one of my prouder moments, but it was over with and now it was his. Regardless of how it might be received, I had at least tried to make amends.

Mr. Tibaldo looked at me for a moment, then looked around. He jostled his head back and forth in consideration. The cold wind seemed to knock on the glass. When he turned back to me, he said, "I accept your apology, Jamie, because I think you mean it." After I thanked him, a moment of silence passed between us. I reveled in it. We were two men, acting like adults.

"You can see the admissions counselor, who will work out your schedule to complete your credits. In doing this, you can take the easy way and load up with the bare-bones requirements, or you can challenge yourself. I think, if I know you, you will consider the latter." He stood up and we shook hands.

I recall thinking that I wished he had been a bigger jerk about it. The fact that he had accepted my apology so well, magnified the sensation that the letter I wrote was underhanded and out of line. Regardless, I left his office feeling like I had reclaimed something of my past.

I walked out of the school grateful. I had shaken off a burden of pride and acquired the promise of a new life. I had left this town thinking there was something wrong with it, but what was wrong was in me. I had been around the world, but now I was home, where I grew up. It wasn't a small, shitty town, the people weren't mean here, and no one was out to get me. The problems I carried around here were within me; I had projected them out and created the turbulence I had experienced. Maybe Damon was right—the world is a giant mirror, reflecting back on me what I put out.

I keyed the ignition of my 1974 AMC Hornet and it started right up. A cold ray of winter daylight broke through the clouds. I felt it touch me with the idea that, even in the dead of winter, some things could grow.

Mr. Tibaldo was right—I wanted a challenge, so I took advanced courses in biology, political science, and college prep courses in English. Having moved around the world in disjointed escapades of frenetic action, I wanted now to embrace a world of structure. I wanted to learn how to study and find out what this brain could do.

I took a computer class taught by Mr. Miller, the cross-country coach. I had run on the cross-country team in the fall and enjoyed racing and getting in shape for wrestling.

Mr. Miller drove a red 1978 Corvette Stingray. He had a big, thick mustache and had been told he looked like Magnum P.I., a character in a television series that was played by Tom Selleck at that time. The series, filmed in Hawaii, featured Magnum P.I. driving around the big island in a Ferrari while solving crimes. Mr. Miller tooled around Merrill in his Corvette, like Tom Selleck had nothing on him. He walked around with the kind of swagger that came from knowing that you look like a current television star and that it was about time people recognized your potential.

He would send us out on training jogs out to Highway Q, a good ten-mile tread of distance running, and drive by us in his Corvette for inspiration. His computer class was the easiest class I had, and I mean a gym teacher could instruct it.

For the first time in my student career, I came home from school with a backpack full of books and homework. I spent the evening reading chapters and completing assignments. During the school day, I showed up to class on time and took copious notes with pens that regularly ran out of ink. I filled spiral notebooks with my hand-scrawled notes from the lectures. I even managed to quit writing fiction during class periods.

As it turned out, if I paid attention, some of the stuff they were teaching was interesting.

I found out I was smart! I could memorize material before a test and then score a high mark on it if I wasn't buzzed up. I could listen and retain information because I wasn't thinking how much I didn't want to be there and steeping in resentment toward the world. I gained a sense of pleasure in being…normal.

And Jamie had come back to town, so that was a big plus. I didn't have any classes with her, but often ran into her in the halls and she made any day brighter.

At lunch hour in the cafeteria, I tried to get a seat by the window to feel the limited sunlight on my face and arms while I gobbled down my tray of food. Then I went into the library and studied where the smart, pretty girls did. I kept to myself, stayed out of trouble, and got the job done.

I was just thinking that I was pulling this off and this could work. I was maneuvering in a new way in life and the road of possibilities before me was endless.

Three weeks into the school year, I went home and went to bed like any other night. I fell into a very deep sleep. I would wake up to a different life from then on. That deep sleep was as though God was preparing me for a change in my life.

My mom shook me awake at four-thirty a.m., crying hysterically. She clutched my shoulders with tears of horror streaming down her face. Her voice barely held back a scream as she spoke. I tried to grasp what was happening as she told me that Shawn was dead.

The words were clear enough, but they didn't make sense. She was speaking English but I couldn't comprehend what she was saying. I had just seen Shawn a month ago at Christmas, here in this house. We had had a great time: laughs, presents, a big dinner with Tim and Deirdre and Judy and Bob. I thought she must be wrong.

She explained that a policeman and a pastor from a church had just been here at the front door with a death notification. She told me what happened, that Shawn had been outside target shooting and, when he didn't come back, some people from Northland Baptist College went out to look for him and had found him dead.

The information kept getting more absurd. I knew that this was a big deal, but I was thinking I would straighten this out—that this mistake would be corrected. I wasn't accepting it as data yet.

I listened in on the phone calls Mom had to make while Bob stood nearby in support. Tim was in college in Eau Claire. Someone had to go get him to the phone. "Jesus Christ," he said in painful exasperation.

Fortunately, we happened to know where to reach Dad. He had called a few weeks back and said he was visiting someone at a house in San Bernardino, California. When Dad heard the report of Shawn's death, he said he would take the next flight back. The hours and days passed in a daze of grief that couldn't be fully realized. The course of our lives had all been changed, but we didn't understand the degree of magnitude. The mind doesn't take it all in right away; it's one of the defense mechanisms.

I remember people arriving: Uncle Mark, Uncle Mike, Aunt Kitsie and Aunt Jane, all landed from flights from Ohio. They swarmed into our house like worker bees and helped quietly with great gentleness.

People showed up at the door with flowers, casseroles, baked brownies, spaghetti dinners with garlic bread, baskets of fruit, and trays of cheese and crackers covered with cellophane. They left pineapple upside-down cakes, cupcakes, and fruit salads with whip cream in them, fruitcakes, green bean salads, and Mexican enchiladas. There were homemade cookies: peanut butter with chocolate chips, oatmeal, and molasses that never lasted long.

All this food kept arriving replace the hole that had been created in our lives. All of it disappeared in the days before the funeral. It didn't seem to matter how much food showed up. The house was full of people, mourning and hungry.

We grieved, stared at the wall and at each other in stunned loss, and touched on feelings that had yet to be fully realized. I replayed memories, hating the fact that I knew they would fade in my mind. I went to sleep, dreamed of conversations with Shawn, woke up, brushed my teeth, and showered. I hated that life was just going on instead of stopping to acknowledge this tragedy.

I kept looking at the door for Shawn to arrive for the family party that I knew he wouldn't want to miss.

In retrospect, his spiritual awakening, and having been born again, offering a new sense of clarity. The "Hand of God" had prepared him for this.

The funeral was brutal. Life rolled us into it, like a kayak toward white water. We selected our clothes as though it were a joyless wedding. I remember Mom ironing Shawn's burial suit, weeping from the pit of her soul in heartbreaking sobs. "Like…he is going back to Greece," she said. As I put my arm around her, she collapsed into me. The hot iron touched my forearm, searing it until I took it from her. I set it on the flimsy, foldout board. It hissed an expression of relief.

In early February, the days are short in northern Wisconsin. The weakened, smeared-out sunlight barely glistens off the frozen snow. With the temperature at thirty degrees below zero and the sun setting on the western horizon at four-forty p.m., the smothering darkness descended on us with God's grace.

At the wake, we stood in line in the funeral parlor, shattered and at our worst, yet having to shake hands and meet everyone that had ever known Shawn. They carried loving wishes of condolences and tore open my heart in a way that was necessary for the grieving process.

It went on for six hours until my endurance wavered, and my feet hurt in the skinny, flat, dress shoes. At the end of it, I looked for a place to sit down and rest. Shawn's open casket showed his waxen face, appearing to look up in peace, but this party, held in his honor, was one he would not attend.

I was in a surreal trance during the funeral service. Then we caravanned to the cemetery through opaque light under the grey, overcast sky. A backhoe had ripped open a hole between some tombstones in the subzero Earth. Shawn was a Marine, so there was an honor guard by the blessed VFW, but Mom insisted they not fire the salute with the 30.06 rifles that looked to be M1 Garand's. A kid from the high school band shivered off to the side of it all, waiting to play "Taps" on his trumpet.

"Taps" had never sounded so beautiful and moving to me as when it did that morning. The forlorn notes rolled through the frosty, brittle air and bounced off the tombstones, reverberating like the sound of icy tuning forks. I cry now, always, when I hear that song.

The priest said a prayer. As the casket was lowered into the grave, Dad fell apart. I looked around to see the stunned misery of my family, as well as the loving, supportive faces of my friends. The cold wind turned my fingers numb. No matter what clothing we were wearing, the wind cut through it. We got into the cars, but Dad stayed at the graveside. He dropped to his knees like he might fall in, looking down into the earth, weeping in gasps from the pit of his being. We waited. He stayed, racked in sobs.

I had no knowledge of what to do.

"Go get your dad," Mom whispered to me. When I got out and closed the car door, the latch froze, and it bounced back open. Under the gray sky, I crouched down next to him on the dirty, crusty snow. The sobbing had stolen his breath like he had been punched in the gut. He trembled and shivered. The air in his lungs was emptying in a long outward sob and I waited for him to breathe in. If he passed out, I would catch him before he fell into the grave.

"Come on, Dad, we have to go now." I prayed that God would strengthen him and us all. Dad said something I didn't understand, but when I lifted him by the shoulders, he struggled to stand. He let me lead him away from the grave, back to the waiting car. Dad, Shawn, and I were dressed in polyester suits in the cold, but Shawn would stay. As Dad slowly got into the car, I witnessed a broken man leaving half of himself back there, forevermore.

CHAPTER 25

No, someone deliberately touched me, for I felt the healing power go out from me.

Luke 9:46

For You, O LORD, will bless the righteous; With favor You will surround him as with a shield.

Psalm 5:12

Dec 20, 1980
Returned from Panama –
Life fly's by quickly, very fast
The cold is great
Winter Solace
QUIET
The search has ended.
I found it.

From a notebook of Shawn Patrick Finucan (The Next to Nothing Book)

November, 2019 Merrill, Wisconsin

I opened the photographs from the Marinette County Sheriff's office again, clicking on the scene of Shawn's death. As I looked at his deceased face, my gut clenched like it does every time. I can't desensitize to it no matter how many times I open this file. Mom tells me she wants to see these photographs, but there is no way I can show her. Instead, I tell her how hard it is to look at them.

What's the point in her seeing them?

I opened the file labeled "scene." The area is lit up by the flash of the camera, revealing the forest floor covered in thick snow with sticks and branches from nearby trees, like pine, maple, and oak. I re-examine the crawl marks in the snow and the position in which Shawn was found. He was crawling on his stomach. Someone had turned him over at some point. His left hand was outstretched in front of him. His face showed a determined acceptance.

I clicked forward and opened the image of the rifle lying on the ground. I noted its odd position; the barrel is down in the snow and the stock lies on top of the snow. I tried to imagine what had happened to make the barrel dive down into the snow right after the weapon fired.

I took out a mop, leaned over the handle, and pressed it into my chest. Then I simulated firing it and falling. The mop drops to the hardwood floor, but the top doesn't dive into the floor. I tried it again and flailed in surprise. My arm brushed the barrel as I fell and the tip of the handle that was on my chest speared into the floor.

He had jerked in surprise.

I returned to my laptop and again examined the photo of the rifle lying in the snow. This time my eye caught something that I did not see before. All my motions stopped.

There was a stick lying on the rifle. I tried to focus on it more. The image did not change. I hurried down to the office on the first floor, found the big magnifying glass, then ran back up the stairs. The stick was jammed in the trigger guard of the rifle and extended across the butt of the rifle. It's about seventeen inches long, crooked, and the width of a man's pinky finger. I looked away to clear my vision. I didn't want to see something just because I needed to see it. I wanted to know the truth.

I refocused on the image and saw that it *is* as I had perceived. A stick is wedged into the trigger guard.

This photograph would have been taken before the rifle was touched.

I reread the report from the sheriff's office. There is no mention of the stick in the trigger guard. Did they just pick up the rifle after shooting the photograph without noticing this important fact? It was late evening, dark out, and very cold. It could have been very easy to do. Hadn't I looked at the picture several times before I noticed it?

The deputies missed it but the camera didn't. This evidence is revealed to me with nothing less than supernatural intervention. I prayed to God, and he answered me. I roll out the scene in my mind, like an actor performing a screenplay. Shawn walks down, checks the target, and walks back to the rifle, perhaps clasping his hands together. The temperature is subzero with windchill on top of that. He approaches the rifle, and his boot touches a stick and moves it, wedging it into the trigger guard. He leans down, grabs the rifle, and picks it up. The barrel is aimed at his chest. With the stick wedged on the ground and stuck in the trigger guard, as he picks the rifle up, the barrel is aimed at his chest, the trigger depresses, and the rifle fires.

The weapon blows out of his hands. He spins and drops in shock. The barrel spears down into the snow. Shawn falls back, (or forward?) into the snow. It takes a moment for him to realize what has happened. If he is on his back, he rolls onto his stomach and starts crawling in the direction of the road, where he can get help. Because he is strong and fit, he makes it a good fifteen feet, but shock and blood loss take over. He gradually succumbs to his injuries, knowing where he is going.

I thank God, for He has answered my prayer and revealed to me what happened that day.

I let my imagination put it down and found myself crying. Shawn was humble, kind, and gentle. He lived his final years with a noticeable peace in his demeanor. He had found a solution and offered it freely to others. He loved Jesus and made his life a study of his faith. He adored his Savior and had plans to be a missionary in areas where religious freedom was restricted. He had a love for all whom he met. He was genuine and a real gentleman.

After he was spiritually "saved" and his relationship with God was the most important thing to him, he made amends for all those wrongs to others he felt he had committed during his life, however minor they may have seemed.

In giving his depression to Jesus, Shawn had forged his life like a sword on an anvil to serve his God with humility.

It was Shawn who was poor in spirit.

Shawn's passing so soon after his religious conversion gave all of us who knew him perspective on how short our lives are, and what eternity may represent to us. He had prepared for the eternal voyage, miraculously before our eyes, and was then whisked away while we all stood, first, awestruck and, then, overwhelmed in agony. What can be learned from tragedy, but astounding humility?

He set an example that I hope to follow the rest of my days—full of hope, faith and love. My prayer is that this document, which is part of my "fourth step," will serve to continue Shawn's ministry in some way and speak the truth.

A few days after the funeral, Dad was getting ready to go to Pembine to collect Shawn's stuff from his former school.

"I'm going with you," I declared. I wanted to see where it happened and talk to the people who knew him. I wanted to start my investigation, knowing perhaps, somehow, that if I didn't do it now, it might take me thirty-seven years to have the courage to do it.

"No. You're going back to school. This is something I have to do alone." Dad was shattered, but through this tragedy, he was displaying strength I didn't know he had. He was doing something for Shawn now. Even if it was too little, too late, it was something. As he moved toward his little pickup truck, he stopped and turned toward me. "Listen, I was wrong about encouraging you to leave school. I shouldn't have taken you with me. I shouldn't have done any of those things. Those actions, all of them, working with the underworld, it angered God. I haven't been a...good example to you. I have been wrong about all the stuff that I've been doing. I won't be working with those people anymore," he said with tender eyes of broken emotion. I felt a tinge of resentment. Was I supposed to be glad that he had come to his senses and found the moral high ground after dragging me all over the globe in dangerous situations? Then I remembered that no one had drug me and that I had gone looking for adventure, and found it. "I'm coming with you," I said again, putting my backpack down and moving toward his truck.

"No. You go back to school and complete your diploma. That's final." It made me angry when he pulled rank like this with me—after being my friend. It seemed unconscionable to play both sides of the fence.

So I went back to school with the class of 1985 and resumed my studies. I had lost a few days and had to catch up. Now I was humbled as a flunky in that class. I was grief-stricken and trying to adjust to the change in my life. Overwhelmingly, I felt the pain and loss of a young family member's death. I had always felt pity for all those families touched by this affliction of loss. Now I was one of them.

Shawn's birthday, March nineteenth, was looming. We didn't speak of it but acknowledged it with trepidation. I was grinding out a day of school, going from class to class, and trying to focus. In Mr. Miller's computer class, the computer wasn't responding, and I hit the escape key. I must have hit it harder than Mr. Miller liked because he walked over and yelled next to my head, "If you bang on that escape key one more time, I'm going to bang on your head!"

I don't recall how hard I had been hitting the escape key. Perhaps, figuratively, it was about me wanting to escape in general. But I do recall not liking his tone, his self-important stance, or his Magnum P.I. wannabe persona. The thought crossed my mind to cock-off and say something engaging, but that had never been my style.

I have never liked it when students are disrespectful to teachers in front of the class. As teachers are in a profession of service, they are at a disadvantage when they are on their job. When Dave Barry writes, "If someone is nice to you but rude to the waiter, they are not a nice person," I think this applies to classroom situations. If you really want to tell a teacher off, wait until the class files out of the room.

So, rather than take any more guff from Mr. Miller, or return it, I picked up my books and walked out of the room. "Good!" he yelled with a little too much emotion in a falsetto, cracking voice. "And don't come back!"

So I walked into Mr. Hull's office, the guidance counselor. He chastised me for being a pain in the ass and didn't I want to graduate. What was my problem with authority in my life, anyway? But, being a good counselor, he got me into another class so that I would have the right number of credits to graduate in May.

I remember going home after that school day and finding Mom in the yard crying. I sat down next to her and shared Shawn's birthday in mourning, but I know he was there, embracing both of us.

In the fall of 2019, my oldest son Brandon was married in Fort Collins, Colorado. The family gathered for the event, and we were enjoying a wonderful reception.

"I have to tell you, I had a dream last night," my brother Tim said to me over the live reggae music. "I dreamt I was walking down a trail and up ahead of me was Shawn. He was just strolling along. So I hurried up to him. I approached him and said, 'Hi Shawn, how are you?' He said, 'Hi, Tim. I'm fine. How are you?' It was so good to see him. I said, 'What are you doing here?' He replied, 'Brandon's wedding is this weekend, and I 'm going to attend, I'll be with you there.'"

As Tim recalled his dream, I sat back in my chair. Of course, Shawn was here with us. Hadn't I felt it in my soul? I looked around at all the family dressed up for this wonderful celebration. It was Shawn's nephew's wedding. He wouldn't miss it. Jesus conquered death.

Deirdre sat down with a smile. "You know what the difference is between reggae music and a funeral procession?"

"No, what?" I had to ask.

"You can dance at a funeral procession." We laughed like Finucan's, strengthening our family bond with joy.

On Dad's birthday, November ninth, in 2020, I found his gravestone, the small one with the veteran's plate on it we got for free because he served in the Marines. I remembered the summer day we buried him. I played Taps on my trumpet and the veteran's honor guard fired off their rifles in salute.

As I stood now in the late fall wind, I could still hear his voice and his laughter. Dad loved to laugh. He was not well and suffered from mental illness and depression, but we could still make each other laugh at the farce in this world.

I stepped back a few yards to where Shawn's grave was, just a short distance away. I could see both of their headstones and I could imagine them being there with me. The acute sadness left, and I felt them there, if only for a moment.

I pulled out a folded piece of paper from my pocket, something I had written to Shawn at the conclusion of my investigation. I cleared my throat, blew my nose in a paper towel from my pocket and tried not to smear snot on the page.

Dear Shawn,

You were a fantastic older brother.

I never got a chance to say goodbye to you, you left so quickly. I have thought a great deal about your final moments, out there in the woods. I know it was an accident now and I can put the subject down in peace. I didn't get to tell you that you were a great, positive influence on my life in many ways. You set the example of kindness that I wish I could set for others but so often fail to do.

You were the demonstration in my life of silent strength that I try to emulate when lost.

Without trying you were gentle to everyone, sensitive to their position, and generous with your time and energy. You blessed everyone around you with a calm, happy disposition and exhibited self-control and self-mastery without any effort.

You were a leader to us and unafraid of anyone or anything.

You found the answer to life early and when you tried to share it with us, we didn't understand. We would remember your message and learn later. I think when you did find Christ, God himself wanted you up there with him. Could any of us who knew you blame Him? Anyway, who are any of us to tell God when he can pick his flowers? Sometimes, He does so when they are in bloom.

I know you're up there with Dad and I just wanted to let you know I miss you and I think about you a lot. I love you brother, may God give you a big hug for me.

Love,
Jamie

I folded up the paper and put it in my pocket. A murder of six crows moved overhead and circled me cawing incessantly and I looked up at them in awe. I counted them to make sure I had the number right so I could remember this moment. I watched as they circled directly over my head, making their beautiful, rough throaty sound.

They followed the leader, flying their circular pattern like black, Blue Angels before a football game. When the exhibition was over, they moved off into the lint-colored sky. I knew it was a sign from God. He uses crows to communicate with me frequently when I hunt and walk out of the house. It's an understanding He and I have—a telegraph wire in the air.

I walked back to my Challenger and got into it. These two stories of Dad and Shawn in my life end here at this place of stones and monuments where we all end up. I had found the answers I was looking for. Shawn handled the rifle carelessly and had an accident. A stick was in the trigger guard when the Sheriff's office photographed the rifle. It was that simple.

I didn't know if this would allow me, finally, to say goodbye, but I had investigated it hard and I did my best to find out. I owed Shawn and the whole family that.

The last year of Shawn's life flashed through my mind again, Dad smuggling drugs and setting up tax shelters for criminals, while Shawn smuggled bibles behind the Iron Curtain to bring salvation to those who would listen. Different paths, different outcomes, but both passed on to eternity now.

I walked back to my car, uncertain whether I should leave this place or stay a bit longer.

I started the engine and slowly drove down the narrow road through the cemetery. I passed some of the gravestones, all with stories of incredible human lives buried below them. When I finish a memoir, I gain a level of understanding of life that provides a framework of compassion for myself that wasn't there before. And with that understanding, I can feel more compassion for those around me.

I braked and looked back over my shoulder out the window with the autumn air blowing in on me bringing the smell of dried maple leaves. Over the graves I could see Shawn and Dad standing there, laughing at some joke with each other. They looked at me and waved.

I remembered the song Shawn was singing one day in the kitchen. "This isn't my home, I'm just passing through."

Me too, my brother. And it won't be that long before we are all on the other side, I thought. Then I smiled. I smiled in peace. The work was done; I had found what I was looking for.

And, so did Shawn. And, so did Dad.

ACKNOWLEDGEMENTS

I would like to thank Jesus Christ for my salvation.

To Judy and Bob Weaver, I thank them for their love and support throughout my life.

I would be remiss if I did not acknowledge and thank the Marinette County Sheriff's Office for keeping excellent records through the years and giving me access to what I needed to write this account.

My thanks to Ralph Yearick, Editor in Chief at Lighthouse Point Press, who saw the potential in this memoir as with *Wild Counselor* when many publishing houses did not. He shared my vision and believed in the work and in me. He worked tirelessly on the manuscript without complaint. Ralph gave me direction and questioned my material when it needed to be, and challenged me in content when I overdramatized or over-extended, or got too mushy or romantic. Ralph is the sensei of editors and I am blessed to work with him and call him a friend.

I thank you, dear reader, who turned the pages of this work and shared my life's journey of joy and pain throughout this year in review. I pray that the read helped you feel what reading a memoir has made me feel—that you are not alone in this brief experience of life. Your comments that have reached me affect me profoundly and give me the strength to take pen in hand and, as Ernest Hemingway has written, "bleed." Perhaps the barbers of old were right—this is how we heal.

About the Author

Jim Finucan is the author of *Wild Counselor: 1977—The Summer of the Hunt,* a prequel to *Year of the Smuggler.* He has also published three other books including *Interview Strategy: The Next Move is Yours*; *The Spear* (fiction); and *Past Due!: A Debt Collecting Manual for Business Professionals.*

Year of the Smuggler is a story within a story, in which Finucan recounts his eighteenth year traveling with his father, while in near time, attempting to solve the mysterious death of his older brother thirty-seven years earlier.

A small business owner, Finucan lives in the Northwoods of Wisconsin with the ghosts of his past and tells their stories to make peace with them.